Mathematics

McGraw–Hill Primis
ISBN: 0390-980072

Text:

Intermediate Algebra,
Second Edition
Streeter–Hutchison–Hoelzle

McGraw-Hill

A Division of The McGraw-Hill Companies

The cover photograph is courtesy of Intel® Corporation and was
created from a color photograph of Intel's Pentium™ chip.*

* Pentium™ is a trademark of Intel.

 This book was printed on recycled paper.

Mathematics

http://www.mhhe.com/primis/online

MATH   ISBN: 0-390-98007-2

Mathematics

Contents

Streeter-Hutchison-Hoelzle • *Intermediate Algebra. Second Edition*

Linear Equations in One Variable

OBJECTIVES
1. To solve equations by using the addition and multiplication properties of equality
2. To recognize conditional equations, identities, and contradictions

We begin by considering one of the most important tools of mathematics, the equation. The ability to recognize and solve various types of equations and inequalities is probably the most useful algebraic skill you will learn. To start, let's describe what we mean by an equation.

An *equation* is a mathematical statement in which two expressions represent the same quantity. An equation has three parts. Consider

$$5x \;+\; 6 \;=\; 2x \;-\; 3$$

Left side   Equals sign   Right side

The equation simply says that the expression on the left and the expression on the right represent the same quantity.

In this section, we will work with a particular kind of equation.

Linear equations are also called *first-degree equations* because the highest power of the variable is the first power.

> A *linear equation in one variable* is any equation that can be written in the form
>
> $ax + b = 0$
>
> where a and b are any real numbers and $a \neq 0$.

We also say the solution *satisfies* the equation.

The *solution* for an equation in one variable is any number that will make the equation a true statement. The *solution set* for such an equation is simply the set consisting of all solutions.

Example 1

For

$$5x + 6 = 2x - 3$$

the solution is -3 because replacing x with -3 gives

$$5(-3) + 6 \stackrel{?}{=} 2(-3) - 3$$
$$-15 + 6 \stackrel{?}{=} -6 - 3$$
$$-9 = -9 \qquad \text{A true statement}$$

$-15 + 6$
-9

CHECK YOURSELF 1

Verify that 7 is a solution for the equation.

$$5x - 15 = 2x + 6$$

[handwritten: $5(7) - 15 = 2(7) + 6$
$35 - 15 = 20 = 20$]

Solving linear equations in one variable will require using *equivalent equations*.

> Two equations are *equivalent* if they have the same solution set.

For example, given the three equations

$$5x + 5 = 2x - 4 \qquad 3x = -9 \qquad \text{and} \qquad x = -3$$

[handwritten: $-15 + 5$ 10]

You can easily verify this by replacing x with -3 in each equation.

are all equivalent because they all have the same solution set, $\{-3\}$. Note that replacing x with -3 will give a true statement in the third equation, but it is not as clear that -3 is a solution for the other two equations. This leads us to an equation-solving strategy of *isolating* the variable, as is the case in the equation $x = -3$.

To form equivalent equations that will lead to the solution of a linear equation, we need two properties of equality.

Adding the same quantity to both sides of an equation gives an equivalent equation. This is true whether c is positive or negative.

> **ADDITION PROPERTY OF EQUALITY**
>
> If $\qquad a = b$
>
> then $\qquad a + c = b + c$

Note Since subtraction can always be defined in terms of addition,

$$a - c = a + (-c)$$

the addition property also allows us to *subtract* the same quantity from both sides of an equation. We also have

Multiplying both sides of an equation by the same nonzero quantity gives an equivalent equation.

> **MULTIPLICATION PROPERTY OF EQUALITY**
>
> If $\qquad a = b$
>
> then $\qquad ac = bc \qquad$ where $\qquad c \neq 0$

Since division can be defined in terms of multiplication,

$$\frac{a}{c} = a \cdot \frac{1}{c} \qquad c \neq 0$$

The multiplication property allows us to *divide* both sides of an equation by the same nonzero quantity.

Let's see how these properties are applied to find the solution of linear equations.

Example 2

Solve for x:

$$3x - 5 = 4 \qquad\qquad (1)$$

Why did we add 5? Because it is the *opposite* of −5 and the resulting equation will have the variable term on the left and the constant term on the right.

We start by using the addition property to add 5 to both sides of the equation.

$$3x - 5 + 5 = 4 + 5$$
$$3x = 9 \qquad\qquad (2)$$

Now we want to get the x term alone on the left with a coefficient of 1 (we call this *isolating* the x). To do this we use the multiplication property and both sides are multiplied by $\frac{1}{3}$.

We choose $\frac{1}{3}$ because $\frac{1}{3}$ is the *reciprocal* of 3 and

$$\frac{1}{3} \cdot 3 = 1$$

$$\frac{1}{3}(3x) = \frac{1}{3}(9)$$
$$\left(\frac{1}{3} \cdot 3\right)x = 3$$
$$x = 3 \qquad\qquad (3)$$

Since any application of the addition or multiplication properties leads to an equivalent equation, Equations (1), (2), and (3) all have the same solution, 3.

To check this result, we can replace x with 3 in the original equation:

$$3(3) - 5 \stackrel{?}{=} 4$$
$$9 - 5 \stackrel{?}{=} 4$$
$$4 = 4 \qquad \text{A true statement}$$

Note You may prefer a slightly different approach in the last step of the solution above. From Equation (2)

$$3x = 9$$

The multiplication property can be used to *divide* both sides of the equation by 3. Then

$$\frac{3x}{3} = \frac{9}{3}$$
$$x = 3$$

Of course, the result is the same.

CHECK YOURSELF 2

Solve for x.

$4x - 7 = 17$

[handwritten: $4x - 7 + 7 = 17 + 7$ $4x = 24$ $x = 6$]

The steps involved in using the addition and multiplication properties to solve an equation are the same if more terms are involved in an equation.

Example 3

Solve for x:

$5x - 11 = 2x - 7$

Our objective is to use the properties of equality to isolate x on one side of an equivalent equation. We begin by adding 11 to both sides.

Again, adding 11 leaves us with the constant term on the right.

$5x - 11 + 11 = 2x - 7 + 11$
$$5x = 2x + 4$$

We continue by adding $-2x$ to (or subtracting $2x$ from) both sides.

If you prefer, write

$5x - 2x = 2x - 2x + 4$

Again:

$3x = 4$

$5x + (-2x) = 2x + (-2x) + 4$
$$3x = 4$$

To isolate x, we now multiply both sides by $\frac{1}{3}$.

This is the same as dividing both sides by 3. So

$$\frac{3x}{3} = \frac{4}{3}$$
$$x = \frac{4}{3}$$

$$\frac{1}{3}(3x) = \frac{1}{3} \cdot 4$$
$$x = \frac{4}{3}$$

We leave it to you to check this result by substitution.

CHECK YOURSELF 3

Solve for x.

$7x - 12 = 2x - 9$

[handwritten: $7x - 12 + 12 = 2x - 9 + 12$]

[handwritten: $7x = 2x + 3$]
[handwritten: $7x + (-2x) = 2x + (-2x) + 3$]
[handwritten: $5x = 3$ $\frac{1}{5}(5x) = \frac{1}{5} \times 3$ $\frac{3}{5}$]

4

Recall the discussion of like terms in our coverage of the properties of the real numbers.

Both sides of an equation should be simplified as much as possible *before* the addition and multiplication properties are applied. If like terms are involved on one side (or on both sides) of an equation, they should be combined before an attempt is made to isolate the variable. The following example illustrates.

Example 4

Solve for x:

Note the like terms on the left and right sides of the equation.

$$8x + 2 - 3x = 8 + 3x + 2$$

Here we combine the like terms $8x$ and $-3x$ on the left and the like terms 8 and 2 on the right as our first step. We then have

$$5x + 2 = 3x + 10$$

We can now solve as before.

$$5x + 2 - 2 = 3x + 10 - 2 \qquad \text{Subtract 2 from both sides.}$$
$$5x = 3x + 8$$

Then

$$5x - 3x = 3x - 3x + 8 \qquad \text{Subtract } 3x \text{ from both sides.}$$
$$2x = 8$$
$$\frac{2x}{2} = \frac{8}{2} \qquad \text{Divide both sides by 2.}$$
or
$$x = 4$$

The solution is 4, which can be checked by returning to the *original equation*.

(handwritten) $2x - 4x = 4x - 4x + 10$
$-2x = 10$
$\dfrac{-2x}{3} = \dfrac{10}{3}$

CHECK YOURSELF 4

Solve for x. *(handwritten: -8)*

$$7x - 3 - 5x = 10 + 4x + 3$$

(handwritten) $2x - 3 + 3 = 4x + 13 - 3$
$2x = 4x + 10$
$2x - 3 = 4x + 13$

If parentheses are involved on one or both sides of an equation, they should be removed by applying the distributive property as the first step. Like terms should then be combined before an attempt is made to isolate the variable. Consider the following example.

(handwritten)
$2x - 3 = 4x + 13$
$2x - 3 + 3 = 4x + 13 + 3$
$2x = 4x = 16$
$2x + 3x = 4x + 3x + 16$
$5x \quad 7x + 16$

5

Example 5

Solve for x:

$$x + 3(3x - 1) = 4(x + 2) + 4$$

First, remove the parentheses on the left and right sides.

$$x + 9x - 3 = 4x + 8 + 4$$

Combine like terms on each side of the equation.

$$10x - 3 = 4x + 12$$

Recall that to isolate the x, we must get the x alone on the left side with a coefficient of 1.

Now isolate variable x on the left side.

$$10x - 3 + 3 = 4x + 12 + 3 \qquad \text{Add 3 to both sides.}$$
$$10x = 4x + 15$$
$$10x - 4x = 4x - 4x + 15 \qquad \text{Subtract } 4x \text{ from both sides.}$$
$$6x = 15$$
$$\frac{6x}{6} = \frac{15}{6} \qquad \text{Divide both sides by 6.}$$
$$x = \frac{5}{2}$$

The solution is $\dfrac{5}{2}$. Again, this can be checked by returning to the original equation.

CHECK YOURSELF 5

Solve for x.

$$x + 5(x + 2) = 3(3x - 2) + 18$$

To solve an equation involving fractions, our first step is to multiply both sides of the equation by the least common multiple (LCM) of all denominators in the equation. This will clear the equation of fractions, and we can proceed as before.

Example 6

Solve

$$\frac{x}{2} - \frac{2}{3} = \frac{5}{6}$$

for x.

$$\frac{x}{2} - \frac{2}{3} = \frac{5}{6}$$

We multiply each side by 6, the LCM of 2, 3, and 6.

$$6\left(\frac{x}{2} - \frac{2}{3}\right) = 6\left(\frac{5}{6}\right)$$

Apply the distributive law.

$$6\left(\frac{x}{2}\right) - 6\left(\frac{2}{3}\right) = 6\left(\frac{5}{6}\right)$$

The equation is now cleared of fractions.

$$3x - 4 = 5$$
$$3x = 9$$
$$x = 3$$

The solution, 3, can be checked as before by returning to the original equation.

CHECK YOURSELF 6

Solve for x.

$$\frac{x}{4} - \frac{4}{5} = \frac{19}{20}$$

$20\left(\frac{x}{4} - \frac{4}{5}\right) = 20\left(\frac{19}{20}\right)$ $20\left(\frac{x}{4}\right) - 20\frac{4}{5} = 20\left(\frac{19}{20}\right)$

$5x - 16 = 19$

$5x = 35 \quad x = 7$

Be sure that the distributive property is applied properly so that *every term* of the equation is multiplied by the LCM.

Example 7

Solve

$$\frac{2x - 1}{5} + 1 = \frac{x}{2}$$

for x.

Multiply by 10, the LCM of 5 and 2.

$$10\left(\frac{2x - 1}{5} + 1\right) = 10\left(\frac{x}{2}\right)$$

Apply the distributive law on the left.

$$10\left(\frac{2x - 1}{5}\right) + 10(1) = 10\left(\frac{x}{2}\right)$$
$$2(2x - 1) + 10 = 5x$$
$$4x - 2 + 10 = 5x$$
$$4x + 8 = 5x$$
$$8 = x$$

The solution for the original equation is 8.

CHECK YOURSELF 7

Solve for x.

$$\frac{3x + 1}{4} - 2 = \frac{x + 1}{3}$$

So far, we have considered only equations of the form $ax + b = 0$, where $a \neq 0$. If we allow the possibility that $a = 0$, two additional equation forms arise. The resulting equations can be classified into three types depending on the nature of their solutions. Let's define and see how to recognize the three types.

Note 1: Here the equation can be written in the form $ax + b = 0$, where $a \neq 0$.

Note 2: In this case *both a and b* are 0, so we get the equation $0 = 0$.

Note 3: Here a is 0, but b is nonzero, and we end up with something like $4 = 0$.

1. An equation that is true for only particular values of the variable is called a *conditional equation*.

   This case has been illustrated in all our previous examples and exercises.

2. An equation that is true for all possible values of the variable is called an *identity*.

   This will be the case if both sides of the equation reduce to the same expression (a true statement).

3. An equation that is never true, no matter what the value of the variable, is called a *contradiction*.

   This will be the case if the two sides of the equation reduce to a false statement.

The following example illustrates the second and third cases.

Example 8

(*a*) Solve for x:

$$2(x - 3) - 2x = -6$$
$$2x - 6 - 2x = -6$$
$$-6 = -6 \qquad \text{A } \textit{true} \text{ statement}$$

See note 2 above. By adding 6 to both sides of this equation, we have $0 = 0$.

Since the two sides reduce to a true statement, $-6 = -6$, the original equation is an *identity* and the solution set is the set of all real numbers.

(*b*) Solve for x:

$$3(x + 1) - 2x = x + 4$$
$$3x + 3 - 2x = x + 4$$
$$x + 3 = x + 4$$
$$3 = 4 \qquad \text{A } \textit{false} \text{ statement}$$

See note 3 from previous page. Subtracting 3 from both sides, we have 0 = 1.

Since the two sides reduce to a false statement, $3 = 4$, the original equation is a contradiction. There are no values of the variable that can satisfy the equation. The solution set has nothing in it. We call this the *empty set* and write $\{\ \}$ or $\varnothing$.

CHECK YOURSELF 8

Determine whether each of the following equations is a conditional equation, an identity, or a contradiction.

1. $2(x + 1) - 3 = x$ *conditional*
2. $2(x + 1) - 3 = 2x + 1$ *contradiction*
3. $2(x + 1) - 3 = 2x - 1$ *identity*

An *algorithm* is a step-by-step process for problem solving.

An organized step-by-step procedure is the key to an effective equation-solving strategy. The following algorithm summarizes our work in this section and should give you guidance in approaching the problems that follow.

SOLVING LINEAR EQUATIONS IN ONE VARIABLE

STEP 1   Multiply both sides of the equation by the LCM of any denominators, to clear the equation of fractions.

STEP 2   Remove any grouping symbols by applying the distributive property.

STEP 3   Combine any like terms that appear on either side of the equation.

STEP 4   Apply the addition property of equality to write an equivalent equation with the variable term on *one side* of the equation and the constant term on the *other side*.

STEP 5   Apply the multiplication property of equality to write an equivalent equation with the variable isolated on one side of the equation.

STEP 6   Check the solution in the *original* equation.

Note: If the equation derived in step 5 is always true, the original equation was an identity. If the equation is always false, the original equation was a contradiction.

When you are solving an equation for which a calculator is recommended, it is often easiest to do all calculations as the last step.

Example 9

Solve the following equation for x.

$$\frac{185(x - 3.25) + 1650}{500} = 159.44$$

Following the steps of the algorithm, we get

$$185(x - 3.25) + 1650 = 159.44 \cdot 500 \qquad \text{Multiply by the LCM.}$$

$$185x - 185 \cdot 3.25 + 1650 = 159.44 \cdot 500 \qquad \text{Remove parentheses.}$$

$$185x = 159.44 \cdot 500 + 185 \cdot 3.25 - 1650 \qquad \text{Apply the addition property.}$$

$$x = \frac{159.44 \cdot 500 + 185 \cdot 3.25 - 1650}{185} \qquad \text{Isolate the variable.}$$

Now, remembering to use parentheses around the numerator, we use a calculator to simplify the expression on the right.

$$x = 425.25$$

CHECK YOURSELF 9

Solve the following equation for x.

$$\frac{2200(x + 17.5) - 1550}{75} = 2326$$

CHECK YOURSELF ANSWERS

1. $5(7) - 15 \overset{?}{=} 2(7) + 6$
   $35 - 15 \overset{?}{=} 14 + 6$
   $20 = 20$

   A true statement.

2. 6.   3. $\frac{3}{5}$.   4. -8.

5. $-\frac{2}{3}$.   6. 7.   7. 5.

8. (1) Conditional; (2) contradiction; (3) identity.
9. 62.5.

Name _____

Date _____

Exercises

ANSWERS

Build Your Skills

1. _____

Solve each of the following equations, and check your result.

2. _____

1. $5x - 8 = 17$　　　　　　**2.** $4x + 9 = -11$

3. _____

3. $8 - 7x = -41$　　　　　　**4.** $-7 - 4x = 21$

4. _____

5. _____

5. $7x - 5 = 6x + 6$　　　　　**6.** $9x + 4 = 8x - 3$

6. _____

7. $8x - 4 = 3x - 24$　　　　　**8.** $5x + 2 = 2x - 5$

7. _____

8. _____

9. $7x - 4 = 2x + 26$　　　　　**10.** $11x - 3 = 4x - 31$

9. _____

11. $4x - 3 = 1 - 2x$　　　　　**12.** $8x + 5 = -19 - 4x$

10. _____

11. _____

13. $2x + 8 = 7x - 37$　　　　　**14.** $3x - 5 = 9x + 22$

12. _____

15. $6x + 5 = 8x - 10$　　　　　**16.** $4x + 7 = 9x - 38$

13. _____

14. _____

Simplify and then solve each of the following equations.

15. _____

17. $5x - 2 + x = 9 + 3x + 10$　　　**18.** $5x + 5 - x = -7 + x - 2$

16. _____

19. $7x - 3 - 4x = 5 + 5x - 13$　　　**20.** $8x - 3 - 6x = 7 + 5x + 17$

17. _____

18. _____

21. $5x = 3(x - 6)$　　　　　　**22.** $2(x - 15) = 7x$

19. _____

20. _____

21. _____

22. _____

ANSWERS

23. _____

24. _____

25. _____

26. _____

27. _____

28. _____

29. _____

30. _____

31. _____

32. _____

33. _____

34. _____

35. _____

36. _____

37. _____

38. _____

39. _____

40. _____

41. _____

42. _____

43. _____

44. _____

23. $5(8 - x) = 3x$

24. $7x = 7(6 - x)$

25. $2(2x - 1) = 3(x + 1)$

26. $3(3x - 1) = 4(3x + 1)$

27. $8x - 3(2x - 4) = 17$

28. $7x - 4(3x + 4) = 9$

29. $7(3x + 4) = 8(2x + 5) + 13$

30. $-4(2x - 1) + 3(3x + 1) = 9$

31. $9 - 4(3x + 1) = 3(6 - 3x) - 9$

32. $13 - 4(5x + 1) = 3(7 - 5x) - 15$

33. $5 - 2[x - 2(x - 1)] = 55 - 4[x - 3(x + 2)]$

34. $7 - 5[x - 3(x + 2)] = 25 - 2[x - 2(x - 3)]$

Clear of fractions and then solve each of the following equations.

35. $\dfrac{2x}{3} - \dfrac{5}{3} = 3$

36. $\dfrac{3x}{4} + \dfrac{1}{4} = 4$

37. $\dfrac{x}{6} + \dfrac{x}{5} = 11$

38. $\dfrac{x}{6} - \dfrac{x}{8} = 1$

39. $\dfrac{2x}{3} - \dfrac{x}{4} = \dfrac{5}{2}$

40. $\dfrac{5x}{6} + \dfrac{2x}{3} = \dfrac{5}{6}$

41. $\dfrac{x}{5} - \dfrac{x - 7}{3} = \dfrac{1}{3}$

42. $\dfrac{x}{6} + \dfrac{3}{4} = \dfrac{x - 1}{4}$

43. $\dfrac{5x - 3}{4} - 2 = \dfrac{x}{3}$

44. $\dfrac{6x - 1}{5} - \dfrac{2x}{3} = 3$

ANSWERS

45. _____

46. _____

47. _____

48. _____

49. _____

50. _____

51. _____

52. _____

53. _____

54. _____

55. _____

56. _____

57. _____

58. _____

59. _____

60. _____

45. $\dfrac{2x + 3}{5} - \dfrac{2x - 1}{3} = \dfrac{8}{15}$

46. $\dfrac{3x}{5} - \dfrac{3x - 1}{2} = \dfrac{11}{10}$

47. $0.5x - 6 = 0.2x$

48. $0.7x - 7 = 0.3x - 5$

49. $0.15x + 1.2 = 0.05x + 2$

50. $0.25x - 0.8 = 0.13x + 1.6$

Classify each of the following equations as a conditional equation, an identity, or a contradiction.

51. $3(x - 1) = 2x + 3$

52. $2(x + 3) = 2x + 6$

53. $3(x - 1) = 3x + 3$

54. $2(x + 3) = x + 5$

55. $3(x - 1) = 3x - 3$

56. $2(x + 3) = 3x + 5$

57. $3x - (x - 3) = 2(x + 1) + 2$

58. $5x - (x + 4) = 4(x - 2) + 4$

59. $\dfrac{x}{2} - \dfrac{x}{3} = \dfrac{x}{6}$

60. $\dfrac{3x}{4} - \dfrac{2x}{3} = \dfrac{x}{6}$

ANSWERS

Skillscan (Operations with Signed Numbers)

a. _____

If $a = 3$, $b = -2$, $c = 4$, and $d = -1$, evaluate each of the following expressions.

b. _____

a. $\dfrac{b}{c}$ b. $\dfrac{ab}{c}$

c. _____

c. $\dfrac{b}{cd}$ d. $\dfrac{c}{2ab}$

d. _____

e. $\dfrac{c - b}{ad}$ f. $\dfrac{d - ac}{b}$

e. _____

g. $\dfrac{c - 2b}{d}$ h. $\dfrac{2c - 3a}{b}$

f. _____

g. _____

h. _____

ANSWERS

1. 5   **3.** 7   **5.** 11   **7.** -4 **9.** 6   **11.** $\dfrac{2}{3}$ **13.** 9   **15.** $\dfrac{15}{2}$ **17.** 7

19. $\dfrac{5}{2}$ **21.** -9 **23.** 5   **25.** 5   **27.** $\dfrac{5}{2}$ **29.** 5   **31.** $-\dfrac{4}{3}$ **33.** -13 **35.** 7

37. 30   **39.** 6   **41.** 15   **43.** 3   **45.** $\dfrac{3}{2}$ **47.** 20   **49.** 8   **51.** Conditional

53. Contradiction   **55.** Identity   **57.** Contradiction   **59.** Identity   **a.** $-\dfrac{1}{2}$ **b.** $-\dfrac{3}{2}$

c. $\dfrac{1}{2}$ **d.** $-\dfrac{1}{3}$ **e.** -2 **f.** $\dfrac{13}{2}$ **g.** -8 **h.** $\dfrac{1}{2}$

WORD PROBLEMS

NUMBER PROBLEMS

1. 5 & 9 The sum of two numbers is 14. Their difference is 4. Find the two numbers.
2. 12 13 The sum of two numbers is 25. Their difference is 1. Find the two numbers.
3. The sum of two numbers is 20. Their difference is 10. Find the two numbers.
4. The sum of two numbers is 32. Their difference is 2. Find the two numbers.
5. The sum of two numbers is 36. One of the numbers is twice as large as the other. Find the two numbers.
6. The sum of two numbers is 44. One of the numbers is three times as large as the other. Find the two numbers.
7. The sum of two numbers is 36. One of the numbers is three less than twice the other. Find the two numbers.
8. The sum of two numbers is 63. One of the numbers is three more than twice the other. Find the two numbers.
9. Find two numbers whose sum is 33 and who difference is 9.
10. One number is three times as large as another, and their sum is 50. Find the two numbers.
11. The sum of two consecutive integers is 191. Find the two integers.
12. The sum of two consecutive integers is 65. Find the two integers.
13. The sum of two consecutive integers is 297. Find the two integers.
14. The sum of two consecutive even integers is 186. Find the two integers.
15. The sum of two consecutive even integers is 214. Find the two integers.
16. The sum of two consecutive odd integers is 44. Find the two integers.

GEOMETRY PROBLEMS   Rectangle: Perimeter = 2(length + width)

W 14 L 28
17. The perimeter of a rectangle is 42 inches. The length is twice the width. Find the length and width of the rectangle.
18. The perimeter of a rectangle is 62 inches. The length is four more than twice the width. Find the length and width of the rectangle.
19. The perimeter of a rectangle is 58 inches. The length is ten less than twice the width. Find the length and width of the rectangle.
20. The perimeter of a rectangle is 110 inches. The length is five less than three times the width. Find the length and width of the rectangle.
21. The length of a rectangle is 7 inches more than the width. The perimeter is 52 inches. Find the length and width.
22. The width of a rectangle is 4 feet less than the length. The perimeter is 32 feet. Find the length and width.
23. The perimeter of a square is 28 meters. Find the length of one side.
24. The perimeter of a square is 44 inches. Find the length of one side.

25. The perimeter of a square is 100 feet. Find the length of one side.

26. One side of a triangle is twice the smallest side. The third side is four inches more than the shortest side. The perimeter is 24 inches. Find all three sides.

27. The length of a rectangle is three inches less than twice the width. The perimeter is 33 inches. Find the length and width.

28. The length of a rectangle is 3 feet less than five times the width. The sum of the length and width is 22 more than the width. Find the width.

COIN PROBLEMS

29. A child has 15 coins, made up of only quarters and dimes. The coin collection is worth $2.85. How many quarters and how many dimes are there?

30. A child has 31 coins, made up of only quarters and dimes. The coin collection is worth $4.75. How many quarters and how many dimes are there?

31. A child has a collection of only nickels and dimes. The collection is worth $5.60. There are 81 coins in all. How many dimes are there?

32. A child has 33 coins, made up of only nickels and dimes. The coin collection is worth $2.70. How many nickels and how many dimes are there?

33. Mark has $1.55 in dimes and nickels. He has two more dimes than nickels. How many dimes does he have?

34. Adam has $4.25 in dimes and nickels. He has 5 more dimes than nickels. How many nickels does he have?

35. Ann has $3.60 in dimes and quarters. She has twice as many quarters as dimes. How many dimes does she have?

36. Matt has $4.95 in dimes and quarters. He has three times as many dimes as quarters. How many dimes does he have?

37. Susan has $2.55 in nickels, dimes and quarters. She has four more nickels than dimes, and five fewer quarters than dimes. How many dimes does she have?

INVESTMENTS

38. A college graduate has $3,500 to invest. He places part of the money in an account which earns 9% interest per year, and the rest of the money in an account paying 7% per year. The total interest earned on both accounts during the first year is $295.00. How much money was invested in each account?

39. A college graduate has $10,000 to invest. She places part of the money in an account which earns 6% interest per year, and the rest of the money in an account paying 9% per year. The total interest earned on both accounts during the first year is $660.00. How much money was invested in each account?

40. Suppose you have money invested in two accounts, one paying 8% per year, and the other paying 9.5% per year. If you have $3,000 more invested at 9.5% than at 8%, and if you earn $1160 in interest in one year, how much money was invested in each account?

41. Suppose you have invested twice as much money at 6% than you have at 4.5% an

that your total interest on the two accounts during the year was $495.00. How much money was invested in each account?

42. Suppose you have invested money in three accounts. The accounts pay 8%, 8.5%, and 9% interest each year. Suppose also that you have $500 more invested at 8.5% than at 8% and $2000 more at 9% than at 8%. If the total interest earned on the three accounts during the year was $732.50, how much money was invested in each account?

43. Suppose you invest money in three accounts that pay 9%, 10% and 11% in annual interest. If you have twice as much invested at 9% as at 10% and three times as much invested at 11% as at 10%, and if the total interest from the three accounts during one year was $2135, how much money was invested in each account?

MISCELLANEOUS

44. Andy received these scores on his "hour" math tests: 79, 67, and 77. The "hour" tests were worth 100 points each. If the Final Exam is worth 200 points, how many points does he need to score on the Final if he needs an overall average of 70% to pass?

45. Michael has a piggy bank in which he saves only dimes and quarters. He has nine more dimes than he has quarters. He has $6.15 in the piggy bank. How many dimes and quarters does he have?

46. Adam's mom needs to give him lunch money for school. Adam needs quarters and dimes, since he buys his lunch from vending machines, and the school has no change machines. If Adam's mom gives him $4.25 in dimes and quarters, and if there were 23 coins making up the $4.25, how many of each coin did he receive?

47. Jennifer needs a new computer. At Best Buy, Packard Bell computers are on sale at 15% off. If a computer's sale price is $2,826.25, what was the original price?

48. If Jennifer buys one of the computers on sale at Best Buy described in problem 47, how much will she pay for it, since Indiana collects 5% in sales tax?

49. A man sold two cars and received $12,500. If he sold one car for $1,600 more than the other car, what were the selling prices for the two cars?

50. A man and wife have an estate worth $380,500. If the husband's portion of the estate is worth $4,000 more than twice the wife's portion, how much is each portion worth?

51. The attendance at a tennis tournament was 44,000. Suppose that tickets cost $13 and $15 and that $618,000 was collected in ticket sales. How many of each type of ticket were sold?

Answers

1. 9 & 5
2. 12 & 13
3. 15 & 5
4. 15 & 17
5. 12 & 24
6. 11 & 33
7. 13 & 23
8. 20 & 43
9. 12 & 21
10. 12.5 and 37.5
11. 95 & 96
12. 32 & 33
13. 148 & 149
14. 92 & 94
15. 106 & 108
16. 21 & 23
17. 14" by 7"
18. 22" by 9"
19. 13" by 16"
20. 15" by 40"
21. 9.5" by 16.5"
22. 6' by 10'
23. 7 m
24. 11"
25. 25'
26. 5", 9", 10"
27. 6.5" by 10"
28. 5' (by 22')
29. 9 quarters, 6 dimes
30. 11 quarters, 20 dimes
31. 31 dimes (50 nickels)
32. 12 nickels, 21 dimes
33. 11
34. 25
35. 6
36. 27
37. 9 dimes (13 nickels, 4 quarters)
38. $2,500 at 9%, $1,000 at 7%
39. $8,000 at 6%, $2,000 at 9%
40. $5,000 at 8%, $8,000 at 9.5%
41. $3,000 at 4.5%, $6,000 at 6%
42. $2,000 at 8%; $2,500 at 8.5%; $4,000 at 9%
43. $7,000 at 9%; $3,500 at 10%; $10,500 at 11%
44. 127
45. 24 dimes; 15 quarters
46. 10 dimes, 13 quarters
47. $3,325
48. $2,967.56
49. $5,450 and $7,050
50. Husband: $255,000; Wife: $125,500
51. 21,000 of $13 tickets; 23,000 of $15 tick

The Cartesian Coordinate System

OBJECTIVES
1. To plot points in a plane, given their coordinates
2. To give the coordinates of a point in the plane

Each point on the number line corresponds to a real number. For our work here, it will be useful to establish a similar correspondence between points in the plane and ordered pairs of real numbers.

As we will see, this correspondence is accomplished through the use of the *Cartesian coordinate system.* This coordinate system is the basis for the union of the subjects of algebra and geometry into a branch of mathematics called *analytic geometry.* Essentially, analytic geometry allows us to consider the behavior of algebraic equations through the study of their corresponding geometric figures or graphs and to study geometric figures by looking at the corresponding algebraic equations.

To summarize: Analytic geometry considers two basic types of questions:

1. If we have an algebraic equation, can we draw the corresponding geometric "picture" or graph?
2. If we have a set of geometric conditions, can we find the corresponding algebraic equation?

All our work here involves the investigation of these two questions.

We must begin our work in analytic geometry by constructing the Cartesian coordinate system. We start with a horizontal number line and then intersect that line with a vertical number line, so that the point of intersection of the two lines is the respective zero point of the lines.

We call the horizontal line the *x axis* and the vertical line the *y axis.* The point at which the two axes intersect is called the *origin.* The normal positioning of the axes is such that the positive directions are to the *right* on the *x* axis and *upward* on the *y* axis.

With the coordinate system so constructed, we can now establish a one-to-one correspondence between points in the plane and *ordered pairs* of real numbers, written as

(x, y)

We agree that the first number is always the *x* value, or the *x coordinate,* and that the second number is always the *y* value, or the *y coordinate.*

The point *P* with coordinates (x, y)—often shortened for convenience to "the point (x, y)," and written $P(x, y)$—is located in the plane by the following rule:

Although there are differences of opinion about the "inventor" of analytic geometry, much of the subject's development is credited to René Descartes (1596–1650), a French mathematician and philosopher. The Cartesian coordinate system is named in his honor.

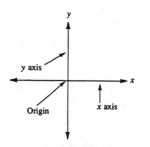

That is, for each point in the plane there is a unique ordered pair, and for every ordered pair there corresponds a unique point in the plane.

Other names are *abscissa* for the *x* coordinate and *ordinate* for the *y* coordinate.

LOCATING POINTS IN THE PLANE

For point P corresponding to the ordered pair (x, y):

1. The first number, or x coordinate, gives the directed distance from the y axis to the point

   To the right if the x coordinate is positive
   To the left if the x coordinate is negative

2. The second number, or y coordinate, gives the directed distance from the x axis to the point

   Upward if the y coordinate is positive
   Downward if the y coordinate is negative

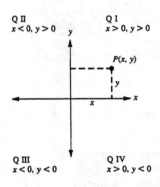

Q II
$x < 0, y > 0$

Q I
$x > 0, y > 0$

$P(x, y)$

Q III
$x < 0, y < 0$

Q IV
$x > 0, y < 0$

Note from our drawing that the coordinate axes separate the plane into four regions, called *quadrants*. They are numbered in a counterclockwise direction from the upper right, as shown. Each point in the plane is either in one of the four quadrants or on one of the coordinate axes.

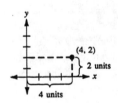

(4, 2)
2 units
4 units

Applying the rule above to *graph* (or *plot*) the point in the plane corresponding to the ordered pair (4, 2), we can move 4 units from the origin to the *right* along the x axis. We then move 2 units *upward* parallel to the y axis.

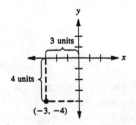

3 units
4 units
$(-3, -4)$

To locate the point corresponding to the ordered pair $(-3, -4)$, we move 3 units from the origin to the *left* along the x axis and then move 4 units *downward* and parallel to the y axis.

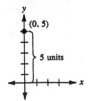

(0, 5)
5 units

To locate the point corresponding to the ordered pair $(0, 5)$, there is *no* movement along the x axis. We move 5 units *upward* along the y axis.

Example 1

Graph (or plot) in the plane points A, B, C, D, and E with the following coordinates:

In this text, we usually use the same scale on the x and y axes, but that is *not* required. In fact, for many applications, different scales are desirable.

$A(3, 5)$ $B(-2, -3)$ $C(-4, 0)$

$D(5, -1)$ $E(0, -6)$

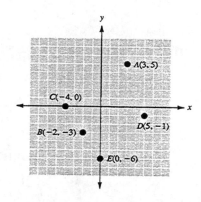

CHECK YOURSELF 1

Graph (or plot) the points with the following coordinates:

$P(2, 4)$ $Q(-5, 7)$ $R(3, 0)$

$T(0, 4)$ $S(-4, -3)$

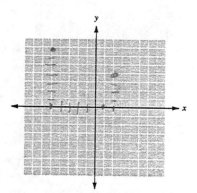

If we are given a point in the plane, reversing the process allows us to write the coordinates of that point by observing the distance and direction of the point from the x and y axes.

Example 2

Points U, W, X, Y, and Z are located in a Cartesian coordinate system, as shown. Give the coordinates of each point.

$U(4, 4)$, $W(-2, 0)$, $X(-4, -5)$,
$Y(5, -5)$, and $Z(-5, 6)$.

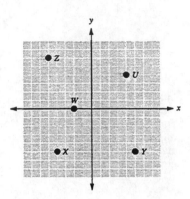

CHECK YOURSELF 2

Points A, B, C, D, and E are located in the Cartesian coordinate system, as shown. Give the coordinates of each point.

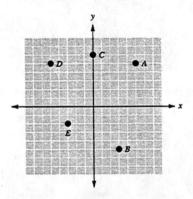

With the structure of the Cartesian coordinate system established, we now have the tools to approach the first basic question of analytic geometry. In our coverage on graphing linear equations we associate ordered pairs of real numbers with equations. Those ordered pairs will then be plotted in the plane to form the desired picture or graph.

CHECK YOURSELF ANSWERS

1.

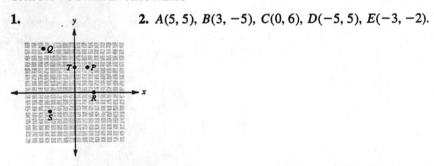

2. $A(5, 5)$, $B(3, -5)$, $C(0, 6)$, $D(-5, 5)$, $E(-3, -2)$.

Name _____

Date _____

Exercises

ANSWERS

Build Your Skills

1. _____

2. _____

Give the quadrant in which each of the following points is located or the axis on which the point lies.

3. _____

1. (4, 5)   **2.** (−3, 2)

4. _____

3. (−4, −3)   **4.** (2, −4)

5. _____

5. (5, 0)   **6.** (−5, 7)

6. _____

7. (−4, 7)   **8.** (−3, −7)

7. _____

9. (0, −7)   **10.** (−3, 0)

8. _____

9. _____

Graph each of the following points in the Cartesian coordinate system.

10. _____

11. A(3, 5)   **12.** B(−4, 6)

11. _____

13. C(−4, −6)   **14.** D(4, −6)

12. _____

15. E(−5, 0)   **16.** F(6, 0)

13. _____

17. G(−3, −4)   **18.** H(0, 4)

14. _____

15. _____

19. I(0, −5)   **20.** J(2, −3)

16. _____

17. _____

18. _____

19. _____

20. _____

ANSWERS

Give the coordinates (ordered pairs) associated with each of the indicated points.

21. _____   **21.** *P*   **22.** *Q*

22. _____   **23.** *R*   **24.** *S*

23. _____   **25.** *T*   **26.** *U*

24. _____   **27.** *V*   **28.** *W*

25. _____

              29. *X*   **30.** *Y*

26. _____

Skillscan (Linear Equations in One Variable)

27. _____   Solve each of the following equations for *y*.

28. _____   **a.** $2(3) + y = 4$ **b.** $3(-1) - y = -7$

29. _____   **c.** $5(-2) - y = -3$ **d.** $(-3)(-2) + y = 3$

30. _____   **e.** $3(-3) + 2y = 5$ **f.** $5(2) - 3y = -5$

a. _____   **g.** $(-2)(4) - 5y = 7$ **h.** $7(-3) + 2y = 1$

b. _____

c. _____

d. _____

ANSWERS

e. _____   **1.** Q I   **3.** Q III   **5.** On the *x* axis   **7.** Q II
              9. On the *y* axis   **11–19.** See figure at right   **21.** (3, 5)
              23. (−6, 0)   **25.** (−5, −4)   **27.** (0, −4)   **29.** (6, −2)
f. _____   **a.** −2   **b.** 4   **c.** −7   **d.** −3   **e.** 7   **f.** 5   **g.** −3
              h. 11

g. _____

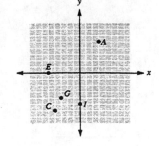

h. _____

Summary Text

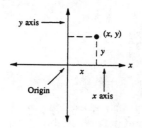

The *Cartesian coordinate system* allows us to establish a one-to-one correspondence between points in the plane and ordered pairs of real numbers:

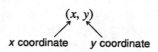

To *graph* (or *plot*) a point (x, y) in the plane:

1. Start at the origin.
2. Move to the right or left along the x axis according to the value of the x coordinate.
3. Move upward or downward and parallel to the y axis according to the value of the y coordinate.

Summary Exercises

Graph each of the following points in the Cartesian coordinate system.

1. $A(2, -3)$

2. $B(4, 5)$

3. $C(0, 5)$

4. $D(-2, -6)$

5. $E(-4, 1)$

6. $F(-6, 0)$

7. $G(5, -5)$

8. $H(0, -2)$

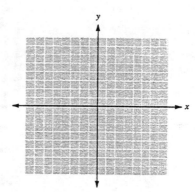

Graphing Linear Equations

OBJECTIVES
1. To graph linear equations
2. To graph linear equations by using intercepts
3. To graph vertical and horizontal lines

We will show in this section how the coordinate system can be used to provide "pictures," or graphs, of the solution set of an equation in two variables. First let's review the idea of a solution set.

We know that the solution set for an equation in one variable such as

In this case, the solution set has the single element 4. That value for *x* *satisfies* the equation—the equation is a true statement when 4 is substituted for *x*.

$$2x - 3 = x + 1$$

is the set of real number values for x which will make the equation a true statement.

What about an equation in two variables such as this?

$$x + 2y = 6$$

The solution set is defined in a similar fashion.

SOLUTION SET FOR AN EQUATION IN TWO VARIABLES

The *solution set* for an equation in two variables is the set containing all ordered pairs of real numbers (x, y) that will make the equation a true statement.

Example 1

The ordered pair (4, 1) is a member of the solution set of the equation

$$x + 2y = 6$$

because substituting 4 for x and 1 for y results in the true statement

$$4 + 2 \cdot 1 \overset{?}{=} 6$$
$$4 + 2 \overset{?}{=} 6$$
$$6 = 6$$

CHECK YOURSELF 1

Verify that $(2, -3)$ is a member of the solution set of the equation $2x - y = 7$.

To find solutions for an equation in two variables, note that in most cases, when a specific value for x is substituted in the equation, we can find the corresponding y value.

Example 2

We can also solve for y and write the equation as

$y = -3x + 9$

In this case, x is called the *independent variable* and y is the *dependent variable.*

As we assign values to x, we can find the corresponding values for y. The value for y *depends on* the value for x.

Suppose that $3x + y = 9$.

Let $x = 1$:

$$3 \cdot 1 + y = 9$$
$$3 + y = 9$$
$$y = 6$$

and the ordered pair $(1, 6)$ is a solution.

Let $x = 3$:

$$3 \cdot 3 + y = 9$$
$$9 + y = 9$$
$$y = 0$$

and $(3, 0)$ is a solution.

CHECK YOURSELF 2

Find three solutions for the equation $x - 3y = 6$.

The graph of the solution set of an equation in two variables, usually called the *graph of the equation,* is the set of all points with coordinates (x, y) that will satisfy the equation.

In this section we are interested in a particular type of equation in x and y and the graph of that equation. The equations considered involve x and y to the first power, and they are called *linear equations.*

LINEAR EQUATIONS

An equation of the form

ax + by = c

where *a* and *b* cannot both be zero, is called the *standard form for a line.* Its graph is always a straight line.

Example 3

Graph the equation

$$x + y = 5$$

Since two points determine a straight line, technically two points are all that is needed to graph the equation. You may want to locate at least one other point as a check of your work.

This is a linear equation in two variables. To draw its graph, we can begin by assigning values to x and finding the corresponding values for y. For instance, if $x = 1$, we have

$$1 + y = 5$$
$$y = 4$$

Therefore (1, 4) satisfies the equation and is in the graph of $x + y = 5$.

Similarly, (2, 3), (3, 2), and (4, 1) are also in the graph. Often these results are recorded in a table of values, as shown below.

$$x + y = 5$$

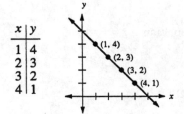

x	y
1	4
2	3
3	2
4	1

We then plot the points determined, and a straight line is drawn through those points. Every point on the graph of the equation $x + y = 5$ has coordinates which satisfy the equation, and every point with coordinates that satisfy the equation lies on the line.

CHECK YOURSELF 3

Graph the equation $2x - y = 6$.

The following algorithm summarizes our first approach to graphing a linear equation in two variables.

Streeter-Hutchison-Hoelzle:
Intermediate Algebra
Form A

Section
Graphing Linear Equations

Text

From Section 3.2 of the
traditional text

© McGraw-Hill, Inc., 1993

TO GRAPH A LINEAR EQUATION

STEP 1   Find at least three solutions for the equation, and write your re-
          sults in a table of values.

STEP 2   Graph the points associated with the ordered pairs found in step
          1.

STEP 3   Draw a straight line through the points plotted above to form the
          graph of the equation.

If the x intercept exists, it can be found by setting $y = 0$ in the equation and solving for x.

Similarly, if the y intercept exists, it is found by letting $x = 0$ and solving for y.

Two particular points are often used in graphing an equation because they are very easy to find. The *x intercept* of a line is the x coordinate of the point where the line crosses the x axis. The *y intercept* is the y coordinate of the point where the line crosses the y axis.

Example 4

Use the intercepts to graph the equation

$$x - 2y = 6$$

To find the x intercept, let $y = 0$.

$$x - 2 \cdot 0 = 6$$
$$x = 6$$

To find the y intercept, let $x = 0$.

$$0 - 2y = 6$$
$$-2y = 6$$
$$y = -3$$

Graphing the intercepts and drawing the line through those intercepts, we have the desired graph.

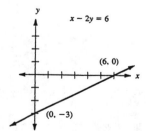

CHECK YOURSELF 4

Graph, using the intercept method.

$4x + 3y = 12$

The following algorithm summarizes the steps of graphing a straight line by the intercept method.

GRAPHING BY THE INTERCEPT METHOD

STEP 1   Find the x intercept. Let $y = 0$ and solve for x.

STEP 2   Find the y intercept. Let $x = 0$ and solve for y.

STEP 3   Plot the two intercepts determined in steps 1 and 2.

STEP 4   Draw a straight line through the intercepts.

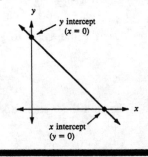

When can the intercept method not be used? Some straight lines have only one intercept. For instance, the graph of $x + 2y = 0$ passes through the origin. In this case, other points must be used to graph the equation.

Example 5

Graph $x + 2y = 0$.

Letting $y = 0$ gives

$$x + 2 \cdot 0 = 0$$
$$x = 0$$

The line passes through the origin.

Thus $(0, 0)$ is a solution, and the line has only one intercept.

We proceed by choosing any other convenient values for x.

If $x = 2$:

$$2 + 2y = 0$$
$$2y = -2$$
$$y = -1$$

So $(2, -1)$ is a solution. You can easily verify that $(4, -2)$ is also a solution.

Again, plotting the points and drawing the line through those points, we have the desired graph.

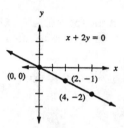

CHECK YOURSELF 5

Graph the equation $x - 3y = 0$.

There are two particular types of equations worthy of special attention. Their graphs are lines that are parallel to the x or y axis, and the equations are special cases of the general form

Again a and b cannot both be 0.

$$ax + by = c$$

in which either $a = 0$ or $b = 0$.

Here h and k are both constants.

VERTICAL OR HORIZONTAL LINES

1. A line with an equation of the form

$$x = h$$

is *vertical* (parallel to the y axis).
2. A line with an equation of the form

$$y = k$$

is *horizontal* (parallel to the x axis).

The following example illustrates both cases.

Example 6

(*a*) Graph the line with equation

$y = 3$

You can think of the equation in the equivalent form

$0 \cdot x + y = 3$

Note that any ordered pair of the form (__, 3) will satisfy the equation. Since x is multiplied by 0, y will always be equal to 3.

For instance, $(-2, 3)$ and $(5, 3)$ are on the graph. The graph, a horizontal line, is shown below.

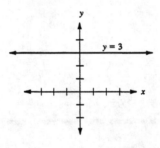

(*b*) Graph the line with equation

$x = -2$

In this case you can think of the equation in the equivalent form

$x + 0 \cdot y = -2$

Now any ordered pair of the form $(-2, \_\_)$ will satisfy the equation. Examples are $(-2, -1)$ and $(-2, 5)$. The graph, a vertical line, is shown below.

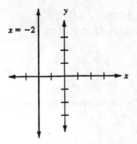

CHECK YOURSELF 6

Graph each equation.

1. $y = -3$ **2.** $x = 5$

Many applications involve linear relationships between variables, and the methods of this section can be used to picture or graph those relationships.

In our coverage of the Cartesian coordinate system we mention that the axes may have different scales. The following example is such an application involving a linear equation.

Example 7

A car rental agency advertises daily rates for a midsize automobile at \$20 per day plus 10¢ per mile. The cost per day C and the distance driven in miles s are then related by the following linear equation:

$$C = 0.10s + 20 \tag{1}$$

Graph the relationship between C and s.

First, we proceed by finding three points on the graph.

s	C
0	20
100	30
200	40

So as the distance s varies from 0 to 200 mi, the cost C changes from \$20 to \$40. To draw a "reasonable" graph, it makes sense to choose a different scale for the horizontal (or s) axis than for the vertical (or C) axis.

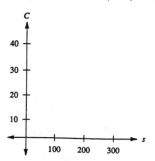

We have chosen units of 100 for the s axis and units of 10 for the C axis.

The graph can then be completed as shown below.

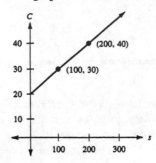

Note that the graph of Equation (1) does not extend beyond the first quadrant. This is due to the nature of our problem in which solutions are only realistic when $s \geq 0$.

CHECK YOURSELF 7

A salesperson's monthly salary S is based on a fixed salary of $1200 plus 8 percent of all monthly sales x. The linear equation relating S and x is

$$S = 0.08x + 1200$$

Graph the relationship between S and x. *Hint:* Find the monthly salary for sales of $0, $10,000, and $20,000.

$X - 3Y = 4$

CHECK YOURSELF ANSWERS

1. $2(2) - (-3) \stackrel{?}{=} 7$
   $4 + 3 \stackrel{?}{=} 7$
   $7 = 7.$

2. $(0, -2)$, $(3, -1)$, and $(6, 0)$ are three possible solutions.

3. $2x - y = 6.$

x	y
0	−6
1	−4
2	−2

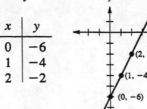

4.

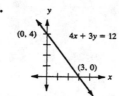

5.

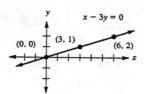

6. (1)

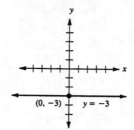

(2)

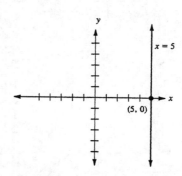

7.

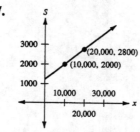

Name _____

Date _____

Exercises

ANSWERS

Build Your Skills

1. _____

2. _____

3. _____

4. _____

5. _____

6. _____

Complete each table of values, and then graph the given equations.

1. $y = x + 1$

x	y
-2	
-1	
0	
1	
2	

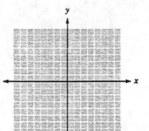

2. $x + y = 3$

x	y
-2	
-1	
0	
1	
2	

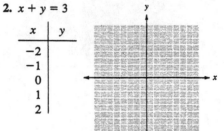

3. $y = x - 4$

x	y
-2	
-1	
0	
1	
2	

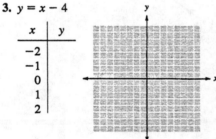

4. $2x - y = 6$

x	y
-1	
0	
1	
2	
3	

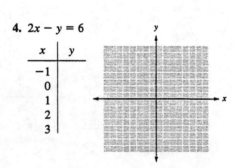

Graph each of the following equations.

5. $x + y = 6$

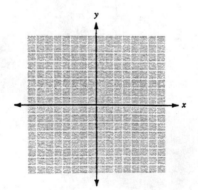

6. $x - y = 5$

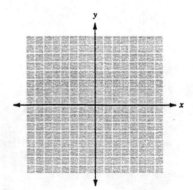

ANSWERS

7. _____

8. _____

9. _____

10. _____

11. _____

12. _____

7. $y = x - 2$

8. $y = x + 4$

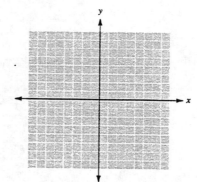

9. $y = x + 1$

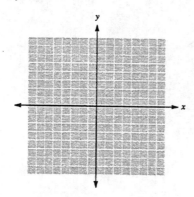

10. $y = 2x + 1$

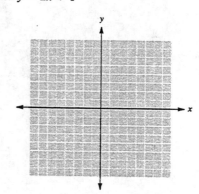

11. $y = -2x + 1$

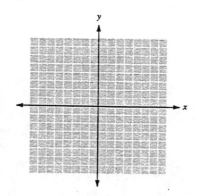

12. $y = -3x + 1$

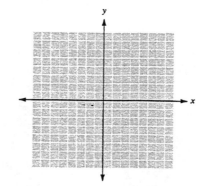

ANSWERS

13. _____

14. _____

15. _____

16. _____

17. _____

18. _____

13. $y = \dfrac{1}{2}x - 3$

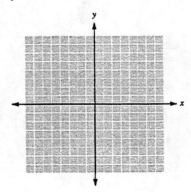

14. $y = 2x - 3$

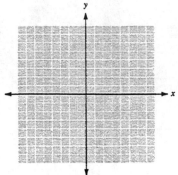

15. $y = -x - 3$

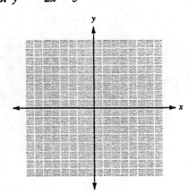

16. $y = -2x - 3$

17. $x + 2y = 0$

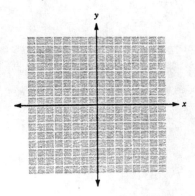

18. $x - 3y = 0$

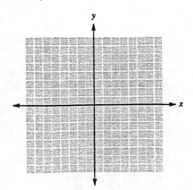

ANSWERS

Find the x and y intercepts, and then graph each of the following equations.

19. _____

19. $x - 2y = 4$

20. _____

20. $x + 3y = 6$

21. _____

22. _____

23. _____

24. _____

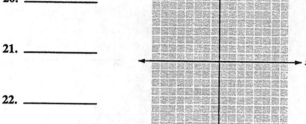

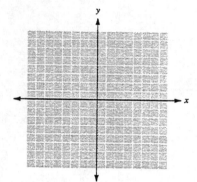

21. $2x - y = 6$

22. $3x + 2y = 12$

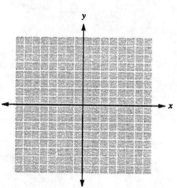

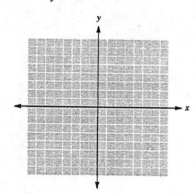

23. $2x + 5y = 10$

24. $2x - 3y = 6$

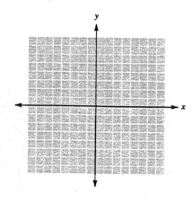

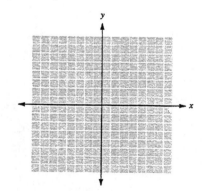

ANSWERS

25. _____

26. _____

27. _____

28. _____

29. _____

30. _____

25. $x + 4y + 8 = 0$

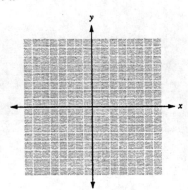

26. $2x - y + 6 = 0$

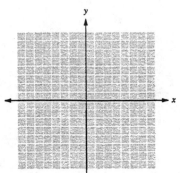

Graph each of the following equations.

27. $x = 4$

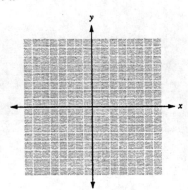

28. $x = -3$

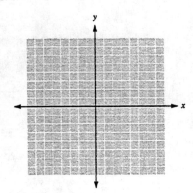

29. $y = 4$

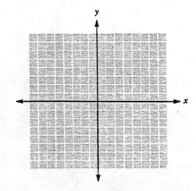

30. $y = -5$

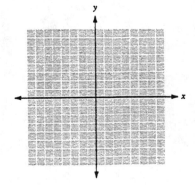

ANSWERS

31. _____

32. _____

33. _____

31. A car rental agency charges $12 per day and 8¢ per mile for the use of a compact automobile. The cost of the rental C and the number of miles driven per day s are related by the linear equation

$$C = 0.08s + 12$$

Graph the relationship between C and s. Be sure to select appropriate scaling for the s and C axes.

32. A bank has the following structure for charges on a checking account. The monthly charge consists of a fixed amount of $8 and an additional charge of 5¢ per check. The monthly cost of an account C and the number of checks written per month n are related by the linear equation

$$C = 0.05n + 8$$

Graph the relationship between C and n.

33. A college has tuition charges based on the following pattern. Tuition is $25 per credit-hour plus a fixed student fee of $40. The total tuition charge T and the number of credit-hours taken h are related by the linear equation

$$T = 25h + 40$$

Graph the relationship between T and h.

ANSWERS

34. _____

34. A salesperson's weekly salary is based on a fixed amount of $200 plus 10 percent of the total amount of weekly sales. The weekly salary S and the amount of weekly sales x (in dollars) are related by the linear equation

$$S = 0.1x + 200$$

Graph the relationship between S and x.

a. _____

b. _____

c. _____

Skillscan (Operations with Signed Numbers)

Evaluate each of the following expressions.

d. _____

a. $\dfrac{6 - 3}{7 - 4}$

b. $\dfrac{11 - 2}{6 - 3}$

e. _____

c. $\dfrac{-8 - 4}{-3 - 3}$

d. $\dfrac{-14 - 2}{2 - 6}$

e. $\dfrac{5 - (-2)}{4 - 2}$

f. $\dfrac{-5 - (-4)}{2 - (-2)}$

f. _____

g. $\dfrac{-5 - (-5)}{7 - 2}$

h. $\dfrac{-8 + (-8)}{-4 + 4}$

g. _____

h. _____

ANSWERS

1. $y = x + 1$

x	y
-2	-1
-1	0
0	1
1	2
2	3

3. $y = x - 4$

x	y
-2	-6
-1	-5
0	-4
1	-3
2	-2

5. $x + y = 6$

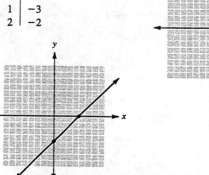

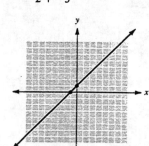

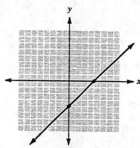

7. $y = x - 2$

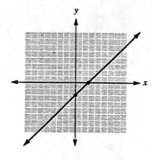

9. $y = x + 1$

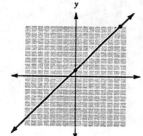

11. $y = -2x + 1$

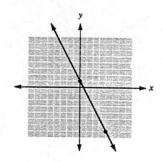

13. $y = \dfrac{1}{2}x - 3$

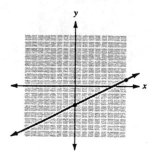

15. $y = -x - 3$

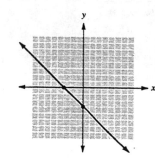

17. $x + 2y = 0$

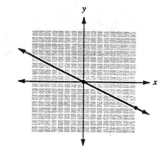

43

19. $x - 2y = 4$
Intercepts: $(4, 0), (0, -2)$

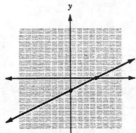

21. $2x - y = 6$
Intercepts: $(3, 0), (0, -6)$

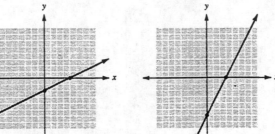

23. $2x + 5y = 10$
Intercepts: $(5, 0), (0, 2)$

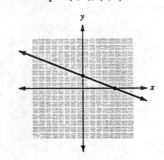

25. $x + 4y + 8 = 0$
Intercepts: $(-8, 0), (0, -2)$

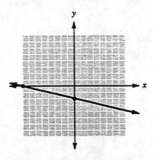

27. $x = 4$

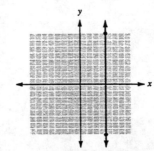

29. $y = 4$

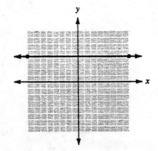

31. $C = 0.08s + 12$

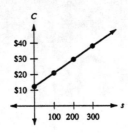

33. $T = 25h + 40$

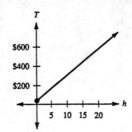

a. 1   **b.** 3   **c.** 2   **d.** 4   **e.** $\dfrac{7}{2}$ **f.** $-\dfrac{1}{4}$ **g.** 0   **h.** Undefined

Summary Text

(1, 3) is a solution for

$3x + 2y = 9$

because

$3 \cdot 1 + 2 \cdot 3 = 9$

is a true statement.

The *solution set* for an equation in two variables is the set of ordered pairs of real numbers (x, y) which will make the equation a true statement.

An equation of the form

$$ax + by = c$$

where a and b cannot both be zero, is a *linear equation in two variables*. The graph of such an equation is always a *straight line*. An equation in form (1) is called the *standard form* for the equation of a line.

To graph

$y = 2x - 3$

(0, −3), (1, −1), and (2, 1) are solutions.

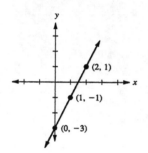

To graph a linear equation:

1. Find at least three solutions for the equation, and write your results in a table of values.
2. Graph the points associated with the ordered pairs found above.
3. Draw a straight line through the points plotted above, to form the graph of the equation.

A second approach to graphing linear equations uses the x and y *intercepts* of the line. The x intercept is the x coordinate of the point where the line intersects the x axis. The y intercept is the y coordinate of the point where the line intersects the y axis.

To graph by the intercept method:

1. Find the x intercept. Let $y = 0$, and solve for x.
2. Find the y intercept. Let $x = 0$, and solve for y.
3. Plot the two intercepts determined above.
4. Draw a straight line through the points of intercept.

Summary Exercises

Graph each of the following equations.

1. $x + y = 7$

2. $x - y = 8$

3. $y = 4x + 3$

4. $y = -3x - 2$

5. $x + 3y = 0$

6. $x - 4y = 0$

7. $x + 4y = 8$

8. $5x - 2y = 10$

9. $3x - 5y = 15$

10. $4x + 3y = 12$

11. $x = 6$

12. $y = -3$

13. $y = x - 4$

14. $y = x - 1$

Self-Test Questions

Graph each of the following equations.

1. $y = 3x + 2$

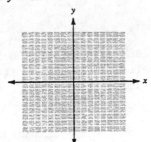

2. $y - 2x = 0$

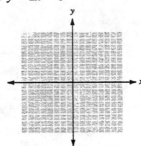

3. $3x - 2y = 6$

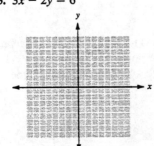

4. $x = -4$

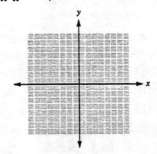

Self-Test Answers

1.

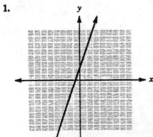

2.

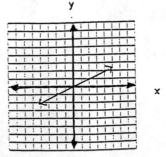

3.

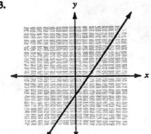

4.

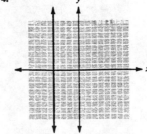

The Slope of a Line

OBJECTIVES

1. To find the slope of a line
2. To find the slope of a line parallel to a given line
3. To find the slope of a line perpendicular to a given line
4. To graph linear equations by using the slope of a line

Given a set of geometric conditions, we must be able to find the corresponding algebraic equation that satisfies those conditions.

For instance, we will be concerned with finding the equation of a line, given information such as a point on the line and the inclination of that line. In this section we start by defining the *slope* of a line, which will give us a numerical measure of the steepness, or inclination, of that line.

To define a formula for slope, choose any two distinct points on the line, say P with coordinates (x_1, y_1) and Q with coordinates (x_2, y_2). As we move along the line from P to Q, the x value, or coordinate, changes from x_1 to x_2. That change in x, also called the *horizontal change*, is $x_2 - x_1$. Similarly, as we move from P to Q, the corresponding change in y, called the *vertical change*, is $y_2 - y_1$. The *slope* is then defined as the ratio of the vertical change to the horizontal change. The letter m is used to represent slope, which we now define as follows.

The difference $x_2 - x_1$ is often called the *run*. The difference $y_2 - y_1$ is the *rise*. So the slope can be thought of as "rise over run."

Note that $x_1 \neq x_2$ or $x_2 - x_1 \neq 0$ ensures that the denominator is nonzero, so that the slope is defined. It also means the line cannot be vertical.

SLOPE OF A LINE

The *slope* of a line through two distinct points $P(x_1, y_1)$ and $Q(x_2, y_2)$ is given by

$$m = \frac{\text{change in } y}{\text{change in } x} = \frac{y_2 - y_1}{x_2 - x_1} \qquad (1)$$

where $x_1 \neq x_2$.

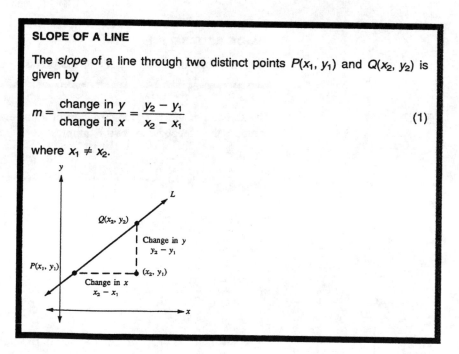

Let's look at some examples using the definition.

47

Example 1

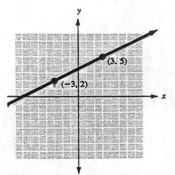

Find the slope of the line through the points $(-3, 2)$ and $(3, 5)$.

Let $(x_1, y_1) = (-3, 2)$ and $(x_2, y_2) = (3, 5)$. From the definition we have

$$m = \frac{5 - 2}{3 - (-3)} = \frac{3}{6} = \frac{1}{2}$$

Note that if the pairs are reversed, so that

$$(x_1, y_1) = (3, 5) \qquad \text{and} \qquad (x_2, y_2) = (-3, 2)$$

then we have

$$m = \frac{2 - 5}{-3 - 3} = \frac{-3}{-6} = \frac{1}{2}$$

The slope in either case is the same.

Note: The work of Example 1 suggests that no matter which point is chosen as (x_1, y_1) or (x_2, y_2), the slope formula will give the same result. You must simply stay with your choice once it is made, and *not* reverse the order of the subtraction in your calculations.

CHECK YOURSELF 1

Find the slope of the line through the points $(-2, -1)$ and $(1, 1)$.

The slope indicates both the direction of a line and its steepness. First we will compare the steepness of two examples.

Example 2

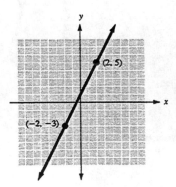

Find the slope of the line through $(-2, -3)$ and $(2, 5)$.

Again, by Equation (1),

$$m = \frac{5 - (-3)}{2 - (-2)} = \frac{8}{4} = 2$$

Compare the lines of Examples 1 and 2. In Example 1 the line has slope $\frac{1}{2}$. The slope here is 2. Now look at the two lines. Do you see the idea of slope as measuring steepness? The greater the absolute value of the slope, the steeper the line.

CHECK YOURSELF 2

Find the slope of the line through the points $(-1, 2)$ and $(2, 7)$. Draw a sketch of this line and the line of the Check Yourself 1 exercise on the same coordinate axes. Compare the lines and the two slopes.

The sign of the slope indicates in which direction the line tilts. The following example illustrates.

Example 3

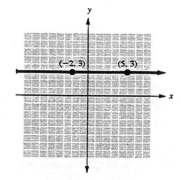

Find the slope of the line through the points $(-1, 2)$ and $(4, -3)$.

We see that

$$m = \frac{-3 - 2}{4 - (-1)} = \frac{-5}{5} = -1$$

Now the slope is negative.

Comparing this with our previous examples, we see that

1. In the first two examples, the lines were rising from left to right, and the slope was *positive*.
2. In this example, the line is falling from left to right, and the slope is *negative*.

CHECK YOURSELF 3

Find the slope of the line through the points $(-2, 5)$ and $(4, -1)$.

Let's continue by looking at the slopes of lines in two particular cases.

Example 4

Find the slope of the line through $(-2, 3)$ and $(5, 3)$.

$$m = \frac{3 - 3}{5 - (-2)} = \frac{0}{7} = 0$$

The slope of the line is 0. Note that the line is parallel to the x axis and $y_2 - y_1 = 0$. *The slope of any horizontal line will be 0.*

CHECK YOURSELF 4

Find the slope of the line through the points $(-2, -4)$ and $(3, -4)$.

Example 5

Find the slope of the line through the points $(1, -3)$ and $(1, 4)$.

$$m = \frac{4 - (-3)}{1 - 1} = \frac{7}{0}$$

Here the line is parallel to the y axis, and $x_2 - x_1$ (the denominator of our slope formula) is 0. Since division by 0 is undefined, we say that the slope is *undefined*, and that will be the case for *any vertical line*.

Note: Be very careful not to confuse a slope of 0 (in the case of a horizontal line) with an undefined slope or no slope (in the case of a vertical line).

CHECK YOURSELF 5

Find the slope of the line through the points $(2, -3)$ and $(2, 7)$.

The following summarizes our work of the previous examples.

1. If the slope of a line is positive, the line is rising from left to right.
2. If the slope of a line is negative, the line is falling from left to right.
3. If the slope of a line is 0, the line is horizontal.
4. If the slope of a line is undefined, the line is vertical. We can also say that the line has no slope in this case.

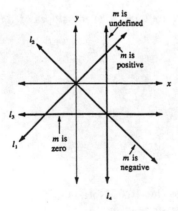

There are two more important results regarding the slope. Recall from geometry that two distinct lines in the plane either intersect at a point or never intersect. Two lines in the plane that do not intersect are called *parallel lines*. It can be shown that two distinct parallel lines will always have the same slope, and we can state the following.

SLOPE OF PARALLEL LINES

For nonvertical lines L_1 and L_2, if line L_1 has slope m_1 and line L_2 has slope m_2, then

L_1 is parallel to L_2 if and only if $m_1 = m_2$

Note: All vertical lines are parallel to each other.

This means that if the lines are parallel, then their slopes are equal. Conversely, if the slopes are equal, then the lines are parallel.

Mathematicians use the symbol

$$\Leftrightarrow$$

to represent "if and only if."

Example 6

Are lines L_1 through $(2, 3)$ and $(4, 6)$ and L_2 through $(-4, 2)$ and $(0, 8)$ parallel, or do they intersect?

$$m_1 = \frac{6 - 3}{4 - 2} = \frac{3}{2}$$

$$m_2 = \frac{8 - 2}{0 - (-4)} = \frac{6}{4} = \frac{3}{2}$$

These come out equal

Unless, of course, L_1 and L_2 are actually the *same line.* In this case a quick sketch will show that the lines are distinct.

Since the slopes of the lines are equal, the lines are parallel. They do *not* intersect.

CHECK YOURSELF 6

Are lines L_1 through $(-2, -1)$ and $(1, 4)$ and L_2 through $(-3, 4)$ and $(0, 8)$ parallel, or do they intersect?

Two lines are perpendicular if they intersect at right angles. Also if two lines (which are not vertical or horizontal) are perpendicular, their slopes are the negative reciprocals of each other. We can then state the following result for perpendicular lines.

$m_1 =$

Streeter-Hutchison-Hoelzle:
Intermediate Algebra
Form A

Section
The Slope of a Line

Text

From Section 3.3 of the
traditional text

© McGraw-Hill, Inc., 1993

SLOPE OF PERPENDICULAR LINES

For nonvertical lines L_1 and L_2, if line L_1 has slope m_1 and line L_2 has slope m_2, then

L_1 is perpendicular to L_2 if and only if $m_1 = -\dfrac{1}{m_2}$

or equivalently

$$m_1 \cdot m_2 = -1$$

Note: Horizontal lines are perpendicular to vertical lines.

Example 7

Are lines L_1 through $(-2, 3)$ and $(1, 7)$ and L_2 through $(2, 4)$ and $(6, 1)$ perpendicular?

Note:

$$\left(\frac{4}{3}\right)\left(-\frac{3}{4}\right) = -1$$

$$m_1 = \frac{7 - 3}{1 - (-2)} = \frac{4}{3}$$

$$m_2 = \frac{1 - 4}{6 - 2} = -\frac{3}{4}$$

Since the slopes are negative reciprocals, the lines are perpendicular.

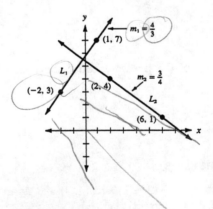

CHECK YOURSELF 7

Are lines L_1 through $(1, 3)$ and $(4, 1)$ and L_2 through $(-2, 4)$ and $(2, 10)$ perpendicular?

Given the equation of a line, we can also find its slope, as the following example illustrates.

Example 8

Note: Let's try solving the original equation for y:

$$3x + 2y = 6$$
$$2y = -3x + 6$$
$$y = -\frac{3}{2}x + 3$$

Consider the coefficient of x. What do you observe?

Find the slope of the line with equation $3x + 2y = 6$.

First, find any two points on the line. In this case, $(2, 0)$ and $(0, 3)$, the x and y intercepts, will work and are easy to find. From our slope formula

$$m = \frac{0 - 3}{2 - 0} = \frac{-3}{2} = -\frac{3}{2}$$

The slope of the line with equation $3x + 2y = 6$ is $-\frac{3}{2}$.

$$4y = -3x + 12$$
$$y = +\frac{3}{4}x + 3$$

CHECK YOURSELF 8

Find the slope of the line with equation $3x - 4y = 12$.

The slope of a line can also be useful in graphing a line. The following example uses the slope of a line in sketching its graph.

Example 9

Suppose a line has slope $\frac{3}{2}$ and passes through the point $(5, 2)$. Graph the line.

First locate the point $(5, 2)$ in the coordinate system. Now since the slope, $\frac{3}{2}$, is the ratio of the change in y to the change in x, move 2 units to the right in the x direction and then 3 units up in the y direction. This determines a second point, here $(7, 5)$, and we can draw our graph.

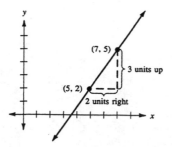

CHECK YOURSELF 9

Graph the line with slope $-\dfrac{3}{4}$ which passes through the point $(2, 3)$.

Hint: Consider the x change as 4 units and the y change as -3 units (down).

___

Since, given a point on a line and its slope, we can graph the line, we should also be able to write its equation.

CHECK YOURSELF ANSWERS

1. $m = \dfrac{2}{3}$.   **2.** $m = \dfrac{5}{3}$.   **3.** $m = -1$.   **4.** 0.

5. Undefined.   **6.** The lines intersect.   **7.** The lines are perpendicular.

8. $m = \dfrac{3}{4}$.   **9.**

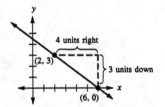

Name _____
Exercises
Date _____

ANSWERS

Build Your Skills

1. _____

Find the slope (if it exists) of the line determined by the following pairs of points. Sketch each line so that you can compare the slopes.

2. _____

1. $(2, 3)$ and $(4, 7)$ **2.** $(-1, 2)$ and $(5, 3)$

3. _____

3. $(2, -3)$ and $(-2, -5)$ **4.** $(0, 0)$ and $(5, 7)$

4. _____

5. _____

5. $(2, 5)$ and $(-3, 5)$ **6.** $(-2, -4)$ and $(5, 3)$

6. _____

7. $(-1, 4)$ and $(-1, 7)$ **8.** $(4, 2)$ and $(-2, 5)$

7. _____

9. $(8, -3)$ and $(-2, -5)$ **10.** $(4, -3)$ and $(-2, 7)$

8. _____

9. _____

11. $(-4, -3)$ and $(2, -7)$ **12.** $(3, 6)$ and $(3, -4)$

10. _____

Find the slope of the line determined by each equation.

11. _____

13. $y = -3x - \dfrac{1}{2}$ **14.** $y = \dfrac{1}{4}x + 3$

12. _____

13. _____

15. $y + \dfrac{1}{2}x = 2$ **16.** $2y - 3x + 5 = 0$

14. _____

15. _____

17. $2x - 3y = 6$ **18.** $x + 4y = 4$

16. _____

19. $3x + 4y = 12$ **20.** $x - 3y = 9$

17. _____

18. _____

19. _____

20. _____

ANSWERS

Are the following pairs of lines parallel, perpendicular, or neither?

21. _____

21. L_1 through $(-2, -3)$ and $(4, 3)$
    L_2 through $(3, 5)$ and $(5, 7)$

22. L_1 through $(-2, 4)$ and $(1, 8)$
    L_2 through $(-1, -1)$ and $(-5, 2)$

22. _____

23. L_1 through $(8, 5)$ and $(3, -2)$
    L_2 through $(-2, 4)$ and $(4, -1)$

24. L_1 through $(-2, -3)$ and $(3, -1)$
    L_2 through $(-3, 1)$ and $(7, 5)$

23. _____

25. L_1 with equation $x - 3y = 6$
    L_2 with equation $2x + 4y = 5$

26. L_1 with equation $x + 2y = 4$
    L_2 with equation $3x + y = 3$

24. _____

25. _____

27. Find the slope of any line parallel to the line through points $(-2, 3)$ and $(4, 5)$.

26. _____

28. Find the slope of any line perpendicular to the line through points $(0, 5)$ and $(-3, -4)$.

27. _____

29. A line passing through $(-1, 2)$ and $(4, y)$ is parallel to a line with slope 2. What is the value of y?

28. _____

30. A line passing through $(2, 3)$ and $(5, y)$ is perpendicular to a line with slope $\dfrac{3}{4}$. What is the value of y?

29. _____

30. _____

If points P, Q, and R are collinear (lie on the same line), the slope of the line through P and Q must equal the slope of the line through Q and R. Use the slope concept to determine whether the following sets of points are collinear.

31. _____

31. $P(-2, -3)$, $Q(3, 2)$, and $R(4, 3)$

32. $P(-5, 1)$, $Q(-2, 4)$, and $R(4, 9)$

32. _____

33. $P(0, 0)$, $Q(2, 4)$, and $R(-3, 6)$

34. $P(-2, 5)$, $Q(-5, 2)$, and $R(1, 12)$

33. _____

35. $P(2, 4)$, $Q(-3, -6)$, and $R(-4, 8)$

36. $P(-1, 5)$, $Q(2, -4)$, and $R(-2, 8)$

34. _____

35. _____

36. _____

ANSWERS

Graph the lines through each of the specified points having the given slope.

37. _____

37. $(0, 1)$, $m = 3$ **38.** $(0, -2)$, $m = -2$ **39.** $(3, -1)$, $m = 2$

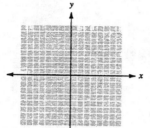  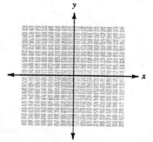

38. _____

39. _____

40. $(2, -3)$, $m = -3$ **41.** $(2, 3)$, $m = \dfrac{2}{3}$ **42.** $(-2, 1)$, $m = -\dfrac{3}{4}$

40. _____

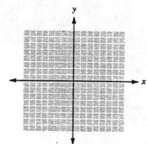 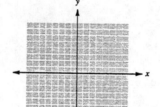 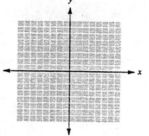

41. _____

43. $(4, 2)$, $m = 0$ **44.** $(3, 0)$, m is undefined

42. _____

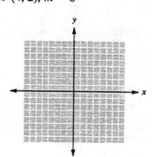 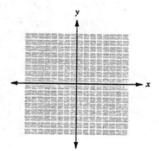

43. _____

45. On the same graph, sketch lines with slope 2 through each of the following points: $(-1, 0)$, $(2, 0)$, and $(5, 0)$.

44. _____

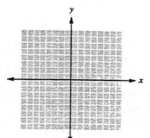

45. _____

57

ANSWERS

46. _____

46. On the same graph, sketch one line with slope $\frac{1}{3}$ and one line with slope -3, having both pass through point $(2, 3)$.

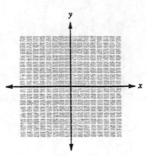

ANSWERS

1. 2   **3.** $\frac{1}{2}$ **5.** 0   **7.** Undefined   **9.** $\frac{1}{5}$ **11.** $-\frac{2}{3}$ **13.** -3 **15.** $-\frac{1}{2}$

17. $\frac{2}{3}$ **19.** $-\frac{3}{4}$ **21.** Parallel   **23.** Neither   **25.** Perpendicular   **27.** $\frac{1}{3}$ **29.** 12

31. Collinear   **33.** Not collinear   **35.** Not collinear

37.   **39.**   **41.**

43.      **45.**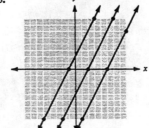

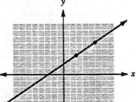

Summary Text

The *slope* of a line gives a numerical measure of the direction and steepness, or inclination, of the line. The slope m of a line containing the distinct points in the plane (x_1, y_1) and (x_2, y_2) is given by

$$m = \frac{y_2 - y_1}{x_2 - x_1} \qquad x_2 \neq x_1$$

The slopes of two nonvertical parallel lines are equal. The slopes of two non-vertical perpendicular lines are the negative reciprocals of each other.

Summary Exercises

Find the slope (if it exists) of the line determined by each of the following pairs of points.

1. $(3, 2)$ and $(5, 8)$

2. $(-2, 5)$ and $(1, -1)$

3. $(2, -4)$ and $(3, 5)$

4. $(-3, -4)$ and $(3, 0)$

5. $(4, -3)$ and $(4, 4)$

6. $(4, -2)$ and $(-2, -2)$

7. $(2, -4)$ and $(-1, -3)$

8. $(5, -2)$ and $(5, 3)$

Find the slope of the line determined by each of the following equations.

9. $3x + 2y = 6$

10. $x - 4y = 8$

Are the following pairs of lines parallel, perpendicular, or neither?

11. L_1 through $(-3, -2)$ and $(1, 3)$
L_2 through $(0, 3)$ and $(4, 8)$

12. L_1 through $(-4, 1)$ and $(2, -3)$
L_2 through $(0, -3)$ and $(2, 0)$

13. L_1 with equation $x + 2y = 6$
L_2 with equation $x + 3y = 9$

14. L_1 with equation $4x - 6y = 18$
L_2 with equation $2x - 3y = 6$

Self-Test Questions

Find the slope of the line determined by each of the following pairs of points.

1. $(-2, -3)$ and $(3, 5)$

2. $(-1, 3)$ and $(3, -2)$

Are the following pairs of lines parallel, perpendicular, or neither?

3. L_1 through $(-1, -4)$ and $(3, 2)$
   L_2 through $(0, 5)$ and $(3, 3)$

4. L_1 through $(-2, 1)$ and $(3, 4)$
   L_2 through $(-4, 4)$ and $(1, 7)$

Find the slope of each line.

5. $2x - 3y = 5$

6. $5x + 2y = 1$

Self-Test Answers

1. $\dfrac{8}{5}$ 2. $-\dfrac{5}{4}$ 3. Perpendicular   4. Parallel   5. $\dfrac{2}{3}$ 6. $-\dfrac{5}{2}$

Forms of Linear Equations

OBJECTIVES

1. To write the equation of a line given its slope and y intercept
2. To write the equation of a line given its slope and any point on the line
3. To write the equation of a line given two points
4. To write the equation of a line given a point and a parallel or perpendicular line

The special form

$$ax + by = c$$

where a and b cannot both be zero, is called the *standard form* for a linear equation. In this section we use the slope concept developed in our coverage of the slope of a line to write the equations of lines, given various sets of geometric conditions. For this purpose we develop two further special forms for the equations of a line which will prove useful in a variety of situations.

First, suppose we know the y intercept of a line L and its slope m. Since b is the y intercept, we know that the point with coordinates $(0, b)$ is on the line. Let $P(x, y)$ be any other point on that line. Using $(0, b)$ as (x_1, y_1) and (x, y) as (x_2, y_2) in our slope formula, we have

> Just as m is used for the slope, b is used for the y intercept.

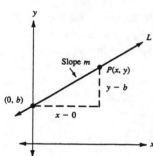

$$m = \frac{y - b}{x - 0} \tag{1}$$

or

$$m = \frac{y - b}{x} \tag{2}$$

Multiplying both sides of Equation (2) by x gives

$$mx = y - b$$

or

$$y = mx + b \tag{3}$$

Equation (3) will be satisfied by any point on line L, including $(0, b)$. It is called the *slope-intercept form* for a line, and we can state the following general result.

SLOPE-INTERCEPT FORM FOR THE EQUATION OF A LINE

The equation of a line with y intercept b and slope m can be written as

$$y = mx + b$$

Example 1

Write the equation of the line with slope 2 and y intercept 3.

Here $m = 2$ and b (the y intercept) = 3. Applying the slope-intercept form, we have

$$y = 2x + 3$$

as the equation of the specified line.

The x coefficient is 2; the y intercept is 3.

It is easy to see that whenever a linear equation is written in slope-intercept form (that is, solved for y), the slope of the line is simply the x coefficient and the y intercept is given by the constant.

CHECK YOURSELF 1

Write the equation of the line with slope $-\dfrac{2}{3}$ and y intercept -3.

Note that the slope-intercept form now gives us a second (and generally more efficient) means of finding the slope of a line whose equation is written in standard form. Recall that in our coverage of the slope of a line we determined two specific points on the line and then applied the slope formula. Now, rather than using specific points, we can simply solve the given equation for y to rewrite the equation in the slope-intercept form and identify the slope of the line as the x coefficient.

Example 2

Find the slope and y intercept of the line with equation

$$2x + 3y = 3$$

To write the equation in slope-intercept form, we solve for y:

$$2x + 3y = 3$$

Subtract $2x$ from both sides.

$$3y = -2x + 3$$

Divide by 3.

$$y = -\frac{2}{3}x + 1$$

We now see that the slope of the line is $-\dfrac{2}{3}$, and the y intercept is 1.

CHECK YOURSELF 2

Find the slope and y intercept of the line with equation

$$3x - 4y = 8$$

We can also use the slope-intercept form to determine whether the graphs of given equations will be parallel, intersecting, or perpendicular lines.

Example 3

Show that the graphs of the equations $3x + 2y = 4$ and $6x + 4y = 12$ are parallel lines.

First, we solve each of the equations for y:

$$3x + 2y = 4$$
$$2y = -3x + 4$$
$$y = -\frac{3}{2}x + 2 \tag{1}$$

Note that the slopes are the same, but the y intercepts are different. Therefore the lines are distinct.

$$6x + 4y = 12$$
$$4y = -6x + 12$$
$$y = -\frac{3}{2}x + 3 \tag{2}$$

Since the two lines have the same slope, here $-\frac{3}{2}$, the lines are parallel.

CHECK YOURSELF 3

Show that the graphs of the equations

$$-3x + 2y = 4 \qquad \text{and} \qquad 2x + 3y = 9$$

are perpendicular lines.

The slope-intercept form can also be used in graphing a line, as the following example illustrates.

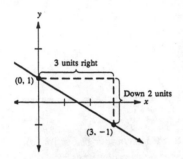

We treat $-\dfrac{2}{3}$ as $\dfrac{-2}{+3}$ to move over 3 units and down 2 units.

Example 4

Graph the line $2x + 3y = 3$.

In Example 2, we found that the slope-intercept form for this equation was

$$y = -\frac{2}{3}x + 1$$

To graph the line, plot the y intercept at $(0, 1)$. Now since the slope m is equal to $-\dfrac{2}{3}$, from $(0, 1)$ we move *over* 3 units and then *down* 2 units, to locate a second point on the graph of the line, here $(3, -1)$.

We can now draw a line through the two points to complete the graph.

CHECK YOURSELF 4

Graph the line with equation

$$3x - 4y = 8$$

Hint: You worked with this equation in a previous Check Yourself exercise.

The following algorithm summarizes the use of graphing with the slope-intercept form.

The desired form for the equation is

$y = mx + b$

GRAPHING BY USING THE SLOPE-INTERCEPT FORM

1. Write the original equation of the line in slope-intercept form.
2. Determine the slope m and the y intercept b.
3. Plot the y intercept at $(0, b)$.
4. Use m (the change in y over the change in x) to determine a second point on the desired line.
5. Draw a line through the two points determined above to complete the graph.

Often in mathematics it is useful to be able to write the equation of a line, given its slope and *any* point on the line. We will now derive a third special form for a line for this purpose.

Suppose that a line has slope m and that it passes through the known point $P(x_1, y_1)$. Let $Q(x, y)$ be any other point on the line. Once again we can use the definition of slope and write

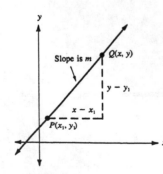

$$m = \frac{y - y_1}{x - x_1} \tag{1}$$

Multiplying both sides of Equation (1) by $x - x_1$, we have

$$m(x - x_1) = y - y_1$$

or

$$y - y_1 = m(x - x_1) \qquad (2)$$

Equation (2) is called the *point-slope form* for the equation of a line, and all points lying on the line [including (x_1, y_1)] will satisfy this equation. We can state the following general result.

The equation of a line with undefined slope passing through the point (x_1, y_1) is given by $x = x_1$.

POINT-SLOPE FORM FOR THE EQUATION OF A LINE

The equation of a line with slope m that passes through point (x_1, y_1) is given by

$$y - y_1 = m(x - x_1)$$

Example 5

Write the equation for the line that passes through point $(3, -1)$ with a slope of 3.

Letting $(x_1, y_1) = (3, -1)$ and $m = 3$ in point-slope form, we have

$$y - (-1) = 3(x - 3)$$

or

$$y + 1 = 3x - 9$$

We can write the final result in slope-intercept form as

$$y = 3x - 10$$

CHECK YOURSELF 5

Write the equation of the line that passes through point $(-2, -4)$ with a slope of $\dfrac{3}{2}$. Write your result in slope-intercept form.

Since we know that two points determine a line, it is natural that we should be able to write the equation of a line passing through two given points. Using the point-slope form together with the slope formula will allow us to write such an equation.

Example 6

Write the equation of the line passing through $(2, 4)$ and $(4, 7)$.

First, we find m, the slope of the line. Here

$$m = \frac{7 - 4}{4 - 2} = \frac{3}{2}$$

Note: We could just as well have chosen to let

$(x_1, y_1) = (4, 7)$

The resulting equation will be the same in either case. Take time to verify this for yourself.

Now we apply the point-slope form with $m = \dfrac{3}{2}$ and $(x_1, y_1) = (2, 4)$:

$$y - 4 = \frac{3}{2}(x - 2)$$

$$y - 4 = \frac{3}{2}x - 3$$

$$y = \frac{3}{2}x + 1$$

CHECK YOURSELF 6

Write the equation of the line passing through $(-2, 5)$ and $(1, 3)$. Write your result in slope-intercept form.

A line with slope zero is a horizontal line. A line with an undefined slope is vertical. The next example illustrates the equations of such lines.

Example 7

(a) Find the equation of a line passing through $(7, -2)$ with a slope of zero.

We could find the equation by letting $m = 0$. Substituting into the slope-intercept form, we can solve for the y intercept (b).

$$y = mx + b$$
$$-2 = 0(7) + b$$
$$-2 = b$$

So,

$$y = 0 \cdot x - 2 \quad \text{or} \quad y = -2$$

It is far easier to remember that any line with a zero slope is a horizontal line and has the form

$$y = b$$

The value for b will always be the y coordinate for the given point.

(*b*) Find the equation of a line with undefined slope passing through $(4, -5)$.

A line with undefined slope is vertical. It will always be of the form $x = a$, where a is the x coordinate for the given point. The equation is

$$x = 4$$

CHECK YOURSELF 7

1. Find the equation of a line with zero slope that passes through the point $(-3, 5)$.
2. Find the equation of a line passing through $(-3, -6)$ with undefined slope.

Alternate methods for finding the equation of a line through two points do exist and have particular significance in other fields of mathematics, such as statistics. The following example shows such an alternate approach.

Example 8

Write the equation of the line through points $(-2, 3)$ and $(4, 5)$.

First, we find m, as before:

$$m = \frac{5 - 3}{4 - (-2)} = \frac{2}{6} = \frac{1}{3}$$

We now make use of the slope-intercept equation, but in a slightly different form.

Since $y = mx + b$, we can write

$$b = y - mx$$

We substitute these values because the line must pass through $(-2, 3)$

Now letting $x = -2$, $y = 3$, and $m = \frac{1}{3}$, we can calculate b:

$$b = 3 - \left(\frac{1}{3}\right)(-2)$$

$$= 3 + \frac{2}{3} = \frac{11}{3}$$

With $m = \dfrac{1}{3}$ and $b = \dfrac{11}{3}$, we can apply the slope-intercept form, to write the equation of the desired line. We have

$$y = \frac{1}{3}x + \frac{11}{3}$$

CHECK YOURSELF 8

Repeat the Check Yourself 6 exercise, using the technique illustrated in Example 8.

We now know that we can write the equation of a line once we are given appropriate geometric conditions, such as a point on the line and the slope of that line. In some applications the slope may be given not directly but through specified parallel or perpendicular lines.

Example 9

Find the equation of the line passing through $(-4, -3)$ and parallel to the line determined by $3x + 4y = 12$.

First, we find the slope of the given parallel line, as before:

$$3x + 4y = 12$$
$$4y = -3x + 12$$
$$y = -\frac{3}{4}x + 3$$

The slope of the given line is $-\dfrac{3}{4}$.

Now since the slope of the desired line must also be $-\dfrac{3}{4}$, we can use the point-slope form to write the required equation:

The line must pass through $(-4, -3)$ so let $(x_1, y_1) = (-4, -3)$.

$$y - (-3) = -\frac{3}{4}[x - (-4)]$$

This simplifies to

$$y = -\frac{3}{4}x - 6$$

and we have our equation in slope-intercept form.

CHECK YOURSELF 9

Find the equation of the line passing through (5, 4) and perpendicular to the line with equation $2x - 5y = 10$.

Hint: Recall that the slopes of perpendicular lines are the negative reciprocals of each other.

There are many applications of our work with linear equations in various fields. The following is just one of many typical examples.

Example 10

In producing a new product, a manufacturer predicts that the number of items produced x and the cost in dollars C of producing those items will be related by a linear equation.

Suppose that the cost of producing 100 items will be $5000 and the cost of producing 500 items will be $15,000. Find the linear equation relating x and C.

Solution   To solve this problem, we must find the equation of the line passing through points (100, 5000) and (500, 15,000).

Even though the numbers are considerably larger than we have encountered thus far in this section, the process is exactly the same.

First, we find the slope:

$$m = \frac{15{,}000 - 5000}{500 - 100} = \frac{10{,}000}{400} = 25$$

We can now use the point-slope form as before to find the desired equation:

$$C - 5000 = 25(x - 100)$$
$$C - 5000 = 25x - 2500$$
$$C = 25x + 2500$$

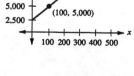

Note how the change in scaling "distorts" the slope of the line.

To graph the equation we have just derived, we must choose our scaling on the x and C axes carefully to get a "reasonable" picture. Here we choose increments of 100 on the x axis and 2500 on the C axis, since those seem appropriate for the given information.

CHECK YOURSELF 10

A company predicts that the value in dollars V and the time that a piece of equipment has been in use t are related by a linear equation. If the equipment is valued at \$1500 after 2 years and at \$300 after 10 years, find the linear equation relating t and V.

The following chart summarizes the various forms for the equation of a line that we have considered in this chapter.

FORM	EQUATION FOR LINE L	CONDITIONS
Standard	$ax + by = c$	a and b cannot both be zero.
Slope-intercept	$y = mx + b$	Line L has y intercept b with slope m.
Point-slope	$y - y_1 = m(x - x_1)$	Line L passes through point (x_1, y_1) with slope m.
Horizontal	$y = b$	Slope is zero.
Vertical	$x = a$	Slope is undefined.

CHECK YOURSELF ANSWERS

1. $y = -\dfrac{2}{3}x - 3$.

2. $y = \dfrac{3}{4}x - 2$, $m = \dfrac{3}{4}$, the y intercept is -2.

3. $m_1 = \dfrac{3}{2}$, $m_2 = -\dfrac{2}{3}$, $m_1 \cdot m_2 = -1$.

4. $y = \dfrac{3}{4}x - 2$. 5. $y = \dfrac{3}{2}x - 1$. 6. $y = -\dfrac{2}{3}x + \dfrac{11}{3}$.

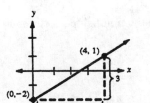

7. (1) $y = 5$; (2) $x = -3$. 8. $y = -\dfrac{2}{3}x + \dfrac{11}{3}$. 9. $y = -\dfrac{5}{2}x + \dfrac{33}{2}$.

10. $V = -150t + 1800$.

Name _____

Date _____

Exercises

ANSWERS

Build Your Skills

1. _____

In Exercises 1 to 8, match the graph with one of the equations on the right.

2. _____

1. 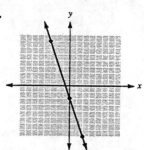   **2.**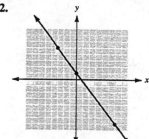

(a) $y = 2x$

(b) $y = x + 1$

(c) $y = -x + 3$

(d) $y = 2x + 1$

(e) $y = -3x - 2$

(f) $y = \dfrac{2}{3}x + 1$

3. _____

(g) $y = -\dfrac{4}{3}x + 1$

(h) $y = -4x$

4. _____

3. 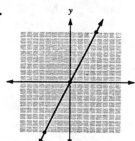   **4.** 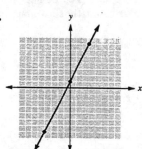   **5.**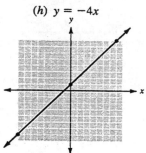

5. _____

6. _____

6. 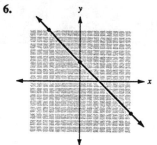   **7.** 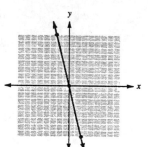   **8.**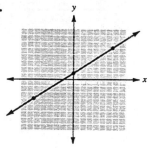

7. _____

8. _____

71

ANSWERS

Write each equation in slope-intercept form. Give its slope and y intercept.

9. _____

10. _____

11. _____

12. _____

13. _____

14. _____

15. _____

16. _____

17. _____

18. _____

19. _____

20. _____

21. _____

22. _____

23. _____

24. _____

25. _____

26. _____

27. _____

28. _____

29. _____

30. _____

9. $x + y = 5$

10. $2x + y = 3$

11. $2x - y = -2$

12. $x + 3y = 6$

13. $x + 3y = 9$

14. $4x - y = 8$

15. $2x - 3y = 6$

16. $3x - 4y = 12$

17. $2x - y = 0$

18. $3x + y = 0$

19. $y + 3 = 0$

20. $y - 2 = 0$

Write the equation of the line passing through each of the given points with the indicated slope. Give your results in slope-intercept form, where possible.

21. $(0, 2), m = 3$

22. $(0, -4), m = -2$

23. $(0, 2), m = \dfrac{3}{2}$

24. $(0, -3), m = -2$

25. $(0, 4), m = 0$

26. $(0, 5), m = -\dfrac{3}{5}$

27. $(0, -5), m = \dfrac{5}{4}$

28. $(0, -4), m = -\dfrac{3}{4}$

29. $(1, 2), m = 3$

30. $(-1, 2), m = 3$

ANSWERS

31. _____

32. _____

33. _____

34. _____

35. _____

36. _____

37. _____

38. _____

39. _____

40. _____

41. _____

42. _____

43. _____

44. _____

45. _____

46. _____

47. _____

48. _____

31. $(-2, -3), m = -3$

32. $(1, -4), m = -4$

33. $(5, -3), m = \dfrac{2}{5}$

34. $(4, 3), m = 0$

35. $(2, -3), m$ is undefined

36. $(2, -5), m = \dfrac{1}{4}$

37. $(5, 0), m = -\dfrac{4}{5}$

38. $(-3, 0), m$ is undefined

Write the equation of the line passing through each of the given pairs of points. Write your result in slope-intercept form, where possible.

39. $(2, 3)$ and $(5, 6)$

40. $(3, -2)$ and $(6, 4)$

41. $(-2, -3)$ and $(2, 0)$

42. $(-1, 3)$ and $(4, -2)$

43. $(-3, 2)$ and $(4, 2)$

44. $(-5, 3)$ and $(4, 1)$

45. $(2, 0)$ and $(0, -3)$

46. $(2, -3)$ and $(2, 4)$

47. $(0, 4)$ and $(-2, -1)$

48. $(-4, 1)$ and $(3, 1)$

ANSWERS

Write the equation of the line L satisfying the given geometric conditions.

49. _____

49. L has slope 4 and y intercept -2.

50. _____

50. L has slope $-\dfrac{2}{3}$ and y intercept 4.

51. _____

51. L has x intercept 4 and y intercept 2.

52. _____

52. L has x intercept -2 and slope $\dfrac{3}{4}$.

53. L has y intercept 4 and a 0 slope.

53. _____

54. L has x intercept -2 and an undefined slope.

55. L passes through the point $(3, 2)$ with a slope of 5.

54. _____

56. L passes through point $(-2, -4)$ with a slope of $-\dfrac{3}{2}$.

55. _____

57. L has y intercept 3 and is parallel to the line with equation $y = 3x - 5$.

56. _____

58. L has y intercept -3 and is parallel to the line with equation $y = \dfrac{2}{3}x + 1$.

57. _____

58. _____

ANSWERS

59. _____

60. _____

61. _____

62. _____

63. _____

64. _____

65. _____

66. _____

67. _____

68. _____

59. L has y intercept 4 and is perpendicular to the line with equation $y = -2x + 1$.

60. L has y intercept 2 and is parallel to the line with equation $y = -1$.

61. L has x intercept 3 and is perpendicular to the line with equation $y = 2$.

62. L has y intercept 2 and is perpendicular to the line with equation $2x - 3y = 6$.

63. L passes through point $(-3, 2)$ and is parallel to the line with equation $y = 2x - 3$.

64. L passes through point $(-4, 3)$ and is parallel to the line with equation $y = -2x + 1$.

65. L passes through point $(3, 2)$ and is parallel to the line with equation $y = \frac{4}{3}x + 4$.

66. L passes through point $(-2, -1)$ and is perpendicular to the line with equation $y = 3x + 1$.

67. L passes through point $(5, -2)$ and is perpendicular to the line with equation $y = -3x - 2$.

68. L passes through point $(3, 4)$ and is perpendicular to the line with equation $y = -\frac{3}{5}x + 2$.

69 _____   69. L passes through (-2, 1) and is parallel to the line with equation x + 2y = 4.

70 _____   70. L passes through (-3, 5) and is parallel to the x axis.

71 _____   71. L passes through (-3, -2) and is perpendicular to the line with the equation 2x + 5y = 10.

72 _____   72. L passes through (5, 2) and is perpendicular to the x axis.

73. Line 1 has the same slope as the line 4x + 3y = 9. Line 1 passes through the origin. Find the equation of line 1. Graph both lines.

74. Line 2 passes through the points (1,5) and (-3,-7). Find the x- and y-intercepts of Line 2. Draw the graph of Line

75. Line 3 has slope -3 and passes through the point (4,-6). Find the area of the triangle formed by Line 3 and the (positive parts of the) x- and y-axes. Sketch the graph of Line 3 and shade the triangle.

76. Line 4 has y-intercept at 2. If Line 4 forms a triangle with the (positive parts of the) x- and y-axes, and if that triangle has area 8 square units, find the slope of Line 4. Sketch the graph of Line 4 and shade the triangle.

77. Line 5 is parallel to the y-axis and has the same x-intercept as this line: 5x - 3y = 15. Find the equation of Line 5. Draw the graph of both lines.

78. Line 6 passes through the point (2, 5). The y-intercept of Line 6 is twice the x-intercept. Find the equation of Line 6. Sketch its graph.

79. Line 7 passes through the point (-2,-1) and has no x-intercept. Find the equation of Line 7. Sketch its graph.

80. Line 8 passes through the point (-1,4) and has no y-intercept. Find the equation of Line 8. Sketch its graph.

81. Line 9 passes through the x-intercept of this line: 5x - 2y = 10. Line 9 has no y-intercept. Find the equation of Line 9. Draw the graph of both lines.

82. Line 10 passes through the point (-3,2) and has the x-intercept 0. Find the equation of Line 10. Sketch its graph

83. Line 11 passes through the x-intercept of this line: 6x + 3y = 12. Line 11 has y-intercept 0. Find the equation of Line 11. Graph both lines.

Skillscan (Solving Linear Inequalities)

Graph each of the following inequalities.

a. $x < 3$

b. $x \geq -2$

c. $2x \leq 8$

d. $3x > -9$

e. $-3x < 12$

f. $-2x \leq 10$

g. $\dfrac{2}{3}x \leq 4$

h. $-\dfrac{3}{4}x \geq \dfrac{5}{6}$

1. (e)   3. (a)   5. (b)   7. (h)   9. $y = -x + 5$. $m = -1$. y intercept is 5

11. $y = 2x + 2$. $m = 2$. y intercept is 2   13. $y = -\frac{1}{3}x + 3$. $m = -\frac{1}{3}$. y intercept is 3

15. $y = \frac{2}{3}x - 2$. $m = \frac{2}{3}$. y intercept is -2 17. $y = 2x$. $m = 2$. y intercept is 0

19. $y = -3$. $m = 0$. y intercept is -3 21. $y = 3x + 2$ 23. $y = \frac{3}{2}x + 2$ 25. $y = 4$

27. $y = \frac{5}{4}x - 5$ 29. $y = 3x - 1$ 31. $y = -3x - 9$ 33. $y = \frac{2}{5}x - 5$ 35. $x = 2$

37. $y = -\frac{4}{5}x + 4$ 39. $y = x + 1$ 41. $y = \frac{3}{4}x - \frac{3}{2}$ 43. $y = 2$ 45. $y = \frac{3}{2}x - 3$

47. $y = \frac{5}{2}x + 4$ 49. $y = 4x - 2$ 51. $y = -\frac{1}{2}x + 2$ 53. $y = 4$ 55. $y = 5x - 13$

57. $y = 3x + 3$ 59. $y = \frac{1}{2}x + 4$ 61. $x = 3$ 63. $y = 2x + 8$ 65. $y = \frac{4}{3}x - 2$

67. $y = \frac{1}{3}x - \frac{11}{3}$ 69. $y = -\frac{1}{2}x$ 71. $y = \frac{5}{2}x + \frac{11}{2}$

73.

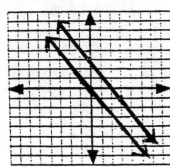

74.

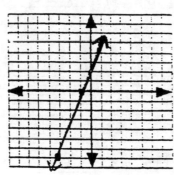

75.

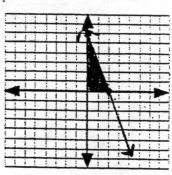

Equation ___ $y = -\frac{4}{3}x$ ___   x-intercept: ___ $\left(-\frac{2}{3}, 0\right)$ ___   Area: ___6 sq. units___

y-intercept: ___(0,2)___

76.

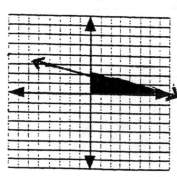

77.

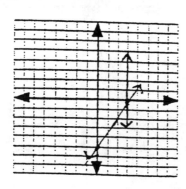

78.

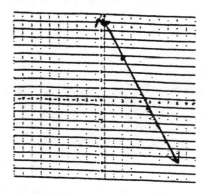

Slope ___ $-\frac{1}{4}$ ___   Equation ___$x = 3$___   Equation $y = -2x + 9$

79.

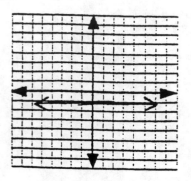

Equation ___y = -1___

80.

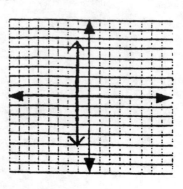

Equation ___x = -1___

81.

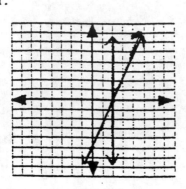

Equation ___x = 2___

82.

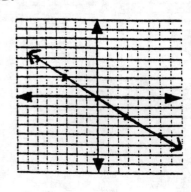

83.

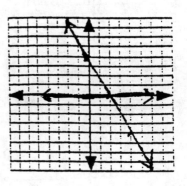

Equation ___$y = -\dfrac{2}{3}x$___   Equation ___y = 0 (x-axis)___

a. $x < 3$ **b.** $x \geq -2$

c. $2x \leq 8$ **d.** $3x > -9$

e. $-3x < 12$ **f.** $-2x \leq 10$

g. $\dfrac{2}{3}x \leq 4$ **h.** $-\dfrac{3}{4}x \geq 6$

78

Summary Text

$y = \frac{2}{3}x + 4$ is in slope-intercept form. The slope m is $\frac{2}{3}$, and the y intercept is 4.

There are two useful special forms for the equation of a line. The *slope-intercept form* for the equation of a line is $y = mx + b$, where the line has slope m and intercept b. The *point-slope form* for the equation of a line is $y - y_1 = m(x - x_1)$, where the line has slope m and passes through the point (x_1, y_1). $x = x_1$ is the equation of a line through (x, y) with undefined slope.

If line l has slope $m = -2$ and passes through $(-2, 3)$, its equation is

$y - 3 = -2[x - (-2)]$
$y - 3 = -2(x + 2)$
$y - 3 = -2x - 4$
$\quad y = -2x - 1$

Summary Exercises

Write the equation of the line passing through each of the following points with the indicated slope. Give your results in slope-intercept form, where possible.

1. $(0, 3)$, $m = 2$

2. $(0, -5)$, $m = \frac{2}{3}$

3. $(0, -3)$, $m = 0$

4. $(2, 3)$, $m = 3$

5. $(-3, -4)$, $m = -3$

6. $(4, 3)$, m undefined

7. $(3, -2)$, $m = \frac{5}{3}$

8. $(-2, -3)$, $m = 0$

9. $(-2, -4)$, $m = -\frac{5}{2}$

10. $(-3, 2)$, $m = -\frac{4}{3}$

11. $\left(\frac{2}{3}, -5\right)$, $m = 0$

12. $\left(-\frac{5}{2}, -1\right)$, m is undefined

Write the equation of the line L satisfying each of the following sets of geometric conditions.

13. L passes through $(-3, -1)$ and $(3, 3)$.

14. L passes through $(0, 4)$ and $(5, 3)$.

15. L has slope $\dfrac{3}{4}$ and y intercept 3.

16. L passes through $(4, -3)$ with a slope of $-\dfrac{5}{4}$.

17. L has y intercept -4 and is parallel to the line with equation $3x - y = 6$.

18. L passes through $(3, -2)$ and is perpendicular to the line with equation $3x - 5y = 15$.

19. L passes through $(2, -1)$ and is perpendicular to the line with the equation $3x - 2y = 5$.

20. L passes through the point $(-5, -2)$ and is parallel to the line with the equation $4x - 3y = 9$.

Self-Test Questions

Write the equation of the line L satisfying each of the following sets of geometric conditions.

1. L has y intercept -3 and slope $-\dfrac{2}{3}$.

2. L passes through the points $(-4, 3)$ and $(-1, 7)$.

3. L passes through $(4, -5)$ and is parallel to $y = -\dfrac{1}{2}x + 5$.

4. L passes through $(-3, 7)$ and is perpendicular to $2x - 3y = 7$.

Self-Test Answers

1. $y = -\dfrac{2}{3}x - 3$ **2.** $y = \dfrac{4}{3}x + \dfrac{25}{3}$ **3.** $y = -\dfrac{1}{2}x - 3$ **4.** $y = -\dfrac{3}{2}x + \dfrac{5}{2}$

Systems of Linear Equations in Two Variables

OBJECTIVES
1. To solve systems of linear equations in two variables by graphing
2. To solve systems by the addition method
3. To solve systems by the substitution method

Our work here focuses on systems of equations and the various solution techniques available for your work with such systems. First, let's consider what we mean by a system of equations.

In many applications you will find it helpful to use two variables when labeling the quantities involved. Often this leads to a *linear equation in two variables.* A typical equation might be

It might be helpful to read our coverage of graphing linear equations at this point.

$$x - 2y = 6$$

A solution for such an equation is any ordered pair of real numbers (x, y) that satisfies the equation. For example, the ordered pair $(4, -1)$ is a solution for the equation above since substituting 4 for x and -1 for y results in the true statement

Of course, there are an infinite number of solutions for an equation of this type. You might want to verify that $(2, -2)$ and $(6, 0)$ are also solutions.

$$4 - 2(-1) \overset{?}{=} 6$$
$$4 + 2 \overset{?}{=} 6$$
or $$6 = 6$$

Whenever two or more equations are considered together, they form a *system of equations.* If the equations of the system are linear, the system is called a *linear system.* Our work here and in our coverage of systems of linear equations in three variables and solutions of systems by matrices involves finding solutions for such systems. Let's look at a definition.

A *solution* for a linear system of equations in two variables is an ordered pair of real numbers (x, y) that satisfies both equations in the system. For instance, given the linear system

$$x - 2y = -1$$
$$2x + y = \quad 8$$

the pair $(3, 2)$ is a solution because, substituting 3 for x and 2 for y in the two equations of the system, we have the *two* true statements

Both equations are satisfied by (3, 2).

$$3 - 2(2) \overset{?}{=} -1 \quad \text{and} \quad 2(3) + 2 \overset{?}{=} 8$$
$$-1 = -1 \qquad\qquad\qquad 8 = 8$$

Since a solution to a system of equations represents a point on both lines, one approach to finding the solution for a system is to graph each equation on the same set of coordinate axes and then identify the point of intersection. This is shown in the following example.

Streeter-Hutchison-Hoelzle:
Intermediate Algebra
Form A

Section
Systems of Linear Equations
in Two Variables

Text

From Section 4.1 of the
traditional text

© McGraw-Hill, Inc., 1993

Example 1

Solve the system by graphing:

$$2x + y = 4$$
$$x - y = 5$$

Here we used the intercept method to graph the lines.

We graph the lines corresponding to the two equations of the system.

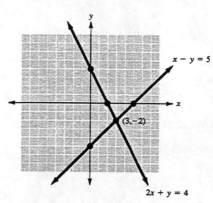

Each equation has an infinite number of solutions (ordered pairs) corresponding to points on a line. The point of intersection, here $(3, -2)$, is the *only* point lying on both lines, and so $(3, -2)$ is the only ordered pair satisfying both equations, and $(3, -2)$ is the solution for the system.

CHECK YOURSELF 1

Solve the system by graphing.

$$3x - y = 2$$
$$x + y = 6$$

In Example 1, the two lines are nonparallel and intersect at only one point. The system has a unique solution corresponding to that point and is called a *consistent* system. In our next example, we examine a system representing two lines that have no point of intersection.

Example 2

Solve the system by graphing:

$$2x - y = 4$$
$$6x - 3y = 18$$

The lines corresponding to the two equations are graphed.

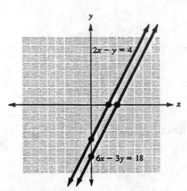

The lines are distinct and parallel. There is no point at which they intersect. So the system has no solution and is called an *inconsistent* system.

CHECK YOURSELF 2

Solve the system if possible.

$$3x - y = 1$$
$$6x - 2y = 3$$

Sometimes the equations in a system have the same graph.

Example 3

Solve the system by graphing:

$$2x - y = 2$$
$$4x - 2y = 4$$

The equations are graphed.

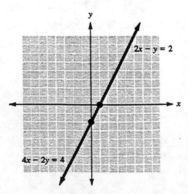

Note that every point on the line is a point of intersection.

Since the lines representing the equations coincide, the system has an infinite number of solutions and is called a *dependent* system. The lines are called *coincident lines.* The solution is the set of all points on the line.

Solve the system, if possible.

$$x - 3y = 1$$
$$-2x + 6y = -2$$

We can summarize our consideration of the nature of the solutions of a linear system in two variables as follows.

SOLUTIONS FOR A LINEAR SYSTEM OF TWO EQUATIONS IN TWO VARIABLES

Consider the lines determined by the equations of the system. The solutions are illustrated by one of the following graphs.

1. The lines are not parallel. They intersect in exactly one point. There is (only) one solution, and the system is *consistent*.

2. The lines are distinct and parallel. There is no solution, and the system is *inconsistent*.

3. The lines coincide. That is, although the two equations may appear to be different, they will have the same graph. There are infinitely many solutions, and the system is *dependent*.

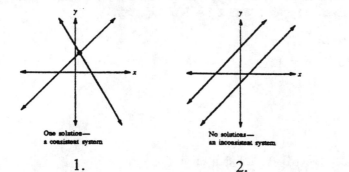 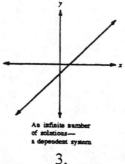

| One solution— a consistent system | No solutions— an inconsistent system | An infinite number of solutions— a dependent system |

    1.   **2.**   **3.**

---

here is nothing wrong with aphing, and then timating, a solution. In fact, is an excellent first proach to the problem. But act solutions may not sult from the graphical ethod.

The graphical method of solution is not always practical, particularly if the coordinates of the point of intersection are not integers. In that case, we can only "guess at," or estimate, the solution.

Because of this, we will turn to algebraic methods that allow us to find exact solutions. The first algebraic approach we consider is the *addition method* of solution. We will need the following definition.

> Two systems of equations are *equivalent* if they have the same solution sets.

The addition method of solving systems is based on the following result regarding equivalent systems:

An equivalent system is formed whenever

1. One of the equations is multiplied by a non-zero number.
2. One of the equations is replaced by the sum of a constant multiple of another equation and that equation.

The following examples illustrate the addition method of solution.

Example 4

Solve the system by the addition method.

$$5x - 2y = 12 \tag{1}$$
$$3x + 2y = 12 \tag{2}$$

The addition method is sometimes called *solution by elimination* for this reason.

In this case, adding the equations will eliminate the variable y, and we have

$$8x = 24$$
$$x = 3 \tag{3}$$

Now Equation (3) can be paired with either of the original equations to form an equivalent system. We let $x = 3$ in Equation (1):

$$5(3) - 2y = 12$$
$$15 - 2y = 12$$
$$-2y = -3$$
$$y = \frac{3}{2}$$

The solution should be checked by substituting these values into Equation (2). Here

$$3(3) + 2\left(\frac{3}{2}\right) \stackrel{?}{=} 12$$
$$9 + 3 \stackrel{?}{=} 12$$
$$12 = 12$$

is a true statement.

and $\left(3, \dfrac{3}{2}\right)$ is the solution for our system.

CHECK YOURSELF 4

Solve the system by the addition method.

$$4x - 3y = 19$$
$$-4x + 5y = -25$$

Remember that multiplying one or both of the equations by a nonzero constant produces an equivalent system.

Example 4 and the above check yourself were straightforward, in that adding the equations of the system immediately eliminated one of the variables. The following example illustrates the fact that often we must multiply one or both of the equations by a nonzero constant before the addition method is applied.

Example 5

Solve the system by the addition method.

$$3x - 5y = 19 \qquad\qquad (1)$$
$$5x + 2y = 11 \qquad\qquad (2)$$

It is clear that adding the equations of the given system will *not* eliminate one of the variables. Therefore, we must use multiplication to form an equivalent system. The choice of multipliers depends on which variable we decide to eliminate. Here we have decided to eliminate y. We multiply Equation (1) by 2 and Equation (2) by 5. We then have

Note that the coefficients of y are now *opposites* of each other.

$$6x - 10y = 38$$
$$25x + 10y = 55$$

Adding now eliminates y and yields

$$31x = 93$$
$$x = 3 \qquad\qquad (3)$$

Pairing Equation (3) with Equation (1) gives an equivalent system, and we can substitute 3 for x in Equation (1):

$$3 \cdot 3 - 5y = 19$$
$$9 - 5y = 19$$
$$-5y = 10$$
$$y = -2$$

Again, the solution should be checked by substitution in Equation (2).

and $(3, -2)$ is the solution for our system.

CHECK YOURSELF 5

Solve the system by the addition method.

$$2x + 3y = -18$$
$$3x - 5y = 11$$

The following algorithm summarizes the addition method of solving linear systems of two equations in two variables.

SOLVING BY THE ADDITION METHOD

STEP 1 If necessary, multiply one or both of the equations by a constant so that one of the variables can be eliminated by addition.

STEP 2 Add the equations of the equivalent systems formed in step 1.

STEP 3 Solve the equation found in step 2.

STEP 4 Substitute the value found in step 3 into either of the equations of the original system to find the corresponding value of the remaining variable. The ordered pair formed is the solution to the system.

STEP 5 Check the solution by substituting the pair of values found in step 4 into the other equation of the original system.

The next example illustrates two special situations.

Example 6

Solve each system by the addition method.

(a) $4x + 5y = 20$ (1)
   $8x + 10y = 19$ (2)

Multiply Equation (1) by -2. We then have

$$-8x - 10y = -40$$
$$\underline{8x + 10y = 19}$$
$$0 \neq -21$$

We add the two left sides to get 0 and the two right sides to get -21.

The result $0 = -21$ is a *false* statement, a contradiction. The assumption that a point of intersection exists is then *false,* and there is no solution. This system represents two parallel lines. The system is inconsistent and there is no solution.

(b) $5x - 7y = 9$ (1)
   $15x - 21y = 27$ (2)

Multiply Equation (1) by -3. We then have

$$-15x + 21y = -27$$
$$\underline{15x - 21y = 27}$$
$$0 = 0$$

We add the two equations.

The solution set could be written as $\{(x, y)\,|\,5x - 7y = 9\}$. For further discussion on set builder notation, see the appendix coverage of sets and set notation.

Both variables have been eliminated, and the result is a *true* statement. The two lines coincide, and there are an infinite number of solutions, one for each point on that line.

CHECK YOURSELF 6

Solve each system by the addition method, if possible.

1. $3x + 2y = 8$
$\quad 9x + 6y = 11$

2. $x - 2y = 8$
$\quad 3x - 6y = 24$

The results of Example 6 can be summarized as follows:

When a system of two linear equations is solved:

1. If a false statement (such as $3 = 4$) is obtained, then the system is inconsistent and has no solution. The graphs of the two equations will be parallel lines.
2. If a true statement (such as $6 = 6$) is obtained, then the system is dependent and has an infinite number of solutions. The graphs of the two equations will be exactly the same lines.

A third method for finding the solutions of linear systems in two variables is called the *substitution method*. You may very well find the substitution method more difficult to apply in solving certain systems than the addition method, particularly when the equations involved in the substitution lead to fractions. However, the substitution method does have important extensions to systems involving higher-degree equations.

To outline the technique, we solve one of the equations from the original system for one of the variables. That expression is then substituted into the *other* equation of the system to provide an equation in a single variable. That equation is solved, and the corresponding value for the other variable is found as before. The following example illustrates.

Example 7

(*a*) Solve the system by the substitution method.

$$2x - 3y = -3 \tag{1}$$
$$y = 2x - 1 \tag{2}$$

Since Equation (2) is already solved for y, we substitute $2x - 1$ for y in Equation (1):

We now have an equation in the single variable x.

$$2x - 3(2x - 1) = -3$$

Solving for x gives

$$2x - 6x + 3 = -3$$
$$-4x = -6$$
$$x = \frac{3}{2}$$

We now substitute $\dfrac{3}{2}$ for x in Equation (2):

To check this result, we substitute these values in Equation (1) and have

$$2\left(\dfrac{3}{2}\right) - 3 \cdot 2 \stackrel{?}{=} -3$$
$$3 - 6 \stackrel{?}{=} -3$$
$$-3 = -3$$

A true statement!

$$y = 2\left(\dfrac{3}{2}\right) - 1$$
$$= 3 - 1 = 2$$

and $\left(\dfrac{3}{2}, 2\right)$ is the solution for our system.

(*b*) Solve the system by the substitution method.

$$2x + 3y = 16 \tag{1}$$
$$3x - y = 2 \tag{2}$$

We start by solving Equation (2) for y:

Why did we choose to solve for *y* in Equation (2)? We could have solved for *x*, so that

$$x = \dfrac{y + 2}{3}$$

We simply chose the easier case to avoid fractions.

$$3x - y = 2$$
$$-y = -3x + 2$$
$$y = 3x - 2 \tag{3}$$

Substituting in Equation (1) yields

$$2x + 3(3x - 2) = 16$$
$$2x + 9x - 6 = 16$$
$$11x = 22$$
$$x = 2$$

We now substitute 2 for x in Equation (3):

$$y = 3 \cdot 2 - 2$$
$$= 6 - 2 = 4$$

The solution should be checked in *both* equations of the original system.

and $(2, 4)$ is the solution for our system. We leave the check of this result to you.

CHECK YOURSELF 7

Solve each system by the substitution method.

1. $2x + 3y = 6$
$x = 3y + 6$

2. $3x + 4y = -3$
$x + 4y = 1$

The following algorithm summarizes the substitution method for solving linear systems of two equations in two variables.

SOLVING BY THE SUBSTITUTION METHOD

STEP 1 If necessary, solve one of the equations of the original system for one of the variables.

STEP 2 Substitute the expression obtained in step 1 into the *other* equation of the system to write an equation in a single variable.

STEP 3 Solve the equation found in step 2.

STEP 4 Substitute the value found in step 3 into the equation derived in step 1 to find the corresponding value of the remaining variable. The ordered pair formed is the solution for the system.

STEP 5 Check the solution by substituting the pair of values found in step 4 into *both* equations of the original system.

A natural question at this point is, How to decide which solution method to use? First, the graphical method can generally provide only approximate solutions. When exact solutions are necessary, one of the algebraic methods must be applied. Which method to use depends totally on the given system.

If you can easily solve for a variable in one of the equations, the substitution method should work well. However, if solving for a variable in either equation of the system leads to fractions, you may find the addition approach more efficient.

CHECK YOURSELF ANSWERS

1. $x + y = 6$; $3x - y = 2$.

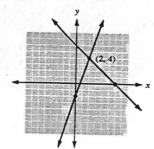

2. The system is inconsistent. The lines are parallel. There is no solution.
3. The system is dependent. The graphs of the two equations will be the same line. The solution set is $\{(x,y) \mid x - 3y = 1\}$.

4. $\left(\dfrac{5}{2}, -3\right)$ 5. $(-3,-4)$

6. (1) The system is inconsistent. The lines are parallel. There is no solution.
   (2) The system is dependent. The graphs of the two equations will be the same line. The solution set is $\{(x,y) \mid x - 2y = 8\}$.

7. (1) $\left(4, -\dfrac{2}{3}\right)$;   (2) $\left(-2, \dfrac{3}{4}\right)$

Name _____

Date _____

Exercises

ANSWERS

Build Your Skills

1. _____

Solve each of the following systems by graphing. If a unique solution does not exist, state whether the system is dependent or inconsistent.

1. $x + y = 6$
$x - y = 4$

2. $x - y = 8$
$x + y = 2$

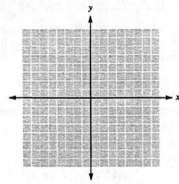

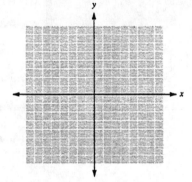

2. _____

3. _____

3. $x + 2y = 4$
$x - y = 1$

4. $x - 2y = 2$
$x + 2y = 6$

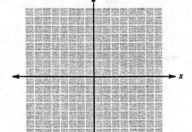

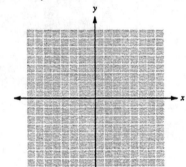

4. _____

5. _____

5. $3x - y = 3$
$3x - y = 6$

6. $3x + 2y = 12$
$y = 3$

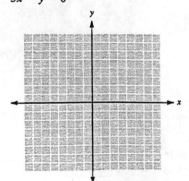

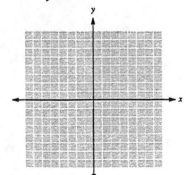

6. _____

ANSWERS

7. _____

8. _____

9. _____

10. _____

11. _____

12. _____

7. $x + 3y = 12$
$2x - 3y = 6$

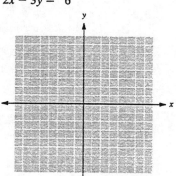

8. $3x - 6y = 9$
$x - 2y = 3$

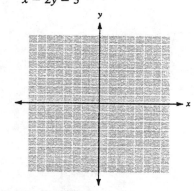

9. $2x - y = 8$
$x = 2$

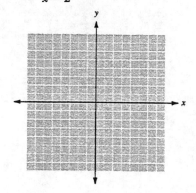

10. $x - 2y = 8$
$3x - 2y = 12$

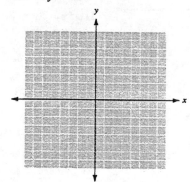

11. $x - y = 4$
$2x - 2y = 8$

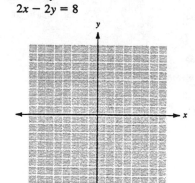

12. $2x - y = 4$
$2x - y = 6$

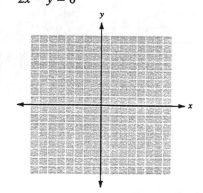

ANSWERS

Solve each of the following systems by the addition method. If a unique solution does not exist, state whether the system is dependent or inconsistent.

13. _____

13. $2x - y = 1$
$-2x + 3y = 5$

14. $x + 3y = 12$
$2x - 3y = 6$

14. _____

15. $x + 2y = -2$
$3x + 2y = -12$

16. $2x + 3y = 1$
$5x + 3y = 16$

15. _____

17. $x + y = 3$
$3x - 2y = 4$

18. $x - y = -2$
$2x + 3y = 21$

16. _____

17. _____

19. $2x + y = 8$
$-4x - 2y = -16$

20. $3x - 4y = 2$
$4x - y = 20$

18. _____

21. $5x - 2y = 31$
$4x + 3y = 11$

22. $2x - y = 4$
$6x - 3y = 10$

19. _____

23. $3x - 2y = 7$
$-6x + 4y = -15$

24. $3x + 4y = 0$
$5x - 3y = -29$

20. _____

25. $-2x + 7y = 2$
$3x - 5y = -14$

26. $5x - 2y = 3$
$10x - 4y = 6$

21. _____

22. _____

27. $7x + 4y = 8$
$5x + 6y = 1$

28. $5x + 4y = 5$
$7x - 6y = 36$

23. _____

24. _____

25. _____

26. _____

27. _____

28. _____

ANSWERS

Solve each of the following systems by the substitution method. If a unique solution does not exist, state whether the system is inconsistent or dependent.

29. _____

29. $x - y = 7$
$\quad\quad y = 2x - 12$

30. $x - y = 4$
$\quad\quad x = 2y - 2$

30. _____

31. $3x + 2y = -18$
$\quad\quad x = 3y + 5$

32. $3x - 18y = 4$
$\quad\quad x = 6y + 2$

31. _____

33. $10x - 2y = 4$
$\quad\quad y = 5x - 2$

34. $4x + 5y = 6$
$\quad\quad y = 2x - 10$

32. _____

35. $3x + 4y = 9$
$\quad\quad y = 3x + 1$

36. $6x - 5y = 27$
$\quad\quad x = 5y + 2$

33. _____

37. $x - 7y = 3$
$\quad 2x - 5y = 15$

38. $4x + 3y = -11$
$\quad 5x + y = -11$

34. _____

39. $4x - 12y = 5$
$\quad -x + 3y = -1$

40. $5x - 6y = 21$
$\quad\quad x - 2y = 5$

35. _____

41. $5x - 4y = 5$
$\quad 4x - y = -7$

42. $8x - 4y = 16$
$\quad -2x + y = -4$

36. _____

37. _____

38. _____

39. _____

40. _____

41. _____

42. _____

ANSWERS

Solve each of the following systems by any method discussed in this section.

43. _____

43. $2x - 3y = 4$
$x = 3y + 6$

44. $5x + y = 2$
$5x - 3y = 6$

44. _____

45. $4x - 3y = 0$
$5x + 2y = 23$

46. $7x - 2y = -17$
$x + 4y = 4$

45. _____

47. $3x - y = 17$
$5x + 3y = 5$

48. $7x + 3y = -51$
$y = 2x + 9$

Solve each of the following systems by any method discussed in this section. *Hint:* You should
multiply to clear of fractions as your first step.

46. _____

49. $\frac{1}{2}x - \frac{1}{3}y = 8$

$\frac{1}{3}x + y = -2$

50. $\frac{1}{5}x - \frac{1}{2}y = 0$

$x - \frac{3}{2}y = 4$

47. _____

48. _____

51. $\frac{2}{3}x + \frac{3}{5}y = -3$

$\frac{1}{3}x + \frac{2}{5}y = -3$

52. $\frac{3}{8}x - \frac{1}{2}y = -5$

$\frac{1}{4}x + \frac{3}{2}y = 4$

49. _____

53. $x + y = 1000$
$0.06x + 0.04y = 48$

54. $x + y = 600$
$0.09x + 0.08y = 50$

50. _____

51. _____

52. _____

53. _____

54. _____

ANSWERS

Skillscan (Operations with Signed Numbers)

a. _____

Simplify each of the following expressions.

a. $(3x - 2y + z) + (5x + 2y - 3z)$ **b.** $(7x - 6y + 3z) - (5x + 2y + 3z)$

c. $(x + 2y - 3z) + 3(2x + y + z)$ **d.** $2(2x + y + z) + (x - 2y + 3z)$

b. _____

e. $2(x + 3y - z) + 3(x - 2y + z)$ **f.** $4(x - 2y - 3z) + 3(2x + y + 4z)$

g. $2(x + 3y - z) - 3(2x + 2y + z)$ **h.** $5(2x - y - z) - 2(5x + y + 3z)$

c. _____

d. _____

e. _____

f. _____

g. _____

h. _____

ANSWERS

1. (5, 1)

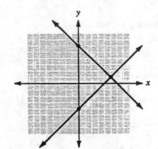

3. (2, 1)

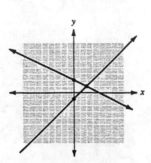

5. Inconsistent

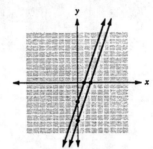

7. (6, 2)

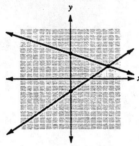

9. (2, −4)

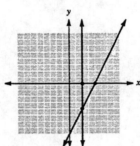

11. Dependent

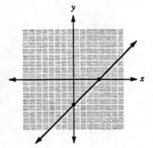

13. (2, 3)   **15.** $\left(-5, \dfrac{3}{2}\right)$ **17.** (2, 1)   **19.** Dependent   **21.** (5, −3)

23. Inconsistent   **25.** (−8, −2)   **27.** $\left(2, -\dfrac{3}{2}\right)$ **29.** (5, −2)   **31.** (−4, −3)

33. Dependent   **35.** $\left(\dfrac{1}{3}, 2\right)$ **37.** (10, 1)   **39.** Inconsistent   **41.** (−3, −5)

43. $\left(-2, -\dfrac{8}{3}\right)$ **45.** (3, 4)   **47.** (4, −5)   **49.** (12, −6)   **51.** (9, −15)

53. (400, 600)   **a.** $8x - 2z$ **b.** $2x - 8y$ **c.** $7x + 5y$ **d.** $5x + 5z$ **e.** $5x + z$
f. $10x - 5y$ **g.** $-4x - 5z$ **h.** $-7y - 11z$

A VISUAL APPROACH TO SOLVING EQUATIONS

Consider the equation $3x - 5 = x + 1$. Associated with this equation is a system of two lines with equations:

$$y = 3x - 5$$
$$y = x + 1 .$$

If we graph these lines (Fig. 1 below), we see that they intersect at $(3,4)$.

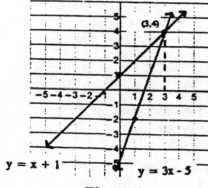

For $x = 3$,

$3x - 5 = 4 = x + 1$, so

$x = 3$ IS THE SOLUTION TO THE

EQUATION $3x - 5 = x + 1$!!

Figure 1

IN GENERAL: When the equation $ax + b = cx + d$ generates two distinct lines, the x-coordinate of the point of intersection of the lines $y = ax + b$ and $y = cx + d$ is the solution to the original equation.

In fact, the system of lines associated with a given equation is not unique: if we start with $3x - 5 = x + 1$ and subtract x from both sides, we get the equivalent equation $2x - 5 = 1$. The lines associated with this new equation are:

$$y = 2x - 5$$
$$y = 1 .$$

These lines are pictured below left (Fig. 2). If we now subtract 1 from both sides of $2x - 5 = 1$, we get still another equivalent equation, $2x - 6 = 0$, and another pair of lines:

$$y = 2x - 6$$
$$y = 0 .$$

These lines are pictured below right (Fig. 3).

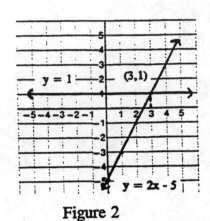

Figure 2

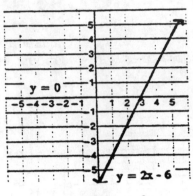

Figure 3

Notice that the x-coordinate of the point of intersection is still 3 in each case. In fact, if we were to graph the three systems in Figs. 1 - 3 on the same axes, the intersection points for each system would all lie on the vertical line x = 3 !

An equation of the form ax + b = 0 , as we had in Fig. 3, is particularly easy to picture, since we are graphing the lines y = ax + b and y = 0 . Since y = 0 is just the x-axis, this means that

> The solution to the equation   ax + b = 0 is the x-intercept of the
> line y = ax + b !!

Example: $-\dfrac{3}{2}x + 6 = 0$.

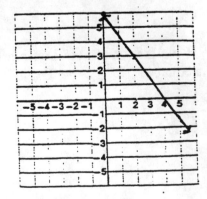

The x-intercept is 4 , so x = 4 IS THE

SOLUTION TO THE EQUATION

$$-\frac{3}{2}x + 6 = 0 \ .$$

100

EXERCISES

Build Your Skills

For each of the following linear equations, a) associate a system of two lines, b) graph these lines, and c) use their point of intersection to determine the solution of the original equation.

1. $-x + 3 = x - 1$

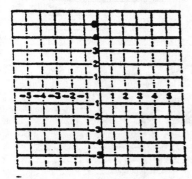

System: _____

_____

Solution: _____

2. $x - 6 = -x - 2$

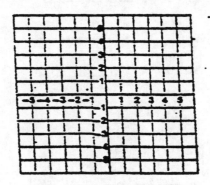

System: _____

_____

Solution: _____

3. $3x + 3 = -x - 1$

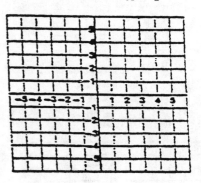

System: _____

_____

Solution: _____

4. $x + 3 = 3x + 5$

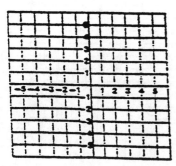

System: _____

_____

Solution: _____

5. $3x + 1 = -2x + 6$

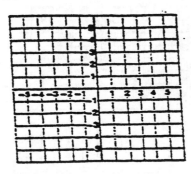

System: _____

_____

Solution: _____

6. $2x = -3x - 5$

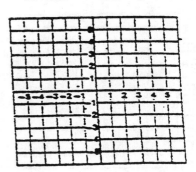

System: _____

_____

Solution: _____

7. $4x - 6 = -x + 4$

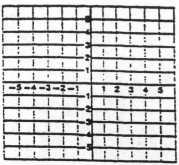

System: _____

_____

Solution: _____

8. $-5x - 3 = 2 - 5x$

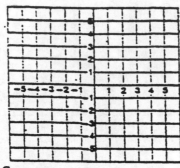

System: _____

_____

Solution: _____

9. $4x - 2 = -2(2 - x)$

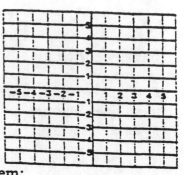

System: _____

_____

Solution: _____

10. $4 - x = x + 2$

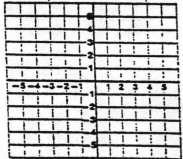

System: _____

_____

Solution: _____

11. $x - 3 = 5 - x$

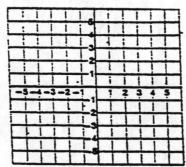

System: _____

_____

Solution: _____

12. $\frac{1}{2}x + 4 = 6$

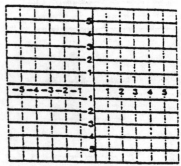

System: _____

_____

Solution: _____

13. $3x - 5 = \frac{2}{3}x + 2$

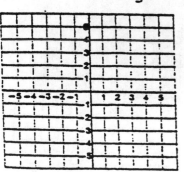

System: _____

_____

Solution: _____

14. $\frac{1}{2}(x - 4) = 5 + \frac{x}{2} - 7$

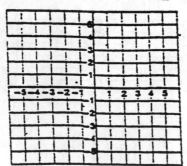

System: _____

_____

Solution: _____

15. $x - 1 = -2x + 5$

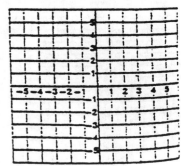

System: _____

_____

Solution: _____

16. $x - 3 = 7x + 3$

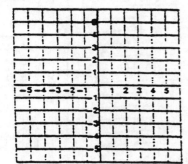

System: _____

_____

Solution: _____

17. $\frac{2}{3}x = x + 1$

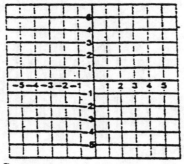

System: _____

_____

Solution: _____

18. $-3x - 4 = 2$

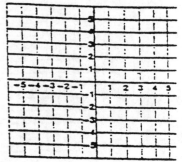

System: _____

_____

Solution: _____

19. $-3x + 6 = 0$

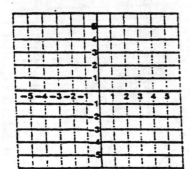

System: _____

_____

Solution: _____

20. $-\frac{1}{4}x + 1 = \frac{1}{2}x - 2$

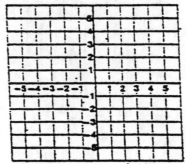

System: _____

_____

Solution: _____

21. $1 - 3x = 4$

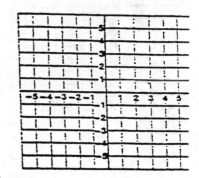

System: _____

_____

Solution: _____

22. $-2x + 4 = \frac{4}{3}x - 6$

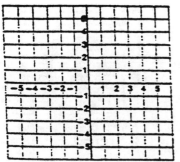

System: _____

_____

Solution: _____

23. $\frac{1}{2}x - 2 = \frac{7}{4}x + 3$

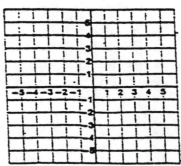

System: _____

_____

Solution: _____

24. $2x - 3 = 2x - 5$

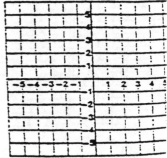

System: _____

_____

Solution: _____

1. $-x + 3 = x - 1$

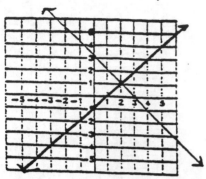

System: $\quad y = -x + 3$

$y = x - 1$

Solution: $\quad x = 2$

4. $x + 3 = 3x + 5$

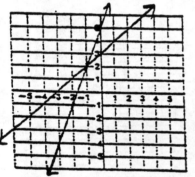

System: $\quad y = x + 3$

$y = 3x + 5$

Solution: $\quad x = -1$

7. $4x - 6 = -x + 4$

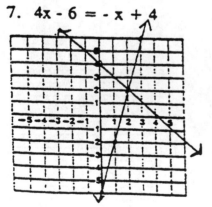

System: $\quad y = 4x - 6$

$y = -x + 4$

Solution: $\quad x = 2$

2. $x - 6 = -x - 2$

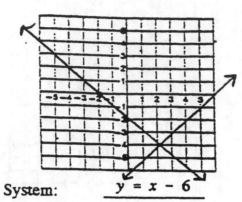

System: $\quad y = x - 6$

$y = -x - 2$

Solution: $\quad x = 2$

5. $3x + 1 = -2x + 6$

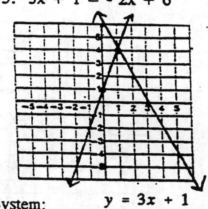

System: $\quad y = 3x + 1$

$y = -2x + 6$

Solution: $\quad x = 1$

8. $-5x - 3 = 2 - 5x$

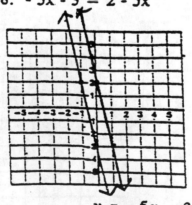

System: $\quad y = -5x - 3$

$y = -5x + 2$

104

Solution: $\quad$ no solution

3. $3x + 3 = -x - 1$

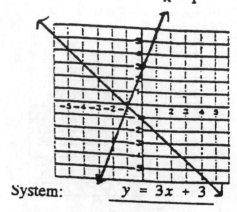

System: $\quad y = 3x + 3$

$y = -x - 1$

Solution: $\quad x = -1$

6. $2x = -3x - 5$

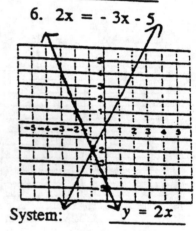

System: $\quad y = 2x$

$y = -3x - 5$

Solution: $\quad x = -1$

9. $4x - 2 = -2(2 - x)$

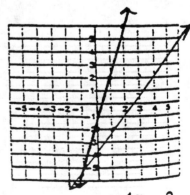

System: $\quad y = 4x - 2$

$y = 2x - 4$

Solution: $\quad x = -1$

10. $4 - x = x + 2$

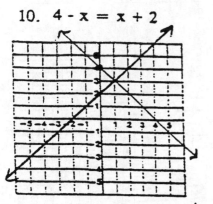

System: $\underline{\quad y = -x + 4 \quad}$

$\underline{\quad y = x + 2 \quad}$

Solution: $\underline{\quad x = 1 \quad}$

11. $x - 3 = 5 - x$

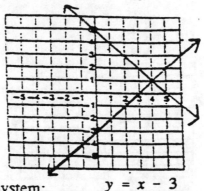

System: $\underline{\quad y = x - 3 \quad}$

$\underline{\quad y = -x + 5 \quad}$

Solution: $\underline{\quad x = 4 \quad}$

12. $\frac{1}{2}x + 4 = 6$

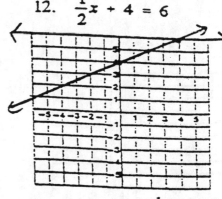

System: $\underline{\quad y = \frac{1}{2}x + 4 \quad}$

$\underline{\quad y = 6 \quad}$

Solution: $\underline{\quad x = 4 \quad}$

13. $3x - 5 = \frac{2}{3}x + 2$

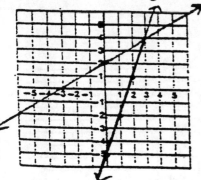

System: $\underline{\quad y = 3x - 5 \quad}$

$\underline{\quad y = \frac{2}{3}x + 2 \quad}$

Solution: $\underline{\quad x = 3 \quad}$

14. $\frac{1}{2}(x - 4) = 5 + \frac{x}{2} - 7$

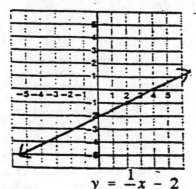

System: $\underline{\quad y = \frac{1}{2}x - 2 \quad}$

$\underline{\quad y = \frac{1}{2}x - 2 \quad}$

Solution: $\underline{\quad \text{same line} \quad}$

15. $x - 1 = -2x + 5$

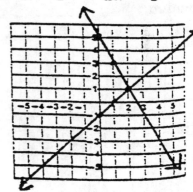

System: $\underline{\quad y = x - 1 \quad}$

$\underline{\quad y = -2x + 5 \quad}$

Solution: $\underline{\quad x = 2 \quad}$

16. $x - 3 = 7x + 3$

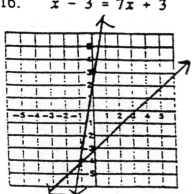

System: $\underline{\quad y = x - 3 \quad}$

$\underline{\quad y = 7x + 3 \quad}$

Solution: $\underline{\quad x = -1 \quad}$

17. $\frac{2}{3}x = x + 1$

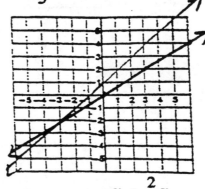

System: $\underline{\quad y = \frac{2}{3}x \quad}$

$\underline{\quad y = x + 1 \quad}$

Solution: $\underline{\quad x = -3 \quad}$

18. $-3x - 4 = 2$

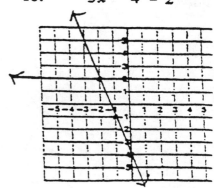

System: $\underline{\quad y = -3x - 4 \quad}$

$\underline{\quad y = 2 \quad}$

Solution: $\underline{\quad x = -2 \quad}$

19. $-3x + 6 = 0$

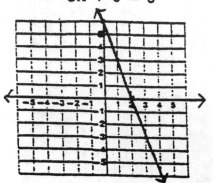

System: $\underline{\quad y = -3x + 6 \quad}$

$\underline{\quad y = 0 \quad}$

Solution: $\underline{\quad x = 2 \quad}$

20. $-\dfrac{1}{4}x + 1 = \dfrac{1}{2}x - 2$

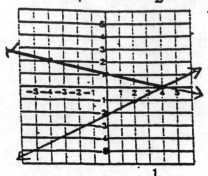

System: $\underline{\quad y = -\dfrac{1}{4}x + 1 \quad}$

$\underline{\quad y = \dfrac{1}{2}x - 2 \quad}$

Solution: $\underline{\quad x = 4 \quad}$

21. $1 - 3x = 4$

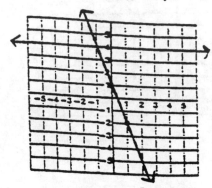

System: $\underline{\quad y = -3x + 1 \quad}$

$\underline{\quad y = 4 \quad}$

Solution: $\underline{\quad x = -1 \quad}$

22. $-2x + 4 = \dfrac{4}{3}x - 6$

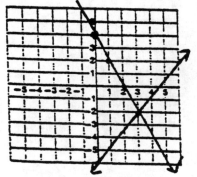

System: $\underline{\quad y = -2x + 4 \quad}$

$\underline{\quad y = \dfrac{4}{3}x - 6 \quad}$

Solution: $\underline{\quad x = 3 \quad}$

23. $\dfrac{1}{2}x - 2 = \dfrac{7}{4}x + 3$

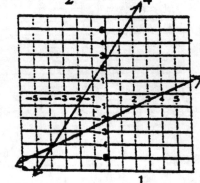

System: $\underline{\quad y = \dfrac{1}{2}x - 2 \quad}$

$\underline{\quad y = \dfrac{7}{4}x + 3 \quad}$

Solution: $\underline{\quad x = -4 \quad}$

24. $2x - 3 = 2x - 5$

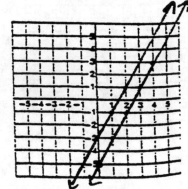

System: $\underline{\quad y = 2x - 3 \quad}$

$\underline{\quad y = 2x - 5 \quad}$

Solution: $\underline{\quad \text{no solution} \quad}$

Equality, Order, and Absolute Value

OBJECTIVES

1. To recognize the properties of equality
2. To use the notation of inequalities
3. To use the absolute value notation

The use of the = symbol to represent equality is due to Robert Recorde (1510–1558), an English mathematician who first used it in print in 1557. According to Recorde, "noe 2 thynges can be moare equalle," referring to the two parallel line segments he used.

Let us now look at relations on the set of real numbers.

The simplest relation is *equality*. The symbol for equality is an equals sign (=), and we write

$$a = b$$

when we want to indicate that the two expressions, a and b, represent the same number.

Listed below are several important properties of the equality relation.

Each property should seem "natural" given your previous understanding of the equality relation.

PROPERTIES OF EQUALITY

For any real numbers a, b, and c:

REFLEXIVE PROPERTY

$$a = a$$

SYMMETRIC PROPERTY

If $a = b$, then $b = a$.

TRANSITIVE PROPERTY

If $a = b$ and $b = c$, then $a = c$.

The following principle follows from the properties above.

SUBSTITUTION PRINCIPLE
If $a = b$, then a may be replaced by b, or b by a, in any statement, without changing the validity of that statement.

Example 1

Which property of equality justifies each of the following statements?

(*a*) If $V = L \cdot W \cdot H$, then $L \cdot W \cdot H = V$.
(*b*) If $2(1 + 3) = 2 + 6$ and $2 + 6 = 8$, then $2(1 + 3) = 8$.
(*c*) $a + 4 = a + 4$
(*d*) If $x = y + 1$ and $2x = 4$, then $2(y + 1) = 4$.

Solution

The form in (b) is, "If $a = b$ and $b = c$, then $a = c$."
We have "replaced" x with $y + 1$.

(a) Symmetric property
(b) Transitive property
(c) Reflexive property
(d) Substitution principle

CHECK YOURSELF 1

Which property of equality justifies each of the following statements?

1. If $7x + 2 = y$, then $y = 7x + 2$.
2. If $3(y + 1) = 2x - 1$ and $x = y + 1$, then $3x = 2x - 1$.
3. $w + 5 = w + 5$.
4. If $x + 1 = y$ and $y = 2$, then $x + 1 = 2$.

Let's now consider two other relations on the set of real numbers. These are the relations of order or inequality known as *less than* and *greater than*.

The set of real numbers is an ordered set. Given any two numbers, we can determine whether one number is less than, equal to, or greater than the other. Let's see how this is expressed symbolically.

We use the *inequality symbol* $<$ to represent "is less than," and we write

As was true with the equals sign, the inequality represents a verb phrase.

$a < b$ This is read "a is less than b."

to indicate that a is less than b. The number line gives us a clear picture of the meaning of this statement. The point corresponding to a must lie *to the left* of the point corresponding to b.

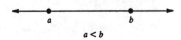

Similarly, the inequality symbol $>$ represents "is greater than," and the statement

$a > b$
and
$b < a$

are equivalent statements. The symbol "points to" the smaller quantity.

$a > b$ This is read "a is greater than b."

indicates that a is greater than b and means that the point corresponding to a on the number line lies *to the right* of the point corresponding to b.

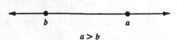

The following example illustrates the use of the inequality symbols.

Example 2

Complete each statement by inserting the $<$ or $>$ symbol between the given numbers.

(a) 2 _____ 8

(b) 2.786 _____ 2.78

(c) -23 _____ -5

(d) $\sqrt{2}$ _____ 1.4

(e) $\dfrac{1}{2}$ _____ $\dfrac{1}{3}$

Solution

(a) $2 < 8$

(b) $2.786 > 2.78$

(c) $-23 < -5$

(d) $\sqrt{2} > 1.4$ Recall that 1.414 is an approximation for $\sqrt{2}$.

(e) $\dfrac{1}{2} > \dfrac{1}{3}$

CHECK YOURSELF 2

Complete each statement by using the proper verb phrase and inserting an inequality symbol.

1. 5 _____ -2

2. 3.14 _____ π

3. -10 _____ -15

4. $\sqrt{15}$ _____ 4

5. 9.78 _____ 9.87

6. -1.3 _____ $-\dfrac{4}{3}$

7. $\dfrac{1}{5}$ _____ $\dfrac{1}{4}$

Suppose we are given an inequality of the form

$$x > -1$$

The *solution set* for an inequality (as it is for an equation) is the set of all values for the variable that make the inequality a true statement. A convenient way to picture that solution set is by a graph on a number line. The following example illustrates.

Example 3

Graph each of the following sets.

This set is read "the set of all *x* such that *x* is greater than -1."

(a) $\{x \,|\, x > -1\}$

Here we want to graph all real numbers greater than -1. This means we want to include all real numbers *to the right* of -1 on the number line.

The *open circle* at −1 means that the point corresponding to −1 is *not included* in the graph. Such a graph is called an *open half line.*

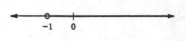

(b) $\{x \mid x < 4\}$

In this case we want to include all real numbers less than 4, that is, *to the left* of 4 on the number line.

Here the "left" arrowhead means the graph continues indefinitely to the left.

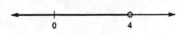

CHECK YOURSELF 3

Graph each of the following sets.

1. $\{x \mid x < 5\}$ 2. $\{x \mid x > -3\}$

Two other symbols, $\leq$ and $\geq$, are also used in writing inequalities. In each case they combine the inequality symbols for less than and greater than with the symbol for equality. The following shows the use of these new symbols. The statement

This combines the symbols < and = and means that either $a < b$ or $a = b$.

$a \leq b$

is read "a is less than or equal to b." Similarly,

Here either $a > b$ or $a = b$.

$a \geq b$

is read "a is greater than or equal to b." We consider the graph of inequalities involving these symbols in our next example.

Example 4

Graph each of the following sets.

(a) $\{x \mid x \leq 3\}$

Now we want to graph all real numbers to the left of 3 but also *including* 3 because of the "is less than or equal to" symbol.

Here the closed circle at 3 means that the point corresponding to 3 is *included* in the graph. Such a graph is called a *closed half line.*

(b) $\left\{x \mid x \geq \dfrac{7}{2}\right\}$

Here we want all numbers to the right of $\dfrac{7}{2}$ and including $\dfrac{7}{2}$.

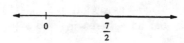

CHECK YOURSELF 4

Graph each of the following sets.

1. $\{x \mid x \leq 7\}$ **2.** $\left\{x \mid x \geq -\dfrac{4}{3}\right\}$

Note You may very well encounter a different notation for indicating the graphs of inequalities. This involves the use of parentheses and brackets to represent open and closed half lines, respectively. For example, the graph of $\{x \mid x > 3\}$ can be drawn as

The left parenthesis, (, is used to indicate the *open* half line, extending to the right and *not including* 3.

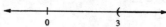

and the graph of $\{x \mid x \leq -2\}$ as

The right bracket,], is used to indicate the *closed* half line, extending to the left and *including* -2.

Our subsequent work with inequalities involves the use of a *double-inequality* statement such as

$$-3 < x < 4$$

We read this "x is greater than -3 and less than 4." This statement combines the two inequalities

The word "and" is implied in any double-inequality statement.

$$x > -3 \qquad and \qquad x < 4$$

or, more formally,

$$\{x \mid x > -3\} \cap \{x \mid x < 4\}$$

For a thorough discussion of sets, see the appendix coverage of sets and set notation.

This set of numbers includes all real numbers between -3 and 4.

In our next example we look at the graphs of inequalities that have this form.

Example 5

Graph each of the following sets.

(a) $\{x \mid -4 < x < 5\}$

For the solution set of this double inequality, we want all points that lie to the right of -4 ($x > -4$) and to the left of 5 ($x < 5$). This means that we should include all points that lie *between* -4 and 5.

The *open* circles indicate that the endpoints, -4 and 5, are *not included* in the graph. This is called an *open interval*.

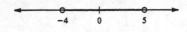

(b) $\{x \mid 2 \le x \le 6\}$

Here we want all points between 2 and 6—in this case we also *include* the endpoints 2 and 6.

The *closed* circles mean that 2 and 6 *are included* in the graph. This is called a *closed interval*.

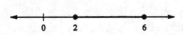

CHECK YOURSELF 5

Graph each of the following sets.

1. $\{x \mid -1 < x < 6\}$
2. $\{x \mid -2 \le x < 8\}$

Once again, we refer to the number line to introduce our final topic of this section. If we locate the number 4 and its opposite, -4, on the number line, we see that both numbers correspond to points that are the same distance (4 units) from the origin.

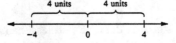

When we are concerned not with the direction (left or right) of a number from the origin, but only with the distance from the origin, we refer to that number's absolute value.

An *absolute value* is the distance (on the number line) between the point named by that real number and the origin. We indicate the absolute value of a number with vertical bars as follows:

$|5|$

This is read "the absolute value of 5," and

$|5| = 5$

We read

$$|-3|$$

Note that the absolute value of a number is always positive or zero.

as "the absolute value of −3," and

$$|-3| = 3$$

In general, we can define the absolute value of any real number a as

The third part of this definition may be hard to see. If a is *negative*, then its opposite, $-a$, must be *positive*, and we want a *positive* absolute value.

$$|a| = \begin{cases} a & \text{if } a \text{ is positive} \\ 0 & \text{if } a \text{ is zero} \\ -a & \text{if } a \text{ is negative} \end{cases}$$

The use of the absolute value notation is illustrated in our final example.

Example 6

Most graphing calculators have a key labeled [abs]. This can be used to evaluate the absolute value of an expression. To evaluate part (b), enter abs (−2.5).

Evaluate each of the following expressions.

(a) $|32|$ (b) $|-2.5|$ (c) $|\sqrt{2}|$

(d) $|-\sqrt{2}|$ (e) $-|-5|$ (f) $|-3| + |-7|$

(g) $\left|-\dfrac{5}{6}\right|$ (h) $\left|-\dfrac{3}{4}\right| + \left|\dfrac{5}{8}\right|$

Solution

(a) $|32| = 32$

(b) $|-2.5| = 2.5$

(c) $|\sqrt{2}| = \sqrt{2}$

(d) $|-\sqrt{2}| = \sqrt{2}$

(e) $-|-5| = -5$ $|-5|$ is 5, so $-|-5|$ must be −5.

(f) $|-3| + |-7| = 3 + 7 = 10$

(g) $\left|-\dfrac{5}{6}\right| = \dfrac{5}{6}$

(h) $\left|-\dfrac{3}{4}\right| + \left|\dfrac{5}{8}\right| = \dfrac{3}{4} + \dfrac{5}{8} = \dfrac{11}{8}$

CHECK YOURSELF 6

Evaluate each of the following expressions.

1. $|121|$ **2.** $|-3.4|$ **3.** $|\sqrt{3}|$

4. $|-\sqrt{5}|$ **5.** $-|-8|$ **6.** $|-9| + |-2|$

CHECK YOURSELF ANSWERS

1. (1) Symmetric; (2) substitution; (3) reflexive; (4) transitive.

2. (1) $5 > -2$; (2) $3.14 < \pi$; (3) $-10 > -15$; (4) $\sqrt{15} < 4$;

(5) $9.78 < 9.87$; (6) $-1.3 > -\dfrac{4}{3}$; (7) $\dfrac{1}{5} < \dfrac{1}{4}$.

3. (1) $\{x \mid x < 5\}$ (2) $\{x \mid x > -3\}$

4. (1) $\{x \mid x \le 7\}$ (2) $\left\{x \mid x \ge -\dfrac{4}{3}\right\}$

5. (1) $\{x \mid -1 < x < 6\}$ (2) $\{x \mid -2 \le x < 8\}$

(This is a *half open* interval.)

6. (1) 121; (2) 3.4; (3) $\sqrt{3}$; (4) $\sqrt{5}$; (5) -8; (6) 11.

Name _____

Date _____

Build Your Skills

Which property of equality justifies each of the following statements?

1. If $2x + 1 = y$, then $y = 2x + 1$.

2. $m + 3n = m + 3n$

3. If $3x - 4 = y$ and $y = 2$, then $3x - 4 = 2$.

4. If $3x - 4 = y$ and $x = 2$, then $3(2) - 4 = y$.

5. If $a^2 + b^2 = c^2$ and $c^2 = 25$, then $a^2 + b^2 = 25$.

6. If $a^2 + b^2 = c^2$ and $b^2 = 16$, then $a^2 + 16 = c^2$.

7. $w + 17 = w + 17$

8. If $2x + y = 2z$, then $2z = 2x + y$.

9. If $3x + 2 = 4y$ and $y = x + 1$, then $3x + 2 = 4(x + 1)$.

10. If $x = 4y - 1$ and $4y - 1 = z$, then $x = z$.

Complete each of the following statements with an inequality symbol ($<$ or $>$) or equality symbol ($=$).

11. 7 ____ 5 **12.** -3 ____ 6

13. -2 ____ -1 **14.** -5 ____ -6

15. -3.8 ____ -3.9 **16.** -6.50 ____ -6.5

ANSWERS

1. _____
2. _____
3. _____
4. _____
5. _____
6. _____
7. _____
8. _____
9. _____
10. _____
11. _____
12. _____
13. _____
14. _____
15. _____
16. _____

17. _____

18. _____

19. _____

20. _____

21. _____

22. _____

23. _____

24. _____

25. _____

26. _____

27. _____

28. _____

29. _____

30. _____

31. _____

32. _____

33. _____

34. _____

35. _____

36. _____

37. _____

38. _____

17. $-\dfrac{5}{4}$ _____ $-\dfrac{4}{3}$

18. -1.3 _____ $-\dfrac{4}{3}$

19. $\sqrt{2}$ _____ 1.41

20. $-\sqrt{3}$ _____ -1.6

21. 1.25 _____ $\dfrac{5}{4}$

22. $\dfrac{7}{3}$ _____ 2.33

23. $|-2|$ _____ -2

24. $|-2|$ _____ $|-1|$

25. $-|4|$ _____ $|-4|$

26. $|5|$ _____ $-|-5|$

Write each of the following inequalities in words.

27. $x > 5$

28. $x \geq 3$

29. $t \leq 3$

30. $y < -2$

31. $x \geq y$

32. $p < q$

33. $m < 0$

34. $x \geq 0$

35. $-2 < x < 5$

36. $-5 \leq x \leq -2$

Graph each of the following sets. Assume x represents a real number.

37. $\{x \mid x < 5\}$

38. $\{x \mid x \geq 3\}$

39. $\{x \mid x > -5\}$ ◄———+———►
                    0

39. _____

40. $\{x \mid x \leq -1\}$ ◄———+———►
                    0

40. _____

41. $\{x \mid -2 \geq x\}$ ◄———+———►
                    0

41. _____

42. $\{x \mid 2 < x\}$ ◄———+———►
                    0

42. _____

43. $\{x \mid x \geq 2\}$ ◄———+———►
                    0

43. _____

44. $\{x \mid 0 \geq x\}$ ◄———+———►
                    0

44. _____

45. $\{x \mid 2 < x < 3\}$ ◄———+———►
                    0

45. _____

46. $\{x \mid -4 \leq x \leq 6\}$ ◄———+———►
                    0

46. _____

47. $\{x \mid -3 < x \leq -1\}$ ◄———+———►
                    0

47. _____

48. $\{x \mid 3 \leq x < 5\}$ ◄———+———►
                    0

48. _____

Rewrite each of the following statements, using inequality symbols. Then graph the solution set for each inequality. Assume that x represents a real number.

49. _____

49. x is less than 2.

◄———+———►
        0

50. x is more than -3.

◄———+———►
        0

50. _____

51. x is at least -1.

◄———+———►
        0

52. x is no more than 6.

◄———+———►
        0

51. _____

53. x is greater than 5.

◄———+———►
        0

54. x is at least 1.

◄———+———►
        0

52. _____

53. _____

54. _____

117

ANSWERS

55. _____

56. _____

57. _____

58. _____

59. _____

60. _____

61. _____

62. _____

63. _____

64. _____

65. _____

66. _____

67. _____

68. _____

69. _____

70. _____

71. _____

72. _____

73. _____

74. _____

75. _____

76. _____

55. x is no more than -1.

56. x is not less than -1.

57. x is between 2 and 5.

58. -5 is less than or equal to x, and x is less than -2.

Write each of the following expressions without the absolute value symbol.

59. $|4|$

60. $|-4|$

61. $|-3.5|$

62. $|2.5|$

63. $\left|\dfrac{7}{8}\right|$

64. $-\left|\dfrac{5}{6}\right|$

65. $-|1.5|$

66. $|-3.4|$

67. $-|-2|$

68. $-|-7|$

69. $-\left|\dfrac{3}{4}\right|$

70. $\left|-\dfrac{5}{2}\right|$

71. $|-4| + |-6|$

72. $|-3| + |-7|$

73. $-(|2| + |-3|)$

74. $-(|-5| + |-6|)$

Think About These

Label each statement as true or false. If it is false, explain.

75. $|-3| \geq 3$

76. $|0| = 0$

77. $|-15| = |15|$

78. $|1 - 2| > |0 - 1|$

79. $|x - 1| = |1 - x|$

80. $|5 - 3| = |5| + |-3|$

81. $|-a| = a$ *Hint:* For this statement to be true, it must be true for all values of the variable.

82. $-|y| = -y$

83. The absolute value of any real number is positive or 0.

84. The absolute value of any real number is equal to the absolute value of its opposite.

85. Some real numbers have no absolute value.

86. There is only one real number which is equal to its own absolute value.

87. The Wilderness Society defines "classic" old-growth forests as "containing at least eight big trees per acre exceeding 300 years in age or measuring more than 40 inches (abbreviated in) in diameter. . . ." Let N represent the number of big trees per acre, A the age in years, and D the diameter in inches. Write three inequalities that can be used to represent this definition of old-growth forests.

88. An old-growth Douglas fir is defined as being between 400 and 1000 years old. Write the age of an old-growth Douglas fir as a double inequality. (Include 400 and 1000.)

77. _____

78. _____

79. _____

80. _____

81. _____

82. _____

83. _____

84. _____

85. _____

86. _____

87. _____

88. _____

89. The typical color television set in U.S. homes uses between 75 and 1000 kilowatthours of electricity E per year (kWh/yr). Write this electricity usage as a double inequality. (Include 15 and 1000.)

90. The average person in the United States creates at least 2 kg of garbage every day. Write an inequality that expresses the number of kilograms of garbage G created by the average person each day in the United States.

ANSWERS

1. Symmetric property **3.** Transitive property or substitution **5.** Transitive property or substitution principle **7.** Reflexive property **9.** Substitution principle **11.** $7 > 5$ **13.** $-2 < -1$

15. $-3.8 > -3.9$ **17.** $-\dfrac{5}{4} > -\dfrac{4}{3}$ **19.** $\sqrt{2} > 1.41$ **21.** $1.25 = \dfrac{5}{4}$ **23.** $|-2| > -2$

25. $-|4| < |-4|$ **27.** x is greater than 5. **29.** t is less than or equal to 3. **31.** x is greater than or equal to y. **33.** m is less than 0 or m is negative. **35.** -2 is less than x, and x is less than 5; or x is between -2 and 5.

37. $x < 5$

39. $x > -5$

41. $-2 \geq x$

43. $x \geq 2$

45. $2 < x < 3$

47. $-3 < x \leq -1$

49. $x < 2$

51. $x \geq -1$

53. $x > 5$

55. $x \leq -1$

57. $2 < x < 5$

59. 4 **61.** 3.5 **63.** $\dfrac{7}{8}$ **65.** -1.5

67. -2 **69.** $-\dfrac{3}{4}$ **71.** 10 **73.** -5 **75.** True **77.** True **79.** True

81. False, this is not true for negative values of a. **83.** True **85.** False, every real number has an absolute value. **87.** $N \geq 8$, $A > 300$, $D > 40$ **89.** $75 \leq E \leq 1000$

INTERVAL NOTATION

In the last section we have seen that an inequality can be represented on a number line. Now let us look at a different way to denote inequalities. An <u>interval</u> is an uninterrupted portion of a number line. Intervals can be either <u>closed or open</u>. We use a parenthesis to indicate an open interval and a bracket to denote a closed interval.

OPEN INTERVALS

An open interval (a,b) is defined as the set of all real numbers between 'a' and 'b' excluding both 'a' and 'b'. We denote this by the inequality notation $a < x < b$. The numbers a and b are called endpoints. The graph of an open interval (a,b) is shown below.

In the graph, the open circles indicate that the endpoints are not included in the interval (a,b). Note that we use the same notation for an open interval and an ordered pair. From the context of the problem, you will be able to distinguish between the two.

Example 1. Draw the open interval (1,5) on the number line.

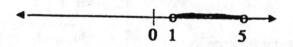

CLOSED INTERVALS

A closed interval [a,b] is defined as the set of all real numbers between 'a' and 'b' including end points 'a' and 'b'. We represent this by the inequality notation $a \leq x \leq b$. Note that the endpoints are included in the graph as shown below.

Example 2. Draw the closed interval [-1,3] on the number line.

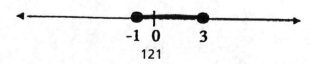

Intervals can be open at one endpoint and closed at the other. They are called **half open/half closed intervals**. For example, the notation (a,b] denotes all the numbers between 'a' and 'b' excluding endpoint 'a' but including endpoint 'b'. We represent this by the inequality $a < x \leq b$.

INFINITE INTERVALS

An interval can be of either finite or infinite length. Consider all the points on the number line greater than 1 (see graph given below).

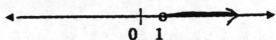

This is an example of an infinite interval and is represented in the interval notation by $(1, \infty)$. You can probably guess what the interval $(-\infty, 1)$ consists of. Remember that $-\infty$ and ∞ do not represent real numbers. They are just symbols to indicate that the interval is of infinite length. (Therefore, intervals like $(2, \infty]$ never make sense.)

Example 3. Write interval notation for each of the following.

    a.   The set of all x such that $x > 3$
         Ans: $(3, \infty)$

    b. The set of all x such that $x < -1$
         Ans: $(-\infty, -1)$

Example 4. Give the interval notation for each of the following graphs.

a.

-3 -2 -1 0

     Ans: $(-\infty, -3)$

b.

0 1 2 3

     Ans: $[3, \infty)$

SUMMARY

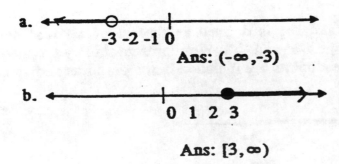

Interval Notation	Graph	Inequality
(a,b)		$a < x <$
[a,b]		$a \leq x \leq$
[a,b)		$a \leq x <$
(a,b]		$a < x \leq$
(a, ∞)		$x > a$
$[a, \infty)$		$x \geq a$
$(-\infty, a)$		$x < a$
$(-\infty, a]$		$x \leq a$

EXERCISES

Fill in the chart below:

	Interval Notation	Graph	Inequality
1.	[-1,2]		
2.		$-2 \quad 3$	
3.			$-4 \leq x \leq 1$
4.	$(-\infty,1)$		
5.		1	
6.			$x \geq 4$
7.	$(4, \infty)$		
8.	$(1,3)$		
9.		3	
10.	$(-\infty,4]$		
11.	$[-3,2]$		
12.		4	
13.			$-2 < x \leq 4$
14.	$(3,\infty)$		
15.		$-3 \quad 3$	
16.			$x < 3$
17.	123		$2 < x \leq 5$

Answers

	Interval Notation	Graph	Inequality
1.	[-1,2]	-1 2	$-1 \leq x \leq 2$
2.	(-2,3)	-2 3	$-2 < x < 3$
3.	[-4,1]	-4 1	$-4 \leq x \leq 1$
4.	(-∞,1)	1	$x < 1$
5.	[1,∞)	1	$x \geq 1$
6.	[4,∞)	4	$x \geq 4$
7.	(4,∞)	4	$x > 4$
8.	(1,3)	1 3	$1 < x < 3$
9.	[3,∞)	3	$x \geq 3$
10.	(-∞,4]	4	$x \leq 4$
11.	[-3,2]	-3 2	$-3 \leq x \leq 2$
12.	(-∞,4)	4	$x < 4$
13.	(-2,4]	-2 4	$2 < x \leq 4$
14.	(3,∞)	3	$x > 3$
15.	(-3,3)	-3 3	$-3 < x < 3$
16.	(-∞,3)	3	$x < 3$
17.	(2,5]	2 5	$2 < x \leq 5$

124

A VISUAL APPROACH TO SOLVING INEQUALITIES

Consider the inequality $3x - 2 < x + 4$. Just as we did with equations, we may associate this inequality with a system of two lines:

$$y = 3x - 2$$

$$y = x + 4$$

As we did for equations, we can graph these lines (Fig. 1) and observe that they intersect at (3,7).

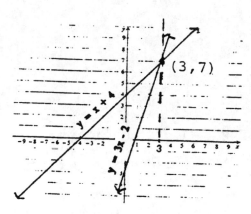

At $x = 3$, the height above the x-axis of both the lines $y = 3x - 2$ and $y = x + 4$ is the <u>same</u>. This is why 3 is the solution to the <u>equation</u> $3x - 2 = x + 4$. To find the solution of the <u>inequality</u> $3x - 2 < x + 4$, we need to find those values on the x-axis for which the line $y = 3x - 2$ is <u>below</u> the line $y = x + 4$.

Fig. 1

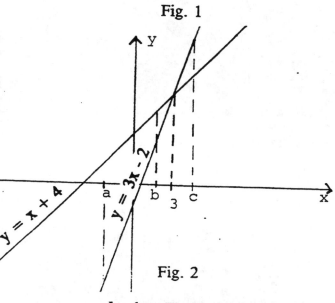

Fig. 2

An illustration of "above" and "below":

At point a, the line $y = 3x - 2$ is <u>below</u> the line $y = x + 4$.

At point b, the line $y = 3x - 2$ is <u>below</u> the line $y = x + 4$.

At point c, the line $y = 3x - 2$ is <u>above</u> the line $y = x + 4$.

Look at Fig. 2. From this, it is clear that the line $y = 3x - 2$ is <u>below</u> the line $y = x + 4$ for values of x that are <u>to the left of 3</u>; that is, on the interval $(-\infty, 3)$. This interval, then, is the solution to the inequality $3x - 2 < x + 4$.

IN GENERAL: to solve visually the inequality $ax + b < cx + d$ OR $ax + b > cx + d$, graph the lines $y = ax + b$ and $y = cx + d$, and determine the x-coordinate of their point of intersection. Then:

1) The solutions to $ax + b < cx + d$ are the values on the x-axis for which the line $y = ax + b$ is <u>below</u> the line $y = cx + d$.
2) The solutions to $ax + b > cx + d$ are the values on the x-axis for which the line $y = ax + b$ is <u>above</u> the line $y = cx + d$.

<u>Note</u>: If the inequality features "$\leq$" or "$\geq$", the procedure is the same, but the solution will be a <u>closed</u> interval instead of an <u>open</u> interval.

Example:

Solve $2x - 5 \geq -\dfrac{1}{2}x - 1$.

The lines $y = 2x - 5$ and $y = -\dfrac{1}{2}x - 1$ are graphed in Fig. 3. Since we observe that these lines don't intersect at a convenient grid point, we find the x-coordinate of the point of intersection by solving the <u>equation</u> $2x - 5 = -\dfrac{1}{2}x - 1$ algebraically. Solving, we get $x = \dfrac{8}{5}$.

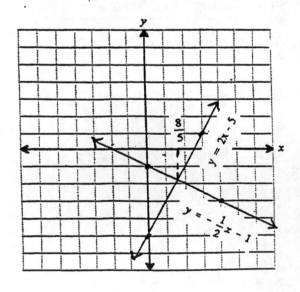

Figure 3

Since we are solving the inequality $2x - 5 \geq -\dfrac{1}{2}x - 1$, we just need to ask ourselves, "On which side of $\dfrac{8}{5}$ is the line $y = 2x - 5$ <u>above</u> the line $y = -\dfrac{1}{2}x - 1$?" From Fig. 3, clearly the answer is "on the <u>right</u> side". Thus, our solution is $\left[\dfrac{8}{5}, \infty\right)$.

EXERCISES

Build Your Skills

For each of the following inequalities, a) associate a system of two lines, b) graph these lines, and c) use the graphs to determine the solution of the original inequality. Write the solution in interval form.

1. $x - 5 < 2$

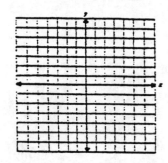

System: _____

_____

Solution: _____

2. $x - 3 < -5$

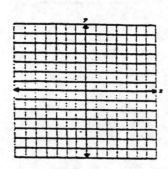

System: _____

_____

Solution: _____

3. $x - 1 \geq 4$

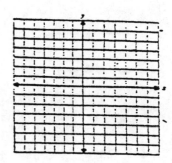

System: _____

_____

Solution: _____

4. $2 < x - 4$

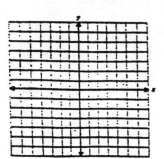

System: _____

_____

Solution: _____

5. $3x < 6$

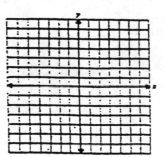

System: _____

_____

Solution: _____

6. $2x < -4$

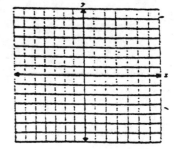

System: _____

_____

Solution: _____

7. $\dfrac{x}{3} > 1$

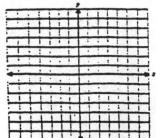

System: _____

_____

Solution: _____

8. $\dfrac{x}{2} \geq 3$

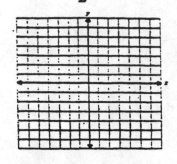

System: _____

_____

Solution: _____

9. $2x - 3 \geq 5$

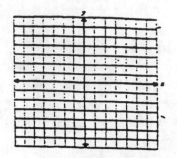

System: _____

_____

Solution: _____

10. $4 - 2x > x - 5$

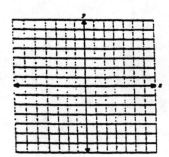

System: _____

_____

Solution: _____

11. $2x - 3 \leq 3$

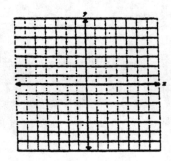

System: _____

_____

Solution: _____

12. $-\dfrac{3}{2}x + 6 \geq \dfrac{5}{2}x - 6$

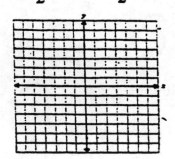

System: _____

_____

Solution: _____

13. $x - 4 < 6 - x$

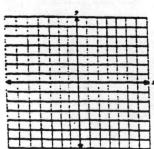

System: _____

_____

Solution: _____

14. $x - 1 \geq -\dfrac{1}{2}x + 2$

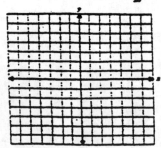

System: _____

_____

Solution: _____ 128

15. $\dfrac{1}{2}x - 1 < -\dfrac{1}{2}x + 3$

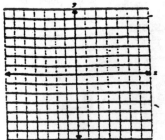

System: _____

_____

Solution: _____

16. $-\dfrac{3}{2}x + 6 > 3$

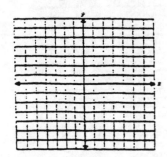

System: _____

_____

Solution: _____

17. $\dfrac{1}{3}x - 4 \le \dfrac{2}{3}x - 2$

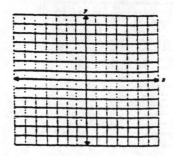

System: _____

_____

Solution: _____

18. $6 - 2x > 3x - 4$

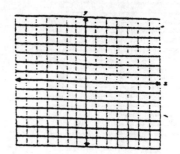

System: _____

_____

Solution: _____

19. $5x - 2 \le 3$

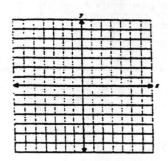

System: _____

_____

Solution: _____

20. $3 - \dfrac{1}{2}x < \dfrac{3}{2}x - 6$

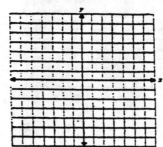

System: _____

_____

Solution: _____

21. $x - 1 > -2x + 5$

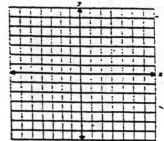

System: _____

_____

Solution: _____

22. $x + 1 \ge \dfrac{2}{3}x$

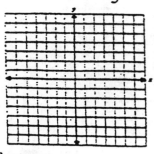

System: _____

_____

Solution: _____

23. $-\dfrac{1}{3}x - 1 > \dfrac{4}{3}x - 6$

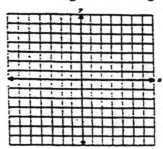

System: _____

Solution: _____

24. $5 > 2x$

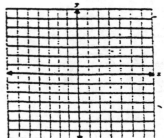

System: _____

_____

Solution: _____

1. $x - 5 < 2$

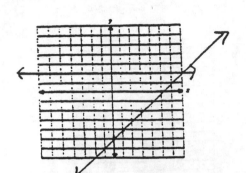

System: $y = x - 5$

$y = 2$

Solution: $(-\infty, 7)$

2. $x - 3 < -5$

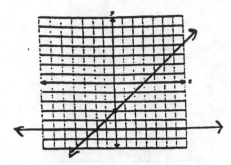

System: $y = x - 3$

$y = -5$

Solution: $(-\infty, -2)$

3. $x - 1 \geq 4$

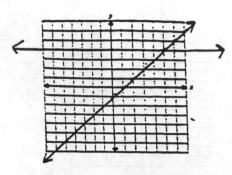

System: $y = x - 1$

$y = 4$

Solution: $[5, \infty)$

4. $2 < x - 4$

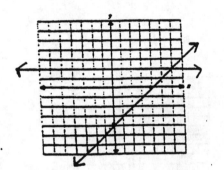

System: $y = 2$

$y = x - 4$

Solution: $(6, \infty)$

5. $3x < 6$

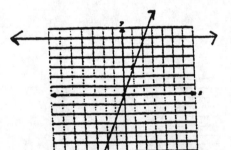

System: $y = 3x$

$y = 6$

Solution: $(-\infty, 2)$

6. $2x < -4$

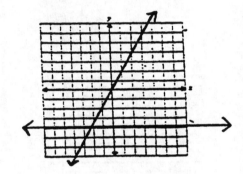

System: $y = 2x$

$y = -4$

Solution: $(-\infty, -2)$

7. $\dfrac{x}{3} > 1$

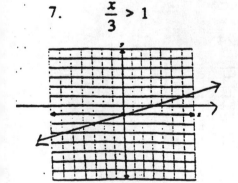

System: $y = \dfrac{1}{3}x$

$y = 1$

Solution: $(3, \infty)$

8. $\dfrac{x}{2} \geq 3$

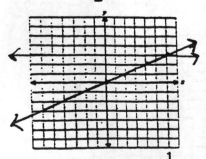

System: $y = \dfrac{1}{2}x$

$y = 3$

130

Solution: $[6, \infty)$

9. $2x - 3 \geq 5$

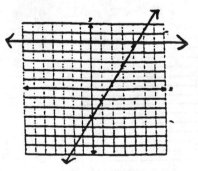

System: $y = 2x - 3$

$y = 5$

Solution: $[4, \infty)$

10. $4 - 2x > x - 5$

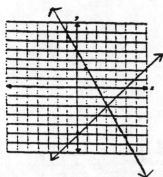

System: $y = -2x + 4$

$y = x - 5$

Solution: $(-\infty, 3)$

11. $2x - 3 \leq 3$

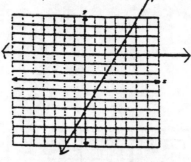

System: $y = 2x - 3$

$y = 3$

Solution: $(-\infty, 3]$

12. $-\frac{3}{2}x + 6 \geq \frac{5}{2}x - 6$

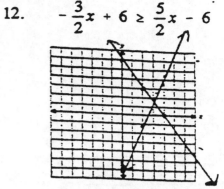

System: $y = -\frac{3}{2}x + 6$

$y = \frac{5}{2}x - 6$

Solution: $(-\infty, 3]$

13. $x - 4 < 6 - x$

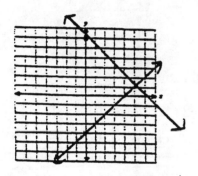

System: $y = x - 4$

$y = -x + 6$

Solution: $(-\infty, 5)$

14. $x - 1 \geq -\frac{1}{2}x + 2$

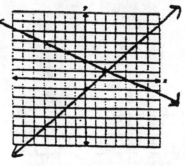

System: $y = x - 1$

$y = -\frac{1}{2}x + 2$

Solution: $[2, \infty)$

15. $\frac{1}{2}x - 1 < -\frac{1}{2}x + 3$

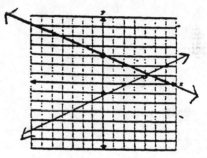

System: $y = \frac{1}{2}x - 1$

$y = -\frac{1}{2}x + 3$

Solution: $(-\infty, 4)$

16. $-\frac{3}{2}x + 6 > 3$

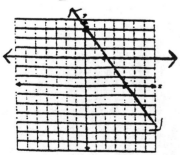

System: $y = -\frac{3}{2}x + 6$

$y = 3$

Solution: $(-\infty, 2)$

17. $\frac{1}{3}x - 4 \leq \frac{2}{3}x - 2$

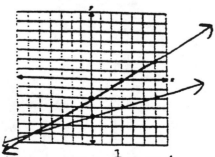

System: $y = \frac{1}{3}x - 4$

$y = \frac{2}{3}x - 2$

Solution: 13$[-6, \infty)$

18. $6 - 2x > 3x - 4$

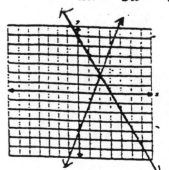

System: $y = -2x + 6$

$y = 3x - 4$

Solution: $(-\infty, 2)$

19. $5x - 2 \le 3$

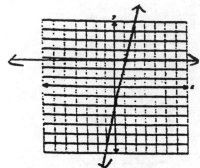

System: $\underline{y = 5x - 2}$

$\underline{y = 3}$

Solution: $\underline{(-\infty, 1]}$

20. $3 - \dfrac{1}{2}x < \dfrac{3}{2}x - 6$

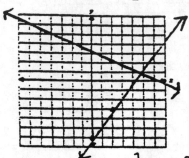

System: $\underline{y = -\dfrac{1}{2}x + 3}$

$\underline{y = \dfrac{3}{2}x - 6}$

Solution: $\underline{\left(\dfrac{9}{2}, \infty\right)}$

21. $x - 1 > -2x + 5$

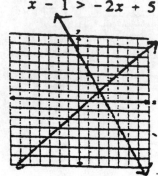

System: $\underline{y = x - 1}$

$\underline{y = -2x + 5}$

Solution: $\underline{(2, \infty)}$

22. $x + 1 \ge \dfrac{2}{3}x$

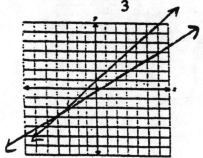

System: $\underline{y = x + 1}$

$\underline{y = \dfrac{2}{3}x}$

Solution: $\underline{[-3, \infty)}$

23. $-\dfrac{1}{3}x - 1 > \dfrac{4}{3}x - 6$

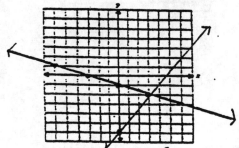

System: $\underline{y = -\dfrac{1}{3}x - 1}$

$\underline{y = \dfrac{4}{3}x - 6}$

Solution: $\underline{(-\infty, 3)}$

24. $5 > 2x$

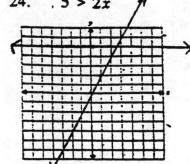

System: $\underline{y = 5}$

$\underline{y = 2x}$

Solution: $\underline{\left(-\infty, \dfrac{5}{2}\right)}$

Solving Linear Inequalities

OBJECTIVES
1. To solve and graph the solution sets for linear inequalities
2. To solve and graph the solution sets for compound inequalities

We defined a linear equation in one variable as an equation that could be written in the form

$$ax + b = 0$$

where a and b are real numbers and $a \neq 0$.

A linear inequality in one variable is defined in a similar fashion.

A *linear inequality* can be written in the form

$$ax + b < 0$$

where a and b are real numbers and $a \neq 0$.

The inequality symbol $<$ can be replaced with any of the other inequality symbols $>$, $\leq$, or $\geq$, so that

$$ax + b > 0 \qquad ax + b \leq 0 \qquad \text{and} \qquad ax + b \geq 0$$

are also linear inequalities.

Fortunately your experience with linear equations provides the groundwork for solving linear inequalities. You will see many similarities.

A *solution* for a linear inequality in one variable is any real number that will make the inequality a true statement when the variable is replaced by that number. The *solution set* for a linear inequality is the set of all solutions.

> We can also say that a solution *satisfies* the inequality.

Our strategy for solving linear inequalities is, for the most part, identical to that used for solving linear equations. We write a sequence of equivalent inequalities in order to isolate the variable on one side of the inequality symbol.

Writing equivalent inequalities for this purpose requires two properties. First:

> Adding the same quantity to both sides of an inequality gives an equivalent inequality.

ADDITION PROPERTY OF INEQUALITY

If $a < b$, then $a + c < b + c$.

Since subtraction is defined in terms of addition, the property also allows us to subtract the same quantity from both sides of an inequality without changing the solutions.

133

Our second property, dealing with multiplication, has an important difference. We begin by writing the true inequality

$$2 < 3$$

Multiplying both sides of that inequality by the same *positive* number, say 3, gives

$$3(2) < 3(3)$$
$$6 < 9 \qquad \text{Another true statement!}$$

Note that the new inequality has the same sense (points in the same direction) as the original inequality.

However, if we now multiply both sides of the inequality by a *negative* number, say -3, we have

$$-3(2) < -3(3)$$
$$-6 < -9 \qquad \text{A } \textit{false} \text{ statement!}$$

To make this a true statement, we must *reverse the sense* of the inequality to write

$$-6 > -9$$

This suggests that if we multiply both sides of an inequality by a negative number, we must reverse the sense of the inequality to form an equivalent inequality. From this discussion we can now state our second property.

Multiplying both sides of an inequality by a positive number gives an equivalent inequality.

Multiplying both sides of an inequality by a negative number and reversing the sense give an equivalent inequality.

MULTIPLICATION PROPERTY OF INEQUALITY

If $\qquad a < b$

then $\qquad ac < bc \qquad$ where c is a *positive* number ($c > 0$)

and

$\qquad ac > bc \qquad$ where c is a *negative* number ($c < 0$)

Again, since division is defined in terms of multiplication, this property also allows us to divide both sides of an inequality by the same nonzero number, reversing the sense of the inequality if that number is negative.

We will use these properties in solving inequalities in much the same way as we did in solving equations, with the one significant difference pointed out above.

The following examples illustrate the solution process for linear inequalities.

Example 1

Solve and graph the inequality

$$4x - 3 < 5 \tag{1}$$

First, we add 3 to both sides.

As in solving equations, we apply the addition property and then the multiplication property, to isolate the variable.

$$4x - 3 + 3 < 5 + 3$$
$$4x < 8 \tag{2}$$

We now divide both sides of the inequality by 4, to isolate the variable on the left.

$$\frac{4x}{4} < \frac{8}{4}$$
$$x < 2 \tag{3}$$

Since inequalities (1), (2), and (3) are all equivalent, the solution set for the original inequality consists of all numbers that are less than 2. That set can be written

$$\{x \mid x < 2\}$$

The graph of the solution set is

The open circle means 2 is not included in the solution set.

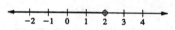

CHECK YOURSELF 1

Solve and graph the inequality.

$$5x + 7 > 22$$

Example 2*

Solve and graph the inequality

$$3x - 5 \geq 5x + 3$$

Add 5 to both sides.

$$3x - 5 + 5 \geq 5x + 3 + 5$$
$$3x \geq 5x + 8$$

*A screen is used to indicate an expression that is being simplified.

Subtract $5x$ from both sides.

$$3x - 5x \geq 5x - 5x + 8$$
$$-2x \geq 8$$

We must now divide both sides by -2. Since the divisor is negative, we reverse the sense of the inequality.

$$\frac{-2x}{-2} \leq * \frac{8}{-2}$$
$$x \leq -4$$

The solution set consists of all numbers that are less than or equal to -4 and is graphed below.

$$\{x \mid x \leq -4\}$$

Here we use the *closed* circle to indicate that −4 is included in the solution set.

CHECK YOURSELF 2

Solve and graph.

$$4x + 3 \leq 7x - 12$$

In working with more complicated inequalities, as was the case with equations, any signs of grouping must be removed, and like terms combined, before the properties of inequalities are applied to isolate the variable.

Example 3

Solve and graph

$$5 - 3(x - 2) \leq 1 - x$$

First, remove the parentheses on the left and combine like terms.

$$5 - 3x + 6 \leq 1 - x$$
$$-3x + 11 \leq 1 - x$$

We now proceed as before.

*A screen is used to indicate an expression that is being simplified.

$$-3x + 11 - 11 \leq 1 - 11 - x \qquad \text{Subtract 11.}$$

$$-3x \leq -10 - x$$

$$-3x + x \leq -10 - x + x \qquad \text{Add } x.$$

$$-2x \leq -10$$

$$\frac{-2x}{-2} \; \underset{}{\geq} \; \frac{-10}{-2} \qquad \text{Divide by } -2, \text{ reversing the sense of the inequality.}$$

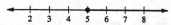

$$x \geq 5$$

The solution set $\{x \mid x \geq 5\}$ is graphed below.

```
 ──┼──┼──┼──●──┼──┼──┼──
   2  3  4  5  6  7  8
```

CHECK YOURSELF 3

Solve and graph.

$$4 - 2(x + 5) \geq -9 - 4x$$

If fractions are involved in an inequality, you should apply the multiplication property to clear the inequality of fractions as your first step.

Example 4

Solve and graph the inequality.

$$\frac{3x + 2}{6} - 1 < \frac{x}{3}$$

Multiply both sides by 6, the LCM of 6 and 3.

$$6\left(\frac{3x + 2}{6} - 1\right) < 6\left(\frac{x}{3}\right)$$

Apply the distributive property on the left.

$$6\left(\frac{3x + 2}{6}\right) - 6(1) < 6\left(\frac{x}{3}\right)$$

$$3x + 2 - 6 < 2x$$

The inequality is now cleared of fractions, and we proceed as before:

$$3x - 4 < 2x$$

$$3x < 2x + 4$$

$$x < 4$$

The solution set is graphed below.

$$\{x \mid x < 4\}$$

```
 ──┼──┼──┼──┼──┼──⊕──┼──┼──
  -1  0  1  2  3  4  5  6
```

CHECK YOURSELF 4

Solve and graph the inequality.

$$\frac{5x - 1}{4} - 2 > \frac{x}{2}$$

The following algorithm summarizes our work thus far in solving linear inequalities.

SOLVING LINEAR INEQUALITIES IN ONE VARIABLE

STEP 1   Clear the inequality statement of any fractions by using the multiplication property.

STEP 2   Remove any grouping symbols, and combine like terms on either side of the equation.

STEP 3   Apply the addition property to write an equivalent inequality with the variable term on one side of the inequality and the constant term on the other.

STEP 4   Apply the multiplication property to write an equivalent inequality with the variable isolated on one side of the inequality. Be sure to reverse the sense of the inequality if you multiply or divide by a negative number.

STEP 5   Graph the solution set of the original inequality.

Let's now consider two types of inequality statements which arise frequently in mathematics. Consider a statement such as

$$-2 < x < 5$$

It is called a *double inequality* because it combines the two inequalities

This is also called a *compound inequality*. In the double inequality the word "and" is understood.

$$-2 < x \quad \text{and} \quad x < 5$$

To solve a double inequality means to isolate the variable in the middle term, as the following example illustrates.

Example 5

Solve and graph the double inequality

$$-3 \leq 2x + 1 \leq 7$$

First, we subtract 1 from each of the three members of the double inequality.

We are really applying the additive property to each of the *two* inequalities that make up the double-inequality statement.

$$-3 - 1 \leq 2x + 1 - 1 \leq 7 - 1$$

or

$$-4 \leq 2x \leq 6$$

We now divide by 2 to isolate the variable x.

$$-\frac{4}{2} \leq \frac{2x}{2} \leq \frac{6}{2}$$
$$-2 \leq x \leq 3$$

The solution set consists of all numbers between -2 and 3, including -2 and 3, and is written

$$\{x \mid -2 \leq x \leq 3\}$$

That set is graphed below.

Because the circles at both ends of the interval are "closed," we sometimes call this a *closed interval*.

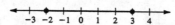

Note: Our solution set is equivalent to

$$\{x \mid x \geq -2 \text{ and } x \leq 3\}$$

Look at the individual graphs.

$\{x \mid x \geq -2\}$

$\{x \mid x \leq 3\}$

$\{x \mid x \geq -2 \text{ and } x \leq 3\}$

Using set notation, we write this as

$\{x \mid x \geq -2\} \cap \{x \mid x \leq 3\}$

The ∩ represents the intersection of the two sets.

Because the connecting word is "and," we want the *intersection* of the sets, that is, those numbers common to both sets.

CHECK YOURSELF 5

Solve and graph the inequality.

$$-5 \leq 2x - 3 \leq 3$$

When the coefficient to the variable is a negative number, care must be taken in isolating the variable.

139

Example 6

Solve and graph the double inequality

$$-3 < 4 - 3x < 13$$

Subtract 4 from each member of the inequality.

$$-7 < -3x < 9$$

Now we must divide by -3. The sense of the inequality is reversed whenever we divide by a negative number.

$$\frac{-7}{-3} > \frac{-3x}{-3} > \frac{9}{-3}$$

$$\frac{7}{3} > \quad x \quad > -3$$

In the standard smallest-to-largest format, we have

$$-3 < x < \frac{7}{3}$$

The solution consists of all numbers between -3 and $\frac{7}{3}$ and is written

$$\left\{ x \mid -3 < x < \frac{7}{3} \right\}$$

That set is graphed below.

The circles are open at both ends, this is sometimes called an open interval.

CHECK YOURSELF 6

Solve and graph the double inequality.

$$-5 < 3 - 2x < 5$$

A compound inequality may also consist of two inequality statements connected by the word "or." The following example illustrates the solution of that type of compound inequality.

Example 7

Solve and graph the inequality

$$2x - 3 < -5 \quad \text{or} \quad 2x - 3 > 5$$

In this case we must work with each of the inequalities *separately*.

$$
\begin{array}{rcl}
2x - 3 < -5 & \text{or} & 2x - 3 > 5 \\
2x < -2 & & 2x > 8 \\
x < -1 & & x > 4
\end{array}
$$

Add 3.

Divide by 2.

The graph of the solution set is shown.

$$\{x \mid x < -1 \text{ or } x > 4\}$$

In set notation we write the union as

$$\{x \mid x < -1\} \cup \{x \mid x > 4\}$$

Note that since the connecting word is "or" in this case, the solution set of the original inequality is the *union* of the two sets, that is, those numbers that belong to either or both of the sets.

CHECK YOURSELF 7

Solve and graph the inequality.

$$3x - 4 \leq -7 \quad \text{or} \quad 3x - 4 \geq 7$$

The following chart summarizes our discussion of solving linear inequalities and the nature of the solution sets of the types of inequalities we have considered in this section.

TYPE OF INEQUALITY	GRAPH OF SOLUTION SET
$ax + b < c$	If $a > 0$: If $a < 0$:
$-c < ax + b < c$	
$ax + b < -c \quad \text{or} \quad ax + b > c$	

CHECK YOURSELF ANSWERS

1. $x > 3$

2. $x \geq 5$

3. $x \geq -\dfrac{3}{2}$

4. $x > 3$

5. $-1 \leq x \leq 3$

6. $-1 < x < 4$ **Note:** This is an *open interval*.

7. $x \leq -1$ or $x \geq \dfrac{11}{3}$

Name _____

Date _____

Exercises

ANSWERS

Build Your Skills

1. _____

Solve each of the following inequalities. Then graph the solution set.

2. _____

1. $x - 2 < 5$

2. $x + 3 > -4$

3. _____

3. $x + 5 \geq 3$

4. $x - 4 \leq -2$

4. _____

5. $5x > 25$

6. $4x < -12$

5. _____

6. _____

7. $-3x \leq -15$

8. $-7x > 21$

7. _____

9. $2x + 3 < 10$

10. $5x - 3 \leq 17$

8. _____

9. _____

11. $-2x - 7 \geq 5$

12. $-3x + 4 < -4$

10. _____

13. $5 - 3x < 14$

14. $2 - 5x \geq 22$

11. _____

15. $3x - 4 > 2x + 5$

16. $4x + 3 \leq 3x + 11$

12. _____

13. _____

17. $8x + 2 \leq 2x + 10$

18. $5x - 1 > x + 9$

14. _____

19. $7x - 3 > 2x - 13$

20. $9x + 2 \geq 2x - 19$

15. _____

16. _____

17. _____

18. _____

19. _____

20. _____

ANSWERS

21. _____

22. _____

23. _____

24. _____

25. _____

26. _____

27. _____

28. _____

29. _____

30. _____

31. _____

32. _____

33. _____

34. _____

35. _____

36. _____

37. _____

38. _____

21. $4x - 3 \leq 6x + 5$

22. $7x - 1 \leq 10x - 6$

23. $5 - 3x > 2x + 3$

24. $7 - 5x > 3x - 9$

Simplify and then solve each of the following inequalities.

25. $5(2x - 1) \leq 25$

26. $3(3x + 1) > -15$

27. $4(5x + 1) > 3(3x + 5)$

28. $3(2x + 4) \leq 5(3x - 3)$

29. $3(x - 1) - 4 < 2(3x + 1)$

30. $3(3x - 1) - 4(x + 3) \leq 15$

31. $3(x + 7) - 11 > 2(3x - 5) + x$

32. $3(2x + 7) - 5 \leq 4(x + 1) - x$

Clear of fractions and then solve each of the following inequalities.

33. $\dfrac{x - 4}{3} < 5$

34. $\dfrac{x + 5}{2} \geq -3$

35. $\dfrac{x + 2}{-3} \leq 3$

36. $\dfrac{x - 2}{-4} > -6$

37. $\dfrac{x}{2} - \dfrac{x}{3} \geq 2$

38. $\dfrac{x}{4} - 2 < \dfrac{x}{5}$

ANSWERS

39. _____

40. _____

41. _____

42. _____

43. _____

44. _____

45. _____

46. _____

47. _____

48. _____

49. _____

50. _____

51. _____

52. _____

53. _____

54. _____

55. _____

56. _____

39. $\dfrac{x}{5} - \dfrac{x-7}{3} < \dfrac{1}{3}$

40. $\dfrac{x}{4} - \dfrac{4x+3}{20} < \dfrac{1}{5}$

41. $\dfrac{x-3}{2} - \dfrac{x+5}{5} \le \dfrac{1}{2}$

42. $\dfrac{x+5}{4} - \dfrac{x+1}{3} \le \dfrac{2}{3}$

Solve each of the following double inequalities. Then graph the solution set.

43. $3 \le x + 1 \le 5$

44. $-2 < x - 3 < 3$

45. $-8 < 2x < 4$

46. $-6 \le 3x \le 9$

47. $1 \le 2x - 3 \le 6$

48. $-2 < 3x - 5 < 4$

49. $-1 < 5 - 3x < 8$

50. $-7 \le 3 - 2x \le 8$

Solve each of the following compound inequalities. Then graph the solution set.

51. $x - 1 < -3$ or $x - 1 > 3$

52. $x + 2 < -5$ or $x + 2 > 5$

53. $2x - 1 < -7$ or $2x - 1 > 7$

54. $2x + 3 < -3$ or $2x + 3 > 3$

55. $3x - 1 < -7$ or $3x - 1 > 7$

56. $4x + 3 < -5$ or $4x + 3 > 5$

ANSWERS

Skillscan (Equality, Order, and Absolute Value)

Simplify each of the following expressions.

a. $|-3|$ **b.** $|7|$

c. $|8 - 2|$ **d.** $|3 - 7|$

e. $|-5| - |5|$ **f.** $|-5| - |-5|$

g. $|2 - 5| + |-3 - 1|$ **h.** $|-5 + 3| + |-2 + 6|$

a. _____

b. _____

c. _____

d. _____

e. _____

f. _____

g. _____

h. _____

ANSWERS

1. $x < 7$

3. $x \geq -2$

5. $x > 5$

7. $x \geq 5$

9. $x < \dfrac{7}{2}$

11. $x \leq -6$

13. $x > -3$

15. $x > 9$

17. $x \leq \dfrac{4}{3}$

19. $x > -2$

21. $x \geq -4$

23. $x < \dfrac{2}{5}$

25. $x \leq 3$ **27.** $x > 1$ **29.** $x > -3$ **31.** $x < 5$ **33.** $x < 19$ **35.** $x \geq -11$
37. $x \geq 12$ **39.** $x > 15$ **41.** $x \leq 10$

43. $2 \leq x \leq 4$

45. $-4 < x < 2$

47. $2 \leq x \leq \dfrac{9}{2}$

49. $-1 < x < 2$

51. $x < -2$ or $x > 4$

53. $x < -3$ or $x > 4$

55. $x < -2$ or $x > \dfrac{8}{3}$ **a.** 3   **b.** 7   **c.** 6   **d.** 4   **e.** 0   **f.** 0   **g.** 7   **h.** 6

A Visual Approach to Absolute Value:
The Graph of y = |ax + b|

Recall that $|a| = \begin{cases} a & \text{if } a \geq 0 \\ -a & \text{if } a < 0 \end{cases}$. It is reasonable to expect that the graph

of the equation $y = |2x + 1|$ will involve the graphs of both $y = 2x + 1$ and
$y = -(2x + 1) = -2x - 1$. The graphs of both of these lines are given in Figure 1.

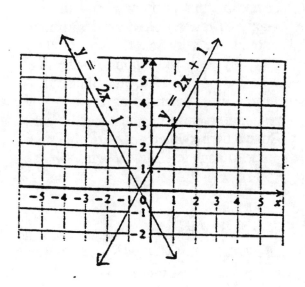

Figure 1

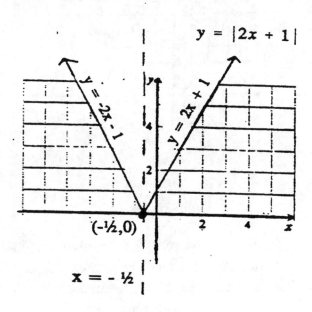

Figure 2

Notice that the graphs of these lines have the same x-intercept (-½,0). Since
$y = |2x + 1|$ implies that y can never be negative, we must eliminate those portions
of both lines that lie below the x-axis. The "V"-shaped graph that is left is the graph of
$y = |2x + 1|$. (See Figure 2.)

In general: The graph of $y = |ax + b|$ is a "V"-shaped graph made up of
the top halves of the lines $y = ax + b$ and $y = -ax - b$. These two
half-lines are called the branches of the "V"-graph, and the tip of the "V"
is called the vertex. The vertex always lies on the x-axis, since the vertex
is the x-intercept of both of the lines $y = ax + b$ and $y = -ax - b$.

In Figure 2, we have added the dotted vertical line $x = -½$, which goes through
the vertex (-½,0). Notice how this line splits the "V"-graph exactly in half. Any point
on one branch of the "V"-graph has a corresponding point on the other branch. These
corresponding points are the same height above the x-axis, and are the same distance
away from the vertical line. This observation about corresponding points leads us to an
alternative method of graphing the equation $y = |ax + b|$. (See Figure 3.)

147

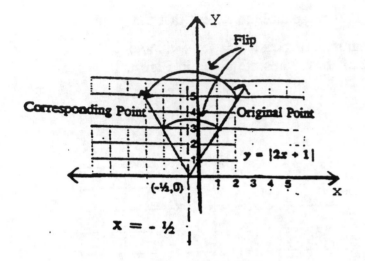

Figure 3

First Alternative Method of Graphing

First Alternative Method of Graphing
$$y = |2x + 1|$$

1) Graph $y = 2x + 1$, but only that part of the line that is on or above the x-axis. Draw a dotted vertical line through the x-intercept.

2) Pick any convenient point on the line $y = 2x + 1$ and flip it around the vertical line, determining the corresponding point on the other branch.

3) Connect the x-intercept with this new point to complete the "V"-graph.

Notice in Figure 1 that the two branches $y = 2x + 1$ and $y = -2x - 1$ __have the same x-intercept but have y-intercepts that are opposites of each other.__ This observations leads to still another quick method of graphing $y = |2x + 1|$. (See Figure 4.)

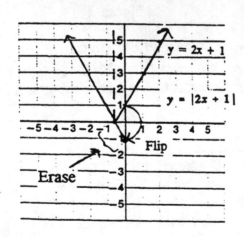

Figure 4

Second Alternative Method of Graphing
$$y = |2x + 1|$$

1) Graph $y = 2x + 1$, but do not go below the x-axis.

2) Now flip the y-intercept around the x-axis, determining a new y-intercept.

3) Connect this new y-intercept with the x-intercept to get the other branch.

4) Finally, to arrive at the "V", erase the part of the graph that is below the x-axis.

<u>Exercises</u>. Construct the "V"-graph of the following absolute-value equations by
determining a) the equations of the two branches of the "V", and b) the coordinates of
the vertex.

1. $y = |x|$

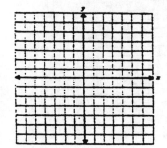

Equation _____

Equation _____

Vertex _____

2. $y = |x - 2|$

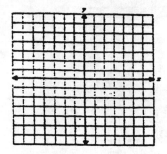

Equation _____

Equation _____

Vertex _____

3. $y = |x + 3|$

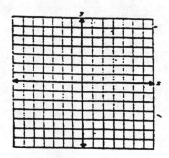

Equation _____

Equation _____

Vertex _____

4. $y = |2x - 1|$

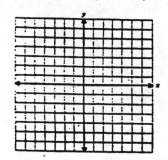

Equation _____

Equation _____

Vertex _____

5. $y = |- 2x + 1|$

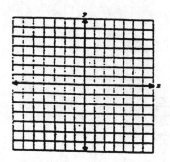

Equation _____

Equation _____

Vertex _____

6. $y = |½x - 1|$

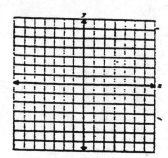

Equation _____

Equation _____

Vertex _____

7. $y = |1 - ½x|$

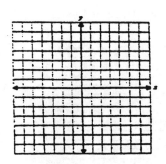

Equation _____

Equation _____

Vertex _____

8. $y = |3x - 2|$

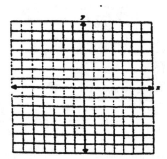

Equation _____

Equation _____

Vertex _____149_____

9. $y = |3x + 2|$

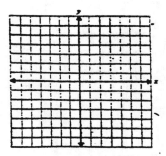

Equation _____

Equation _____

Vertex _____

10. $y = |x + 1|$

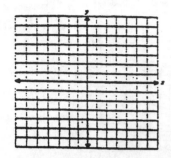

Equation _____

Equation _____

Vertex _____

11. $y = |-x - 1|$

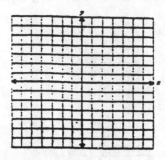

Equation _____

Equation _____

Vertex _____

12. $y = |-2x|$

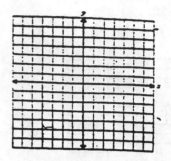

Equation _____

Equation _____

Vertex _____

Answers:

1. $y = |x|$

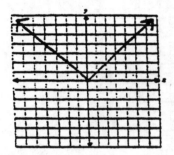

Equation $y = x$

Equation $y = -x$

Vertex $(0, 0)$

2. $y = |x - 2|$

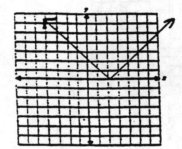

Equation $y = x - 2$

Equation $y = -x + 2$

Vertex $(2, 0)$

3. $y = |x + 3|$

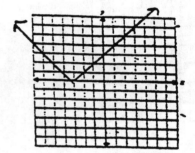

Equation $y = x + 3$

Equation $y = -x - 3$

Vertex $(-3, 0)$

4. $y = |2x - 1|$

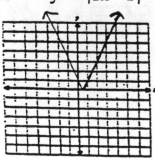

Equation $y = 2x - 1$

Equation $y = -2x + 1$

Vertex $\left(\frac{1}{2}, 0\right)$

5. $y = |-2x + 1|$

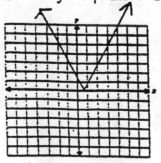

Equation $y = -2x + 1$

Equation $y = 2x - 1$

Vertex $\left(\frac{1}{2}, 0\right)$

6. $y = |\frac{1}{2}x - 1|$

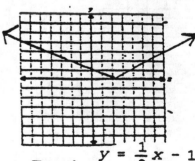

Equation $y = \frac{1}{2}x - 1$

Equation $y = -\frac{1}{2}x + 1$

Vertex $(2, 0)$

7. $y = |1 - \frac{1}{2}x|$

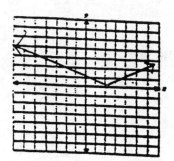

Equation $\underline{y = -\frac{1}{2}x + 1}$

Equation $\underline{y = \frac{1}{2}x - 1}$

Vertex $\underline{(2,0)}$

8. $y = |3x - 2|$

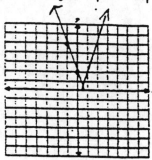

Equation $\underline{y = 3x - 2}$

Equation $\underline{y = -3x + 2}$

Vertex $\underline{\left(\frac{2}{3}, 0\right)}$

9. $y = |3x + 2|$

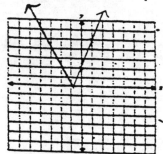

Equation $\underline{y = 3x + 2}$

Equation $\underline{y = -3x - 2}$

Vertex $\underline{\left(-\frac{2}{3}, 0\right)}$

10. $y = |x + 1|$

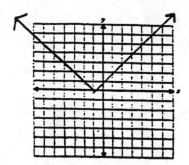

Equation $\underline{y = x + 1}$

Equation $\underline{y = -x - 1}$

Vertex $\underline{(-1,0)}$

11. $y = |-x - 1|$

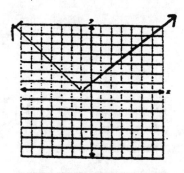

Equation $\underline{y = -x - 1}$

Equation $\underline{y = x + 1}$

Vertex $\underline{(-1,0)}$

12. $y = |-2x|$

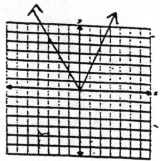

Equation $\underline{y = -2x}$

Equation $\underline{y = 2x}$

Vertex $\underline{(0,0)}$

A Visual Approach to Solving Equations and Inequalities Involving Absolute Value

I.   Equations

Consider the equation $|x - 2| = 5$. We may associate this equation with a system of a "V"-graph and a horizontal line with equations

$$y = |x - 2|$$
$$y = 5$$

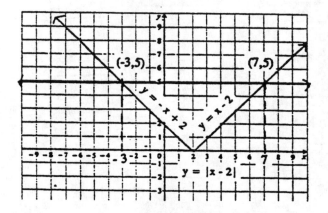

If we graph this system (Figure 1), we see that the graphs intersect at $(-3,5)$ and $(7,5)$. Thus, there are <u>two</u> solutions to the equation $|x - 2| = 5$, namely -3 and 7.

Figure 1

> In general: The solutions to the equation $|ax + b| = c$ are the x-coordinates of the points of intersection of the "V"-graph of $y = |ax + b|$ and the horizontal line $y = c$.

II.   Inequalities

Now consider the inequality $|x - 2| < 5$. We may, as before, associate this inequality with the system of equations

$$y = |x - 2|$$
$$y = 5$$

and the graphs shown in Figure 1. Now recall how we solved inequalities before: by looking for where one graph was <u>below</u> another (for $<$), <u>OR</u> where one graph was <u>above</u> another (for $>$). This approach works just as well in this situation involving absolute value! To solve the inequality $|x - 2| < 5$, we need only ask ourselves, "For what values of x is the "V"-graph of $y = |x - 2|$ <u>below</u> the horizontal line $y = 5$?" A quick inspection of Figure 1 reveals that the "V"-graph is below the line for x-values between -3 and 7. This means that the interval $(-3,7)$ is the solution to the inequality.

152

In general: To solve the inequality $|ax + b| < c$ or $|ax + b| > c$:

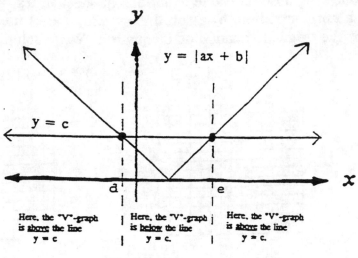

Figure 2

First sketch the "V"-graph $y = |ax + b|$ and the horizontal line $y = c$. (See Figure 2.) Determine the x-coordinates of their points of intersection. Then:

1) The solutions to $|ax + b| < 0$ are the values on the x-axis for which the "V"-graph of $y = |ax + b|$ is <u>below</u> the line $y = c$.

2) The solutions to $|ax + b| > 0$ are the values on the x-axis for which the "V"-graph of $y = |ax + b|$ is <u>above</u> the line $y = c$.

If the "V"-graph of $y = |ax + b|$ intersects the horizontal line $y = c$ at two points with x-coordinates d and e, as in Figure 2 above, the solution of $|ax + b| < c$ will be the interval (d,e), while the solution of $|ax + b| > c$ will be the intervals $(-\infty, d)$ and (e, ∞), taken together. Note: "$\leq$" or "$\geq$" instead of "$<$" or "$>$" yields closed interval solutions instead of open interval solutions.

<u>Example:</u> $|2x - 3| \geq 4$

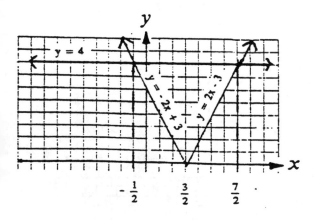

Figure 3

See Figure 3. Since the branches of $y = |2x - 3|$ (the lines $y = 2x - 3$ and $y = -2x + 3$) do not intersect $y = 4$ at grid points, we find the x-coordinates of the intersection points by solving the two equations $2x - 3 = 4$ and $-2x + 3 = 4$. When we solve these equations, we get $x = 7/2$ and $x = -1/2$. We can observe that the "V"-graph of $y = |2x - 3|$ is above the horizontal line $y = 4$ when x is to the right of $7/2$ (i.e., $x \geq 7/2$), and also when x is to the <u>left</u> of -1/2 (i.e., $x \leq -1/2$). This means that our solutions to the inequality $|2x - 3| \geq 4$ are the intervals $(-\infty, \frac{1}{2}]$ and $[3/2, \infty)$, taken together.

Exercises. For each of the following absolute-value equations or inequalities, a) associate a system of a "V"-graph and a horizontal line, b) graph this system, and c) use the graphs to determine the solution(s) of the original equation or inequality. Write solutions to inequalities in interval form.

1. $|x + 2| = 4$

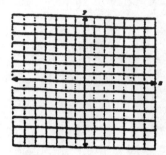

System _____

_____

Solution _____

2. $|2 - x| = 3$

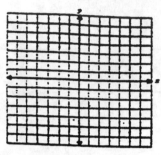

System _____

_____

Solution _____

3. $|2x - 3| = 5$

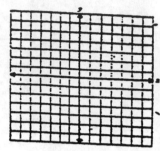

System _____

_____

Solution _____

4. $|4 - 3x| = 2$

System _____

_____

Solution _____

5. $|2x - 1| = 2$

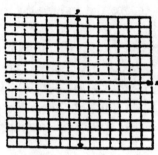

System _____

_____

Solution _____

6. $|x + 2| < 4$

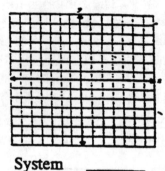

System _____

_____

Solution _____

7. $|2 - x| \geq 3$

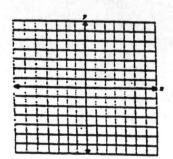

System _____

_____

Solution _____

8. $|2x - 3| < 3$

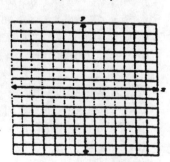

System _____

_____

Solution _____

9. $|2 - 2x| \leq 4$

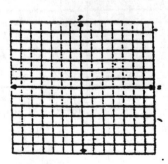

System _____

_____

Solution _____

10. $|2x - 5| > 3$

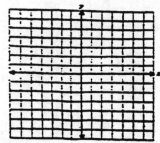

System _____

_____

Solution _____

11. $\left|\dfrac{1}{2}x - 1\right| \leq 2$

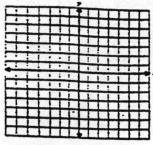

System _____

_____

Solution _____

12. $\left|3 - \dfrac{3}{2}x\right| > 3$

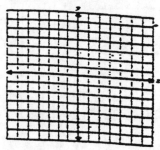

System _____

_____

Solution _____

13. $|2x - 1| < 4$

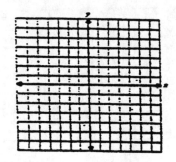

System _____

_____

Solution _____

14. $|2 - 3x| \geq 4$

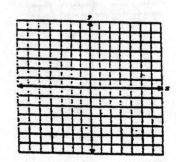

System _____

_____

Solution _____

15. $\left|\dfrac{3}{2}x - 1\right| \leq 3$

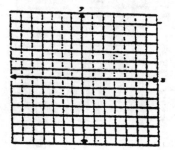

System _____

_____

Solution _____

16. $|3x - 2| > 2$

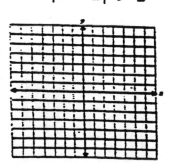

System _____

_____

Solution _____

17. $|2x + 1| \geq 0$

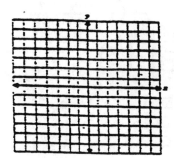

System _____

_____

Solution 55_____

18. $|3x - 2| < 0$

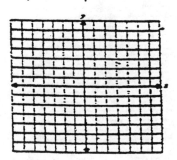

System _____

_____

Solution _____

Answers:

1. $|x + 2| = 4$

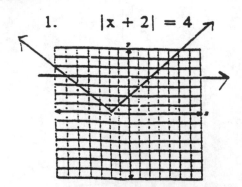

System: $\underline{\quad y = |x + 2| \quad}$

$\underline{\quad y = 4 \quad}$

Solution: $\underline{\quad -6 \text{ and } 2 \quad}$

2. $|2 - x| = 3$

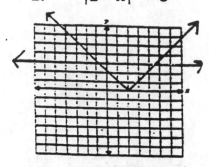

System: $\underline{\quad y = |2 - x| \quad}$

$\underline{\quad y = 3 \quad}$

Solution: $\underline{\quad -1 \text{ and } 5 \quad}$

3. $|2x - 3| = 5$

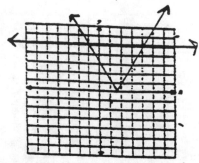

System: $\underline{\quad y = |2x - 3| \quad}$

$\underline{\quad y = 5 \quad}$

Solution: $\underline{\quad -1 \text{ and } 4 \quad}$

4. $|4 - 3x| = 2$

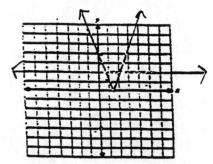

System: $\underline{\quad y = |4 - 3x| \quad}$

$\underline{\quad y = 2 \quad}$

Solution: $\underline{\quad \dfrac{2}{3} \text{ and } 2 \quad}$

5. $|2x - 1| = 2$

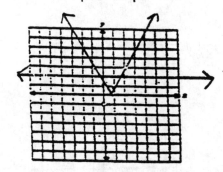

System: $\underline{\quad y = |2x - 1| \quad}$

$\underline{\quad y = 2 \quad}$

Solution: $\underline{\quad -\dfrac{1}{2} \text{ and } \dfrac{3}{2} \quad}$

6. $|x + 2| < 4$

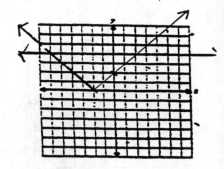

System: $\underline{\quad y = |x + 2| \quad}$

$\underline{\quad y = 4 \quad}$

Solution: $\underline{\quad (-6, 2) \quad}$

7. $|2 - x| \geq 3$

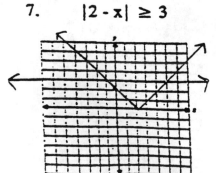

System: $\underline{\quad y = |2 - x| \quad}$

$\underline{\quad y = 3 \quad}$

Solution: $\underline{\quad (-\infty, -1] \cup [5, \infty) \quad}$

8. $|2x - 3| < 3$

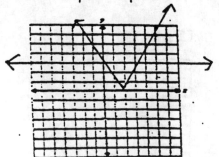

System: $\underline{\quad y = |2x - 3| \quad}$

$\underline{\quad y = 3 \quad}$

Solution: $\underline{\quad (0, 3) \quad}$

9. $|2 - 2x| \leq 4$

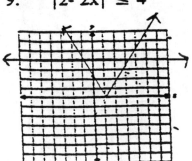

System: $\underline{\quad y = |2 - 2x \quad}$

$\underline{\quad y = 4 \quad}$

Solution: $\underline{\quad [-1, 3] \quad}$

10. $|2x - 5| > 3$

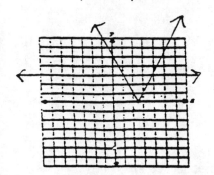

System: $\dfrac{y = |2x - 5|}{y = 3}$

Solution: $(-\infty, 1) \cup (4, \infty)$

11. $\left|\dfrac{1}{2}x - 1\right| \leq 2$

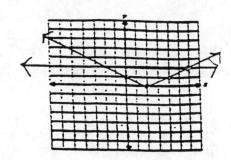

System: $\dfrac{y = \left|\dfrac{1}{2}x - 1\right|}{y = 2}$

Solution: $[-2, 6]$

12. $\left|3 - \dfrac{3}{2}x\right| > 3$

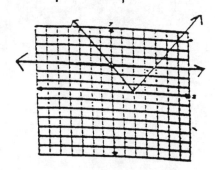

System: $\dfrac{y = \left|3 - \dfrac{3}{2}x\right|}{y = 3}$

Solution: $(-\infty, 0) \cup (4, \infty)$

13. $|2x - 1| < 4$

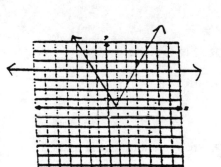

System: $\dfrac{y = |2x - 1|}{y = 4}$

Solution: $\left(-\dfrac{3}{2}, \dfrac{5}{2}\right)$

14. $|2 - 3x| \geq 4$

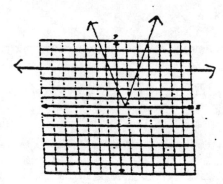

System: $\dfrac{y = |2 - 3x|}{y = 4}$

Solution: $\left(-\infty, -\dfrac{2}{3}\right] \cup [2, \infty)$

15. $\left|\dfrac{3}{2}x - 1\right| \leq 3$

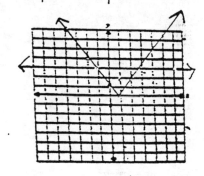

System: $\dfrac{y = \left|\dfrac{3}{2}x - 1\right|}{y = 3}$

Solution: $\left[-\dfrac{4}{3}, \dfrac{8}{3}\right]$

16. $|3x - 2| > 2$

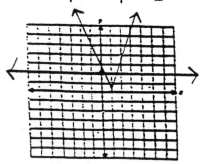

System: $\dfrac{y = |3x - 2|}{y = 2}$

Solution: $(-\infty, 0) \cup \left(\dfrac{4}{3}, \infty\right)$

17. $|2x + 1| \geq 0$

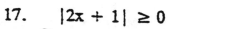

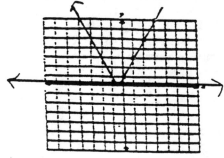

System: $\dfrac{y = |2x + 1|}{y = 0}$

Solution: 157 $(-\infty, \infty)$

18. $|3x - 2| < 0$

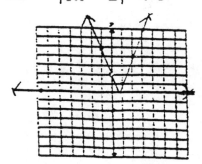

System: $\dfrac{y = |3x - 2|}{y = 0}$

Solution: no solution

Equations and Inequalities Involving Absolute Value

OBJECTIVES
1. To solve equations involving absolute value
2. To solve and graph the solution sets for inequalities involving absolute value

Equations and inequalities may involve the absolute value notation in their statements. In this section we build on the tools developed in our coverage of linear equations in one variable and solving linear inequalities and on our earlier work with absolute value for the necessary solution techniques.

> **Technically we mean the distance between the *point corresponding* to x and the *point corresponding* to 0, the origin.**

Recall from our coverage of equality, order, and absolute value that the absolute value of x, written $|x|$, is the distance between x and 0 on the number line. Consider, for example, the absolute value equation

$$|x| = 4$$

This means that the distance between x and 0 is 4, as is pictured below.

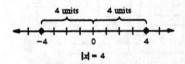

As the sketch illustrates, $x = 4$ and $x = -4$ are the two solutions for the equation.

This observation suggests the more general statement.

> **‹CAUTION›**
>
> **p must be positive because an equation such as**
>
> $$|5x - 2| = -3$$
>
> **has no solution. An absolute-value equation must always be equal to a nonnegative number.**

ABSOLUTE VALUE EQUATIONS—PROPERTY 1

For any positive number p, if

$$|x| = p$$

then

$$x = p \qquad \text{or} \qquad x = -p$$

This property allows us to "translate" an equation involving absolute value to two linear equations which we can then solve separately. The following example illustrates.

Example 1

Solve for x:

$$|3x - 2| = 4$$

From Property 1 we know that $|3x - 2| = 4$ is equivalent to the equations

$$3x - 2 = 4 \quad \text{or} \quad 3x - 2 = -4$$

Add 2.

$$3x = 6 \qquad\qquad 3x = -2$$

Divide by 3.

$$x = 2 \qquad\qquad x = -\frac{2}{3}$$

> ⟨CAUTION⟩
>
> **Be Careful!** A common mistake is to solve *only* the equation $3x - 2 = 4$. You must solve *both* of the equivalent equations to find the two required solutions.

The solutions are $-\dfrac{2}{3}$ and 2. These solutions are easily checked by replacing x with $-\dfrac{2}{3}$ and 2 in the original absolute value equation.

CHECK YOURSELF 1

Solve for x.

$$|4x + 1| = 9$$

An equation involving absolute value may have to be rewritten before you can apply Property 1. Consider the following example.

Example 2

Solve for x:

$$|2 - 3x| + 5 = 10$$

To use Property 1, we must first isolate the absolute value on the left side of the equation. This is easily done by subtracting 5 from both sides for the result:

$$|2 - 3x| = 5$$

We can now proceed as before by using Property 1.

$$2 - 3x = 5 \quad \text{or} \quad 2 - 3x = -5$$

Subtract 2.

$$-3x = 3 \qquad\qquad -3x = -7$$

Divide by −3.

$$x = -1 \qquad\qquad x = \frac{7}{3}$$

The solutions are -1 and $\dfrac{7}{3}$.

CHECK YOURSELF 2

Solve for x.

$$|5 - 2x| - 4 = 7$$

In some applications more than one absolute value is involved in an equation. Consider an equation of the form

$$|x| = |y|$$

Since the absolute values of x and y are equal, x and y are the same distance from 0. This means they are either *equal* or *opposite in sign*. This leads to a second general property of absolute value equations.

ABSOLUTE VALUE EQUATIONS—PROPERTY 2

If

$$|x| = |y|$$

then

$$x = y \quad \text{or} \quad x = -y$$

Let's look at an application of this second property in our next example.

Example 3

Solve for x:

$$|3x - 4| = |x + 2|$$

By Property 2, we can write

$$3x - 4 = x + 2 \quad \text{or} \quad 3x - 4 = -(x + 2)$$
$$3x - 4 = -x - 2$$
$$3x = x + 6 \qquad\qquad 3x = -x + 2$$
$$2x = 6 \qquad\qquad 4x = 2$$
$$x = 3 \qquad\qquad x = \frac{1}{2}$$

The solutions are $\frac{1}{2}$ and 3.

CHECK YOURSELF 3

Solve for x.

$$|4x - 1| = |x + 5|$$

We started this section by noting that the solution set for the equation

$$|x| = 4$$

consists of those numbers whose distance from the origin is equal to 4. Similarly, the solution set for the absolute value inequality

$$|x| < 4$$

consists of those numbers whose distance from the origin is *less than* 4, that is, all numbers between -4 and 4. The solution set is pictured below.

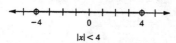

$|x| < 4$

The solution set would be
$\{x \mid -4 < x < 4\}$

The solution set can be described by the double inequality

$$-4 < x < 4$$

and this suggests the following general statement.

ABSOLUTE VALUE INEQUALITIES—PROPERTY 1

For any positive number p, if

$$|x| < p$$

then

$$-p < x < p$$

Let's look at an application of Property 1 in solving an absolute value inequality.

Example 4

Solve and graph the solution set of

$$|2x - 3| < 5$$

With Property 1 we can *translate* an absolute value inequality to an inequality *not* involving absolute value which can be solved by our earlier methods.

From Property 1, we know that the given absolute value inequality is equivalent to the double inequality

$$-5 < 2x - 3 < 5$$

Solving as before, we isolate the variable in the center term.

$-2 < 2x < 8 \qquad$ Add 3 to all three parts.

$-1 < x < 4 \qquad$ Divide by 2.

The solution set is

$$\{x \mid -1 < x < 4\}$$

The graph is shown below.

Note that the solution is an open interval on the number line.

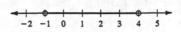

CHECK YOURSELF 4

Solve and graph the solution set.

$$|3x - 4| \leq 8$$

We know that the solution set for the absolute value inequality

$$|x| < 4$$

consists of those numbers whose distance from the origin is *less than* 4. Now what about the solution set for

$$|x| > 4$$

It must consist of those numbers whose distance from the origin is *greater than* 4. The solution set is pictured below.

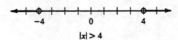

$|x| > 4$

The solution set can be described by the compound inequality

$$x < -4 \qquad \text{or} \qquad x > 4$$

and this suggests the following general statement.

ABSOLUTE VALUE INEQUALITIES—PROPERTY 2

For any positive number p, if

$$|x| > p$$

then

$$x < -p \qquad \text{or} \qquad x > p$$

Let's apply Property 2 to the solution of an absolute value inequality.

Example 5

Again we translate the absolute value inequality to the compound inequality not involving absolute value.

Solve and graph the solution set of

$$|5x - 2| > 8$$

From Property 2, we know that the given absolute inequality is equivalent to the compound inequality

$$5x - 2 < -8 \quad \text{or} \quad 5x - 2 > 8$$

Solving as before, we have

Add 2.

$$5x < -6 \quad \text{or} \quad 5x > 10$$

Divide by 5.

$$x < -\frac{6}{5} \qquad x > 2$$

You could describe the solution set as

$$\{x \mid x < -\tfrac{6}{5}\} \cup \{x \mid x > 2\}$$

The solution set is $\{x \mid x < -\frac{6}{5} \text{ or } x > 2\}$ and the graph is shown below.

CHECK YOURSELF 5

Solve and graph the solution set.

$$|3 - 2x| \geq 9$$

The following chart summarizes our discussion of absolute value inequalities.

As before, p must be a positive number if p > 0.

TYPE OF INEQUALITY	EQUIVALENT INEQUALITY	GRAPH OF SOLUTION SET
$|ax + b| < p$	$-p < ax + b < p$	
$|ax + b| > p$	$ax + b < -p \quad \text{or} \quad ax + b > p$	

CHECK YOURSELF ANSWERS

1. $-\dfrac{5}{2}, 2.$ 2. $-3, 8.$ 3. $2, -\dfrac{4}{5}$

4. $-\dfrac{4}{3} \leq x \leq 4.$

5. $x \leq -3 \text{ or } x \geq 6.$

Name _____

Date _____

Exercises

ANSWERS

Build Your Skills

1. _____

2. _____

3. _____

4. _____

5. _____

6. _____

7. _____

8. _____

9. _____

10. _____

11. _____

12. _____

13. _____

14. _____

15. _____

16. _____

17. _____

18. _____

19. _____

20. _____

21. _____

22. _____

Solve each of the following absolute value equations.

1. $|x| = 5$ 2. $|x| = 7$

3. $|x - 2| = 3$ 4. $|x + 5| = 6$

5. $|x + 6| = 0$ 6. $|x - 3| = 0$

7. $|3 - x| = 7$ 8. $|5 - x| = 4$

9. $|2x - 3| = 9$ 10. $|3x + 5| = 11$

11. $|5 - 4x| = 1$ 12. $|3 - 6x| = 9$

13. $\left|\dfrac{1}{2}x + 5\right| = 7$ 14. $\left|\dfrac{2}{3}x - 4\right| = 6$

15. $\left|4 - \dfrac{3}{4}x\right| = 8$ 16. $\left|3 - \dfrac{2}{5}x\right| = 9$

17. $|3x + 1| = -2$ 18. $|5x - 2| = -3$

Rewrite each of the following absolute value equations, and then solve the equations.

19. $|x| - 3 = 2$ 20. $|x| + 4 = 6$

21. $|x - 2| + 3 = 5$ 22. $|x + 5| - 2 = 5$

ANSWERS

23. _____

24. _____

25. _____

26. _____

27. _____

28. _____

29. _____

30. _____

31. _____

32. _____

33. _____

34. _____

35. _____

36. _____

37. _____

38. _____

39. _____

40. _____

41. _____

42. _____

43. _____

44. _____

23. $|2x - 3| - 1 = 6$

24. $|3x + 5| + 2 = 4$

25. $\left|\dfrac{1}{2}x + 2\right| - 3 = 5$

26. $\left|\dfrac{1}{3}x - 4\right| + 3 = 9$

27. $8 - |x - 4| = 5$

28. $10 - |2x + 1| = 3$

29. $|3x - 2| + 4 = 3$

30. $|5x - 3| + 5 = 3$

Solve each of the following absolute value equations.

31. $|2x - 1| = |x + 3|$

32. $|3x + 1| = |2x - 3|$

33. $|5x - 2| = |2x + 4|$

34. $|7x - 3| = |2x + 7|$

35. $|x - 2| = |x + 1|$

36. $|x + 3| = |x - 2|$

37. $|2x - 5| = |2x - 3|$

38. $|3x + 1| = |3x - 1|$

39. $|x - 2| = |2 - x|$

40. $|x - 4| = |4 - x|$

Find and graph the solution set for each of the following absolute value inequalities.

41. $|x| < 5$

42. $|x| > 3$

43. $|x| \geq 7$

44. $|x| \leq 4$

ANSWERS

45. _____

46. _____

47. _____

48. _____

49. _____

50. _____

51. _____

52. _____

53. _____

54. _____

55. _____

56. _____

57. _____

58. _____

59. _____

60. _____

61. _____

62. _____

63. _____

64. _____

45. $|x - 4| > 2$ **46.** $|x + 5| < 3$

47. $|x + 6| \leq 4$ **48.** $|x - 7| \geq 5$

49. $|3 - x| > 5$ **50.** $|5 - x| < 3$

51. $|x - 7| < 0$ **52.** $|x + 5| \geq 0$

53. $|2x - 5| < 3$ **54.** $|3x - 1| > 8$

55. $|3x + 4| \geq 5$ **56.** $|2x + 3| \leq 9$

57. $|5x - 3| > 7$ **58.** $|6x - 5| < 13$

59. $|2 - 3x| < 11$ **60.** $|3 - 2x| \geq 11$

61. $|3 - 5x| \geq 7$ **62.** $|7 - 3x| < 13$

63. $\left|\dfrac{3}{4}x - 5\right| < 7$ **64.** $\left|\dfrac{2}{3}x + 5\right| \geq 3$

ANSWERS

1. $-5, 5$ **3.** $-1, 5$ **5.** -6 **7.** $-4, 10$ **9.** $-3, 6$ **11.** $1, \dfrac{3}{2}$ **13.** $-24, 4$

15. $-\dfrac{16}{3}, 16$ **17.** No solution   **19.** $-5, 5$ **21.** $0, 4$ **23.** $-2, 5$ **25.** $-20, 12$

27. $1, 7$ **29.** No solution   **31.** $-\dfrac{2}{3}, 4$ **33.** $-\dfrac{2}{7}, 2$ **35.** $\dfrac{1}{2}$ **37.** 2

39. All real numbers

41. $-5 < x < 5$

43. $x \le -7$ or $x \ge 7$

45. $x < 2$ or $x > 6$

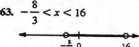

47. $-10 \le x \le -2$

49. $x < -2$ or $x > 8$

51. No solution

53. $1 < x < 4$

55. $x \le -3$ or $x \ge \dfrac{1}{3}$

57. $x < -\dfrac{4}{5}$ or $x > 2$

59. $-3 < x < \dfrac{13}{3}$

61. $x \le -\dfrac{4}{5}$ or $x \ge 2$

63. $-\dfrac{8}{3} < x < 16$

SQUARES AND SQUARE ROOTS

The most intuitive example of square numbers is represented by the area of a square. The area of a square is the length of a side times itself. For example, if we know that the length of a side is 3 , we can find the area. See Figure 1 below.

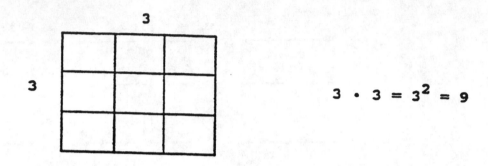

$$3 \cdot 3 = 3^2 = 9$$

Figure 1

It is sometimes convenient to have a way of representing the length of a side of a given square when the area is known. If we know that the area of the square is 9 , then its side can be represented by the symbol $\sqrt{9}$, which must equal $\sqrt{3^2} = 3$. In this way, the $\sqrt{}$ symbol can be thought of as undoing the squaring operation.

Again, if we know that the area of a square is 7, then the side is $\sqrt{7}$. $\sqrt{}$ is called a radical or square root sign. We say "radical 7", or "square root of 7", when we are talking about $\sqrt{7}$.

"Radical A" or "square root of A", written $\sqrt{A}$, will represent the length of a side of a square with area A.

An important application of radicals and square roots occurs in solving equations such as $x^2 = 25$. The solutions to this equation are 5 and -5, since $(5)^2 = 5 \cdot 5 = 25$ and $(-5)^2 = (-5) \cdot (-5) = 25$. We can use the $\sqrt{}$ to solve this equation as follows:

$$x^2 = 25$$

$$\sqrt{x^2} = \pm \sqrt{25}$$

$$x = \pm 5$$

Here are some examples of equations where the $\sqrt{}$ symbol is used in finding solutions to equations.

Example 1:

$$2x^2 - 3 = 27$$
$$2x^2 = 30$$
$$x^2 = 15$$
$$x = \pm\sqrt{15}$$

$x \approx \pm 3.87$, rounded to the nearest hundredth.

Example 2:

$$-2(x - 1)^2 = -70$$
$$(x - 1)^2 = 35$$
$$x - 1 = \pm\sqrt{35}$$
$$x = 1 \pm \sqrt{35}$$
$$x \approx 1 \pm 5.916$$

$x \approx 6.916$ or -4.916, rounded to the nearest thousandth

Example 3:

$$x^2 = -49$$
$$x = \pm\sqrt{-49}$$

Is $x = 7$ or -7?

$$(7)^2 = 7 \cdot 7 = 49 \quad NOT \quad -49$$

Also,

$$(-7)^2 = (-7) \cdot (-7) = 49 \quad NOT \quad -49.$$

In the real number system, we cannot take the square root of a negative number. In the real number system, equations like $x^2 = -49$ have no solution.

In general, the solutions to $x^2 = a$ are the numbers $\sqrt{a}$ and $-\sqrt{a}$. (Of course if a is negative, there are no solutions to $x^2 = a$.)

CUBE ROOTS

We can develop the concept of the cube root using the symbol $\sqrt[3]{}$, by looking at an equation such as $x^3 = 8$. We can use the symbol $\sqrt[3]{}$ to solve this equation:

169

$$x^3 = 8$$
$$x = \sqrt[3]{8}$$
$$x = 2 \, ,$$

since $(2)^3 = 2 \cdot 2 \cdot 2 = 8$. Note that $x = -2$ will not satisfy the given equation since $(-2)^3 = (-2) \cdot (-2) \cdot (-2) = -8$, not 8.

In general, the solution to $x^3 = a$ is the unique number $\sqrt[3]{a}$.

PROPERTIES OF RADICALS

We have two useful properties for radicals that can be used to simplify expressions.

Product Property   Quotient Property

$$\sqrt{a \cdot b} = \sqrt{a} \cdot \sqrt{b} \qquad \text{and} \qquad \sqrt{\frac{a}{b}} = \frac{\sqrt{a}}{\sqrt{b}}$$

Example 1: $\sqrt{32} = \sqrt{16 \cdot 2} = \sqrt{16} \cdot \sqrt{2} = 4\sqrt{2}$

Example 2: $\sqrt{\dfrac{75}{64}} = \dfrac{\sqrt{75}}{\sqrt{64}} = \dfrac{\sqrt{25 \cdot 3}}{8} = \dfrac{5\sqrt{3}}{8}$

Example 3: $\sqrt{27} - \sqrt{48} = \sqrt{9 \cdot 3} - \sqrt{16 \cdot 3} = \sqrt{9}\sqrt{3} - \sqrt{16}\sqrt{3} = 3\sqrt{3} - 4\sqrt{3}$
$$= (3 - 4)\sqrt{3} = (-1)\sqrt{3} = -\sqrt{3}$$

Exercises:

A. Evaluate each of the following roots where possible.

1. $\sqrt{49}$	2. $\sqrt{36}$	3. $-\sqrt{36}$
4. $-\sqrt{81}$	5. $\pm\sqrt{81}$	6. $\pm\sqrt{49}$
7. $\sqrt{-49}$	8. $\sqrt{-25}$	9. $\sqrt[3]{27}$
10. $\sqrt[3]{64}$	11. $\sqrt[3]{-64}$	12. $-\sqrt[3]{125}$
13. $-\sqrt[3]{216}$	14. $\sqrt[3]{-27}$	15. $\sqrt{\dfrac{4}{9}}$

16. $\sqrt{\dfrac{9}{25}}$ 17. $\sqrt{6^2}$ 18. $\sqrt{9^2}$

19. $\sqrt{(-3)^2}$ 20. $\sqrt{(-5)^2}$ 21. $\sqrt[3]{4^3}$

B. Using a calculator, find the cube root, square root, square and cube for each integer given. Round off your answers to four decimal places, if necessary.

$\sqrt[3]{n}$	$\sqrt{n}$	n	n^2	n^3
		1		
		2		
		3		
		4		
		5		
		6		
		7		
		8		
		9		
		10		
		11		
		12		
		13		
		14		
		15		
		16		
		17		
		18		
		19		
		20		

C. Use the Product Property or Quotient Property to write each expression in simplified form.

1. $\sqrt{12}$ 2. $\sqrt{24}$ 3. $\sqrt{50}$

4. $\sqrt{28}$ 5. $-\sqrt{108}$ 6. $\sqrt{32}$

7. $\sqrt{52}$ 8. $-\sqrt{96}$ 9. $\sqrt{60}$

10. $\sqrt{150}$ 11. $-\sqrt{125}$ 12. $\sqrt{128}$

13. $\sqrt{288}$ 14. $-\sqrt{300}$ 15. $\sqrt{450}$

16. $\sqrt{432}$ 17. $\sqrt{\dfrac{5}{16}}$ 18. $\sqrt{\dfrac{11}{36}}$

19. $-\sqrt{\dfrac{50}{81}}$ 20. $-\sqrt{\dfrac{72}{121}}$ 21. $\sqrt{\dfrac{48}{25}}$

22. $\sqrt{\dfrac{20}{49}}$

Solve the following equations for x. Round off your answer to three decimal places, if appropriate.

23. $x^2 = 36$ 24. $x^2 = 51$ 25. $3x^2 = 75$

26. $-3x^2 = -30$ 27. $-2x^2 + 98 = 0$ 28. $-5x^2 + 100 = 0$

29. $0 = -2x^2 - 98$ 30. $0 = -4x^2 - 36$ 31. $(x-1)^2 - 9 = 0$

32. $(x-3)^2 - 16 = 0$ 33. $2\left(x + \dfrac{1}{2}\right)^2 - 32 = 0$

34. $3\left(x - \dfrac{1}{2}\right)^2 - 75 = 0$ 35. $-\dfrac{1}{2}(x+3)^2 = -18$

36. $-\dfrac{1}{3}(x-2)^2 = -12$ 37. $3(x+4)^2 + 21 = 0$

38. $-3(x+4)^2 - 27 = 0$ 39. $-2(x+5)^2 + 10 = 0$

40. $-2(x-5)^2 = 0$ 41. $-\dfrac{1}{2}(x+3)^2 = 0$

42. $0 = -(x+2)^2 - 1$

Simplify, then combine the following radical expressions:

43. $\sqrt{12} + \sqrt{27}$ 44. $\sqrt{18} + \sqrt{8}$

45. $\sqrt{54} - \sqrt{6}$ 46. $\sqrt{80} + \sqrt{20}$

47. $\sqrt{162} - \sqrt{72}$ 48. $\sqrt{125} - \sqrt{45}$

49. $2\sqrt{27} + 3\sqrt{48}$ 50. $5\sqrt{99} - \sqrt{44}$

51. $\sqrt{8} + \sqrt{32} - \sqrt{72}$ 52. $\sqrt{200} + \sqrt{50} + \sqrt{128}$

Answers:

Part A

1.	7	2.	6	3.	-6	4.	-9

5. ± 9   6. ± 7   7. No real number solution

8. No real number solution   9. 3   10. 4

11. -4   12. -5   13. -6   14. -3

15. $\dfrac{2}{3}$ 16. $\dfrac{3}{5}$ 17. 6   18. 9

19. 3   20. 5   21. 4

Part B

$\sqrt[3]{n}$	$\sqrt{n}$	n	n^2	n^3
1	1	1	1	1
1.2599	1.4142	2	4	8
1.4422	1.7321	3	9	27
1.5874	2	4	16	64
1.7100	2.2361	5	25	125
1.8171	2.4495	6	36	216
1.9129	2.6458	7	49	343
2	2.8284	8	64	512
2.0801	3	9	81	729
2.1544	3.1623	10	100	1,000
2.2240	3.3166	11	121	1,331
2.2894	3.4641	12	144	1,728
2.3513	3.6056	13	169	2,197
2.4101	3.7417	14	196	2,744
2.4662	3.8730	15	225	3,375
2.5198	4	16	256	4,096
2.5713	4.1231	17	289	4,913
2.6207	4.2426	18	324	5,832
2.6684	4.3589	19	361	6,859
2.7144	4.4721	20	400	8,000

Part C

1. $2\sqrt{3}$ 2. $2\sqrt{6}$ 3. $5\sqrt{2}$ 4. $2\sqrt{7}$

5.	$-6\sqrt{3}$	6.	$4\sqrt{2}$	7.	$2\sqrt{13}$	8.	$-4\sqrt{6}$
9.	$2\sqrt{15}$	10.	$5\sqrt{6}$	11.	$-5\sqrt{5}$	12.	$8\sqrt{2}$
13.	$12\sqrt{2}$	14.	$-10\sqrt{3}$	15.	$15\sqrt{2}$	16.	$12\sqrt{3}$

17. $\dfrac{\sqrt{5}}{4}$ 18. $\dfrac{\sqrt{11}}{6}$ 19. $\dfrac{-5\sqrt{2}}{9}$ 20. $\dfrac{-6\sqrt{2}}{11}$

21. $\dfrac{4\sqrt{3}}{5}$ 22. $\dfrac{2\sqrt{5}}{7}$ 23. ± 6 24. ± 7.141

25. ± 5 26. ± 3.162 27. ± 7 28. ± 4.472

29. No real number solution   30. No real number solution

31. 4 or -2   32. 7 or -1   33. $3\frac{1}{2}$ or $-4\frac{1}{2}$

34. $5\frac{1}{2}$ or $-4\frac{1}{2}$ 35. -9 or 3   36. 8 or -4

37. No real number solution   38. No real number solution

39. -2.764 or -7.236   40. 5   41. -3

42. No real number solution   43. $5\sqrt{3}$ 44. $5\sqrt{2}$

45. $2\sqrt{6}$ 46. $6\sqrt{5}$ 47. $3\sqrt{2}$ 48. $2\sqrt{5}$

49. $18\sqrt{3}$ 50. $13\sqrt{11}$ 51. 0   52. $23\sqrt{2}$

Integral Exponents and Scientific Notation

OBJECTIVES
1. To define 0 and negative integer exponents
2. To use the properties of integer exponents
3. To use scientific notation

Exponents are a shorthand form for repeated multiplication. Instead of writing

$$a \cdot a \cdot a \cdot a \cdot a$$

we write

We call a the base of the expression and 5 the exponent, or power.

$$a^5$$

which we read as "a to the fifth power."

In general, for any real number a and any natural number n,

$$a^n = \underbrace{a \cdot a \cdot \,\cdots\, \cdot a}_{n \text{ factors}}$$

An expression of this type is said to be in *exponential form*. We call a the *base* of the expression and n the *exponent*, or *power*.

Example 1*

Write each of the following, using exponential notation.

(a) $5y \cdot 5y \cdot 5y = (5y)^3$
(b) $w \cdot w \cdot w \cdot w = w^4$

CHECK YOURSELF 1

Write each of the following, using exponential notation.

1. $3z \cdot 3z \cdot 3z$ **2.** $x \cdot x \cdot x \cdot x$

Let's consider what happens when we multiply two expressions in exponential form with the same base.

*A screen is used to indicate an expression that is being simplified.

We expand the expressions and apply the associative property to regroup.

$$a^4 \cdot a^5 = \underbrace{(a \cdot a \cdot a \cdot a)}_{4 \text{ factors}}\underbrace{(a \cdot a \cdot a \cdot a \cdot a)}_{5 \text{ factors}}$$

$$= \underbrace{a \cdot a \cdot a \cdot a \cdot a \cdot a \cdot a \cdot a \cdot a}_{9 \text{ factors}}$$

$$= a^9$$

Notice that the product is simply the base taken to the power that is the sum of the two original exponents.

In fact, in general, the following holds:

PRODUCT RULE FOR EXPONENTS

For any nonzero real number a and positive integers m and n,

This is our *first property of exponents*

$a^m \cdot a^n = a^{m+n}$

$$a^m \cdot a^n = \underbrace{a \cdot a \cdot \,\cdots\, \cdot a)}_{m \text{ factors}}\underbrace{(a \cdot a \cdot \,\cdots\, \cdot a)}_{n \text{ factors}}$$

$$= \underbrace{a \cdot a \cdot \,\cdots\, \cdot a}_{m + n \text{ factors}}$$

$$= a^{m+n}$$

The next example illustrates the product rule for exponents.

Example 2

Simplify each expression.

(a) $b^4 \cdot b^6 = b^{4+6} = b^{10}$

(b) $(2a)^3 \cdot (2a)^4 = (2a)^{3+4} = (2a)^7$

(c) $(-2)^5(-2)^4 = (-2)^{5+4} = (-2)^9$

(d) $(10^7)(10^{11}) = (10)^{7+11} = (10)^{18}$

CHECK YOURSELF 2

Simplify each product.

1. $(5b)^6(5b)^5$ 2. $(-3)^4(-3)^3$

3. $10^8 \cdot 10^{12}$ 4. $(xy)^2(xy)^3$

Applying the commutative and associative properties of multiplication, we know that a product such as

$2x^3 \cdot 3x^2$

can be rewritten as

$$(2 \cdot 3)(x^3 \cdot x^2)$$

or as

$$6x^5$$

We expand on the ideas illustrated above in our next example.

Example 3

Using the product rule for exponents together with the commutative and associative properties, simplify each product.

Multiply the coefficients and *add* the exponents by the product rule. With practice you will *not need to write* the regrouping step.

(a) $(5x^4)(3x^2) = (5 \cdot 3)x^4x^2 = 15x^6$

(b) $(x^2y^3)(x^2y^4) = (x^2 \cdot x^2)(y^3 \cdot y^4) = x^4y^7$

(c) $(4c^5d^3)(3c^2d^2) = (4 \cdot 3)(c^5c^2)(d^3d^2) = 12c^7d^5$

(d) $(-3p^3q^4)(2p^2q^5) = (-3)(2)(p^3p^2)(p^4q^5) = -6p^5q^9$

(e) $(-2m^2n^5)(-4m^3n^2) = (-2)(-4)(m^2m^3)(n^5n^2) = 8m^5n^7$

CHECK YOURSELF 3

Simplify each expression.

1. $(4a^2b)(2a^3b^4)$
2. $(3x^4)(2x^3y)$
3. $(-2s^3t^4)(3s^2t)$
4. $(-4d^5f^3)(-5d^2f^4)$

Now consider the quotient

$$\frac{a^6}{a^4}$$

If we write this in expanded form, we have

$$\frac{\overbrace{a \cdot a \cdot a \cdot a \cdot a \cdot a}^{6 \text{ factors}}}{\underbrace{a \cdot a \cdot a \cdot a}_{4 \text{ factors}}}$$

This can be reduced to

Divide the numerator and denominator by the four common factors of *a*.

Note that $\frac{a}{a} = 1$, where $a \neq 0$.

$$\frac{\cancel{a} \cdot \cancel{a} \cdot \cancel{a} \cdot \cancel{a} \cdot a \cdot a}{\cancel{a} \cdot \cancel{a} \cdot \cancel{a} \cdot \cancel{a}} \quad \text{or} \quad a^2$$

This means that

$$\frac{a^6}{a^4} = a^2$$

This leads to a second property of exponents.

This is our *second property of exponents*. We write $a \neq 0$ to avoid division by 0.

QUOTIENT RULE FOR EXPONENTS

In general, for any real number a ($a \neq 0$) and positive integers m and n,

$$\frac{a^m}{a^n} = a^{m-n}$$

Example 4

Simplify each expression.

Subtract the exponents, applying the quotient rule.

(a) $\dfrac{x^{10}}{x^4} = x^{10-4} = x^6$

Note that $a^1 = a$; there is no need to write the exponent of 1 because it is understood.

(b) $\dfrac{a^8}{a^7} = a^{8-7} = a$

(c) $\dfrac{63w^8}{7w^5} = 9w^{8-5} = 9w^3$

We *divide* the coefficients and subtract the exponents.

(d) $\dfrac{-32a^4b^5}{8a^2b} = -4a^{4-2}b^{5-1} = -4a^2b^4$

Divide the coefficients and subtract the exponents for *each* variable.

(e) $\dfrac{10^{16}}{10^6} = 10^{16-6} = 10^{10}$

CHECK YOURSELF 4

Simplify each expression.

1. $\dfrac{y^{12}}{y^5}$ 2. $\dfrac{x^9}{x^8}$ 3. $\dfrac{45r^8}{-9r^6}$

4. $\dfrac{49a^6b^7}{7ab^3}$ 5. $\dfrac{10^{13}}{10^5}$

In the quotient rule, suppose that we now allow *m to equal n*. We then have

$$\frac{a^m}{a^m} = a^{m-m} = a^0 \qquad\qquad (1)$$

But we know that it is also true that

$$\frac{a^m}{a^m} = 1 \qquad\qquad (2)$$

With this definition

$$\frac{a^m}{a^n} = a^{m-n}$$

We must have $a \neq 0$ since the form 0^0 is called *indeterminate* and is considered in later mathematics classes.

Comparing (1) and (2), we see that the following definition seems reasonable.

THE ZERO EXPONENT

For any real number a, $a \neq 0$,

$$a^0 = 1$$

Example 5

Use the above definition to simplify each expression.

Note that in $6x^0$ the 0 exponent applies *only* to x.

(*a*) $17^0 = 1$

(*c*) $6x^0 = 6 \cdot 1 = 6$

(*b*) $(a^3b^2)^0 = 1$

(*d*) $-3y^0 = -3$

CHECK YOURSELF 5

Simplify each expression.

1. 25^0 **2.** $(m^4n^2)^0$ **3.** $8s^0$ **4.** $-7t^0$

Now what if we allow one of the exponents to be negative and apply the product rule? Suppose, for instance, that $m = 3$ and $n = -3$. Then

Recall from our coverage of operations with signed numbers that $a^0 = 1$ if $a \neq 0$.

$$a^m \cdot a^n = a^3 \cdot a^{-3} = a^{3+(-3)}$$
$$= a^0 = 1$$

so

$$a^3 \cdot a^{-3} = 1$$

implies that

Divide both sides of the equation by a^3.

$$a^{-3} = \frac{1}{a^3}$$

This leads us to the following general definition.

John Wallis (1616–1702), an English mathematician, was the first to fully discuss the meaning of 0, negative, and rational exponents (which we discuss in our coverage of rational exponents).

NEGATIVE INTEGER EXPONENTS

For any nonzero real number a and whole number n,

$$a^{-n} = \frac{1}{a^n}$$

a^{-n} is the multiplicative inverse of a^n

The next example illustrates this definition.

Example 6

From this point on, to *simplify* will mean to write the expression with *positive exponents only*.

Also, we will restrict all variables so that they represent nonzero real numbers.

Simplify the following expressions.

(a) $y^{-5} = \dfrac{1}{y^5}$

(b) $4^{-2} = \dfrac{1}{4^2} = \dfrac{1}{16}$

(c) $(-3)^{-3} = \dfrac{1}{(-3)^3} = \dfrac{1}{-27} = -\dfrac{1}{27}$

(d) $\left(\dfrac{2}{3}\right)^{-3} = \dfrac{1}{\left(\dfrac{2}{3}\right)^3} = \dfrac{1}{\dfrac{8}{27}} = \dfrac{27}{8}$

CHECK YOURSELF 6

Simplify each of the following expressions.

1. a^{-10} **2.** 2^{-4} **3.** $(-4)^{-2}$ **4.** $\left(\dfrac{5}{2}\right)^{-2}$

The next example illustrates the case where coefficients are involved in an expression with negative exponents. As will be clear, some caution must be used.

Example 7

Simplify each of the following expressions.

Negative exponents do not generate negative coefficients.

(a) $2x^{-3} = 2 \cdot \dfrac{1}{x^3} = \dfrac{2}{x^3}$

The -3 exponent applies only to the variable x, and *not* to the coefficient 2.

(b) $4w^{-2} = 4 \cdot \dfrac{1}{w^2} = \dfrac{4}{w^2}$

(c) $(4w)^{-2} = \dfrac{1}{(4w)^2} = \dfrac{1}{16w^2}$

⬡ CAUTION ⬡

Be Careful! The expressions

$$4w^{-2} \qquad \text{and} \qquad (4w)^{-2}$$

are not the same. Do you see why?

CHECK YOURSELF 7

Simplify each of the following expressions.

1. $3w^{-4}$ **2.** $10x^{-5}$ **3.** $(2y)^{-4}$ **4.** $-5t^{-2}$

Suppose that a variable with a negative exponent appears in the denominator of an expression. Our previous definition can be used to write a complex fraction which can then be simplified. For instance,

$$\frac{1}{a^{-2}} = \frac{1}{\dfrac{1}{a^2}} = 1 \cdot \frac{a^2}{1} = a^2 \longleftarrow \text{Positive exponent in the numerator}$$

Negative exponent
in the denominator

To divide, we
invert and multiply.

To avoid the intermediate steps, we can write that in general

> For any nonzero real number a and integer n.
>
> $$\frac{1}{a^{-n}} = a^n$$

Example 8

Simplify each of the following expressions.

(a) $\dfrac{1}{y^{-3}} = y^3$

(b) $\dfrac{1}{2^{-5}} = 2^5 = 32$

The exponent -2 applies only to x and not to 4.

(c) $\dfrac{3}{4x^{-2}} = \dfrac{3x^2}{4}$

(d) $\dfrac{a^{-3}}{b^{-4}} = \dfrac{b^4}{a^3}$

CHECK YOURSELF 8

Simplify each of the following expressions.

1. $\dfrac{1}{x^{-4}}$ **2.** $\dfrac{1}{3^{-3}}$

3. $\dfrac{2}{3a^{-2}}$ **4.** $\dfrac{c^{-5}}{d^{-7}}$

The product and quotient rules for exponents apply to expressions that involve any integral exponent—positive, negative, or 0. The next example illustrates this.

Example 9

Simplify each of the following expressions, and write the result, using positive exponents only.

We add the exponents by the product rule.

(a) $x^3 \cdot x^{-7} = x^{3+(-7)}$

$$= x^{-4} = \frac{1}{x^4}$$

We *subtract* the exponents by the quotient rule.

(b) $\dfrac{m^{-5}}{m^{-3}} = m^{-5-(-3)} = m^{-5+3}$

$$= m^{-2} = \frac{1}{m^2}$$

Here we apply first the product rule and then the quotient rule.

(c) $\dfrac{x^5 x^{-3}}{x^{-7}} = \dfrac{x^{5+(-3)}}{x^{-7}} = \dfrac{x^2}{x^{-7}} = x^{2-(-7)} = x^9$

Note Typically, in simplifying expressions involving negative exponents, there are often alternate approaches. For instance, in Example 9b, we could have made use of our earlier work to write

Note that m^{-5} in the numerator becomes m^5 in the denominator, and m^{-3} in the denominator becomes m^3 in the numerator. We then simplify as before.

$$\frac{m^{-5}}{m^{-3}} = \frac{m^3}{m^5} = m^{3-5} = m^{-2} = \frac{1}{m^2}$$

CHECK YOURSELF 9

Simplify each of the following expressions.

1. $x^9 \cdot x^{-5}$ **2.** $\dfrac{y^{-7}}{y^{-3}}$ **3.** $\dfrac{a^{-3} a^2}{a^{-5}}$

Suppose that we have an expression of the form

$$(a^2)^4$$

This can be written as

$$\underbrace{(a \cdot a)(a \cdot a)(a \cdot a)(a \cdot a)}_{2 \cdot 4, \text{ or } 8, \text{ factors}} \qquad \text{or} \qquad a^8$$

This suggests in general, the following:

> **POWER RULE**
>
> For any nonzero real number a and integers m and n,
>
> $(a^m)^n = a^{mn}$

This is our *third property of exponents*.

Our next example illustrates the use of this third property for exponents.

Example 10

Using the power rule, simplify each expression.

We *multiply* the exponents.

(a) $(x^3)^5 = x^{3 \cdot 5} = x^{15}$

(b) $(a^2)^8 = a^{2 \cdot 8} = a^{16}$

(c) $(3^2)^3 = 3^{2 \cdot 3} = 3^6$

◁ CAUTION ▷

Be Careful! Students sometimes confuse $(x^3)^5$ or x^{15} with $x^3 \cdot x^5$ or x^8. In the first case we *multiply* the exponents, in the second we *add*!

CHECK YOURSELF 10

Simplify each expression.

1. $(b^4)^7$ **2.** $(10^3)^3$ **3.** $b^4 b^7$

Expressions with negative exponents can also be simplified by using the power rule.

Example 11

Using the power rule, simplify each expression.

(a) $(x^{-3})^5 = x^{(-3)(5)} = x^{-15} = \dfrac{1}{x^{15}}$

(b) $(x^4)^{-3} = x^{(4)(-3)} = x^{-12} = \dfrac{1}{x^{12}}$

(c) $(w^{-3})^{-2} = w^{(-3)(-2)} = w^6$

CHECK YOURSELF 11

Simplify each of the following expressions.

1. $(y^3)^{-4}$ **2.** $(p^{-2})^{-5}$ **3.** $(w^{-5})^6$

Let's develop another property for exponents. An expression such as

$$(2x)^5$$

can be written in expanded form as

$$\underbrace{(2x)(2x)(2x)(2x)(2x)}_{5 \text{ factors}}$$

We could use the commutative and associative properties to write this product as

$$(2 \cdot 2 \cdot 2 \cdot 2 \cdot 2)(x \cdot x \cdot x \cdot x \cdot x)$$

or

Note that each factor of the base has been raised to the fifth power.

$$2^5 x^5$$

This suggests our fourth property for exponents.

RAISING PRODUCTS TO A POWER

For any nonzero real numbers a and b and any integer m,

$$(ab)^m = a^m b^m$$

This is our *fourth property of exponents*. Notice that the exponent is distributed over the product.

The use of this fourth property is illustrated in our next example.

Example 12

Simplify each expression.

(a) $(xy)^5 = x^5 y^5$

(b) $(3a)^4 = 3^4 \cdot a^4 = 81a^4$

Note that we also apply the power rule in simplifying this expression.

(c) $(2p^2 q^3)^3 = 2^3 (p^2)^3 (q^3)^3$
$\qquad\quad = 8p^6 q^9$

Be sure to raise *each factor* to the −2 power.

(d) $(x^{-2} y^3)^{-2} = (x^{-2})^{-2} (y^3)^{-2}$
$\qquad\qquad\quad = x^4 y^{-6} = \dfrac{x^4}{y^6}$

(e) $(2w^{-2} z^4)^3 = 2^3 (w^{-2})^3 (z^4)^3$
$\qquad\qquad\quad = 2^3 w^{-6} z^{12} = \dfrac{8z^{12}}{w^6}$

CHECK YOURSELF 12

Simplify each expression.

1. $(ab)^7$ **2.** $(4p)^3$ **3.** $(3m^4n^2)^2$
4. $(x^5y^{-2})^{-4}$ **5.** $(3a^5b^{-2})^{-2}$

Our fifth (and final) property for exponents can be established in a similar fashion to the fourth property. It deals with a power of quotients rather than the power of a product.

This is our *fifth property of exponents*.

> **RAISING QUOTIENTS TO A POWER**
>
> For any nonzero real numbers *a* and *b* and integer *m*,
>
> $$\left(\frac{a}{b}\right)^m = \frac{a^m}{b^m}$$

Our next example shows the application of this property.

Example 13

Simplify each expression.

(*a*) $\left(\dfrac{x^2}{y}\right)^3 = \dfrac{(x^2)^3}{y^3} = \dfrac{x^6}{y^3}$ Raise the numerator and denominator to the third power.

(*b*) $\left(\dfrac{2a}{b^3}\right)^4 = \dfrac{(2a)^4}{(b^3)^4}$

$= \dfrac{2^4a^4}{b^{12}} = \dfrac{16a^4}{b^{12}}$

Raise both the numerator and the denominator to the −2 power.

(*c*) $\left(\dfrac{a^3}{b^2}\right)^{-2} = \dfrac{(a^3)^{-2}}{(b^2)^{-2}}$

$= \dfrac{a^{-6}}{b^{-4}} = \dfrac{b^4}{a^6}$

(*d*) $\left(\dfrac{2w^{-4}}{z^3}\right)^{-3} = \dfrac{(2w^{-4})^{-3}}{(z^3)^{-3}}$

$= \dfrac{2^{-3}w^{12}}{z^{-9}} = \dfrac{w^{12}z^9}{2^3} = \dfrac{w^{12}z^9}{8}$

CHECK YOURSELF 13

Simplify each expression.

1. $\left(\dfrac{m^3}{n}\right)^4$ **2.** $\left(\dfrac{3t^2}{s^3}\right)^3$ **3.** $\left(\dfrac{x^5}{y^{-2}}\right)^{-3}$ **4.** $\left(\dfrac{3p^{-4}}{q^2}\right)^{-2}$

When a fraction is raised to a negative power (as in Examples 12c and d), the work can often be simplified by the following observation.

RAISING QUOTIENTS TO A NEGATIVE POWER

$$\left(\frac{a}{b}\right)^{-n} = \frac{a^{-n}}{b^{-n}} = \frac{b^n}{a^n} = \left(\frac{b}{a}\right)^n \qquad a \neq 0 \qquad b \neq 0$$

This is used in the next example.

Example 14

Simplify each of the following expressions.

We will not provide a long set of rules about when to use which method. It is better for you to try both techniques and look for clues as to when one might be "better" than the other.

Try both approaches in the Check Yourself 14 exercise that follows.

(a) $\left(\dfrac{3}{q^5}\right)^{-2} = \left(\dfrac{q^5}{3}\right)^2$

$\qquad = \dfrac{q^{10}}{9}$

(b) $\left(\dfrac{x^3}{y^4}\right)^{-3} = \left(\dfrac{y^4}{x^3}\right)^3$

$\qquad = \dfrac{(y^4)^3}{(x^3)^3} = \dfrac{y^{12}}{x^9}$

CHECK YOURSELF 14

Simplify each of the following expressions.

1. $\left(\dfrac{r^4}{5}\right)^{-2}$ **2.** $\left(\dfrac{a^4}{b^3}\right)^{-3}$

The chart on the next page summarizes the five properties of integer exponents introduced in this section.

PROPERTIES OF EXPONENTS $a \neq 0$, $b \neq 0$

General Form	Example
$a^m \cdot a^n = a^{m+n}$	$x^2 \cdot x^3 = x^5$
$\dfrac{a^m}{a^n} = a^{m-n}$	$\dfrac{5^7}{5^3} = 5^4$
$\left(a^m\right)^n = a^{mn}$	$\left(x^5\right)^4 = x^{20}$
$(ab)^m = a^m b^m$	$(4x)^3 = 4^3 x^3 = 64x^3$
$\left(\dfrac{a}{b}\right)^m = \dfrac{a^m}{b^m}$	$\left(\dfrac{2}{3}\right)^6 = \dfrac{2^6}{3^6} = \dfrac{64}{729}$
$a^1 = a$	$(45)^1 = 45$
$a^0 = 1$	$(1{,}289)^0 = 1$

As you might expect, more complicated expressions require the use of more than one of our properties, for simplification. The next examples illustrate such cases.

Example 15

Use the properties of exponents to simplify each of the following expressions.

In (a) the exponents on the parentheses apply to both the 2 and the x.

(a) $(2x)^2(2x)^4 = (2x)^{2+4} = (2x)^6$ Product rule
$\qquad = 2^6 x^6 = 64x^6$ Product to a power

(b) $\dfrac{(x^4)^3}{(x^3)^2} = \dfrac{x^{12}}{x^6} = x^{12-6} = x^6$ Power rule, quotient rule

(c) $\dfrac{6a^4 b^5}{3a^2 b} = 2a^{4-2} b^{5-1} = 2a^2 b^4$ Quotient rule, division

(d) $\dfrac{7.5 \times 10^{14}}{2.5 \times 10^3} = \dfrac{7.5}{2.5} \times 10^{14-3}$ Quotient rule
$\qquad = 3 \times 10^{11}$ Divide.

CHECK YOURSELF 15

Simplify each expression.

1. $(3y)^2(3y)^3$ 2. $\dfrac{(3a^2)^3}{9a^3 187}$ 3. $\dfrac{25x^3 y^4}{5x^2 y}$

Example 16

Simplify each of the following expressions.

Apply the power rule to each factor in the numerator and to the denominator.
Apply the product rule in the numerator.

Apply the quotient rule.

(a) $\dfrac{(a^2)^{-3}(a^3)^4}{(a^{-3})^3} = \dfrac{a^{-6} \cdot a^{12}}{a^{-9}}$

$= \dfrac{a^{-6+12}}{a^{-9}} = \dfrac{a^6}{a^{-9}}$

$= a^{6-(-9)} = a^{6+9} = a^{15}$

It may help to separate the problem into three fractions, one for the coefficients and one for each of the variables.

(b) $\dfrac{8x^{-2}y^{-5}}{12x^{-4}y^3} = \dfrac{8}{12} \cdot \dfrac{x^{-2}}{x^{-4}} \cdot \dfrac{y^{-5}}{y^3}$

$= \dfrac{2}{3}x^{-2-(-4)} \cdot y^{-5-3}$

$= \dfrac{2}{3}x^2 \cdot y^{-8} = \dfrac{2x^2}{3y^8}$

Apply the power rule inside the parentheses.
Apply rule for a product to a power.
Apply the power rule.

(c) $\left(\dfrac{pr^3s^{-5}}{p^3r^{-3}s^{-2}}\right)^{-2} = (p^{1-3}r^{3-(-3)}s^{-5-(-2)})^{-2}$

$= (p^{-2}r^6s^{-3})^{-2}$

$= (p^{-2})^{-2}(r^6)^{-2}(s^{-3})^{-2}$

$= p^4r^{-12}s^6 = \dfrac{p^4s^6}{r^{12}}$

Be Careful! Another possible first step (and generally an efficient one) is to rewrite an expression by using our earlier definitions.

$$a^{-n} = \dfrac{1}{a^n} \quad \text{and} \quad \dfrac{1}{a^{-n}} = a^n$$

For instance, in Example 16b, we would *correctly* write

We leave it to the reader to show that this leads to the same simplified form as above.

$$\dfrac{8x^{-2}y^{-5}}{12x^{-4}y^3} = \dfrac{8x^4}{12x^2y^3y^5}$$

A *common error* is to write

⟨CAUTION⟩

$$\dfrac{8x^{-2}y^{-5}}{12x^{-4}y^3} = \dfrac{12x^4}{8x^2y^3y^5} \qquad \text{This is } not \text{ correct.}$$

The coefficients should not have been moved along with the factors in x. Keep in mind that the negative exponents apply *only* to the variables. The coefficients remain *where they were* in the original expression when the expression is rewritten by using this approach.

CHECK YOURSELF 16

Simplify each of the following expressions.

1. $\dfrac{(x^5)^{-2}(x^2)^3}{(x^{-4})^3}$ **2.** $\dfrac{12a^{-3}b^{-2}}{16a^{-2}b^3}$ **3.** $\left(\dfrac{xy^{-3}z^{-5}}{x^{-4}y^{-2}z^3}\right)^{-3}$

You may have noticed that throughout this section we have frequently used 10 as a base in our examples. You will find that experience useful as we discuss scientific notation.

We begin the discussion with a calculator exercise. On most (scientific) calculators, if you find 2.3 times 1000, the display will read

2300.

Multiply by 1000 a second time. Now you will see

2300000.

Multiplying by 1000 a third time will result in the display

This must equal 2,300,000,000.

2.3 09

And multiplying by 1000 again yields

2.3 12

Consider the following table:

$2.3 = 2.3 \times 10^0$
$23 = 2.3 \times 10^1$
$230 = 2.3 \times 10^2$
$2300 = 2.3 \times 10^3$
$23{,}000 = 2.3 \times 10^4$
$230{,}000 = 2.3 \times 10^5$

Can you see what is happening? This is the way calculators display very large numbers: The number on the left is always between 1 and 10, and the number on the right indicates the number of places the decimal point must be moved to the right to put the answer in standard (or decimal) form.

This notation is used frequently in science. It is not uncommon, in scientific applications of algebra, to find yourself working with very large or very small numbers. Even in the time of Archimedes (287–212 B.C.), the study of such numbers was not unusual. Archimedes estimated that the universe was 23,000,000,000,000,000 m in diameter.

In scientific notation, his estimate for the diameter of the universe would be

$$2.3 \times 10^{16} \, \text{m}$$

In general, we can define scientific notation as follows:

SCIENTIFIC NOTATION

Any number written in the form

$$a \times 10^n$$

where $1 \le a < 10$ and n is an integer, is written in scientific notation.

Example 17

Write each of the following numbers in scientific notation.

Note the pattern for writing a number in scientific notation.

The exponent on the 10 shows the *number of places* we must move the decimal point so that the multiplier will be a number between 1 and 10. A positive exponent tells us to move right, while a negative exponent indicates to move left.

(a) $120,000. = 1.2 \times 10^5$

5 places — The power is 5.

(b) $88,000,000. = 8.8 \times 10^7$

7 places — The power is 7.

(c) $520,000,000. = 5.2 \times 10^8$

8 places

(d) $4,000,000,000. = 4 \times 10^9$

9 places

Note: To convert back to standard or decimal form, the process is simply reversed.

(e) $0.0005 = 5 \times 10^{-4}$

4 places — If the decimal point is to be moved to the left, the exponent will be negative.

(f) $0.0000000081 = 8.1 \times 10^{-9}$

9 places

CHECK YOURSELF 17

Write in scientific notation.

1. 212,000,000,000,000,000
2. 5,600,000
3. 0.00079
4. 0.0000007

Example 18

(a) Light travels at a speed of 3.05×10^8 meters per second (m/s). There are approximately 3.15×10^7 seconds (s) in a year. How far does light travel in a year?

We multiply the distance traveled in 1 s by the number of seconds in a year. This yields

$$(3.05 \times 10^8)(3.15 \times 10^7) = (3.05 \cdot 3.15)(10^8 \cdot 10^7)$$
$$= 9.6075 \times 10^{15}$$

Multiply the coefficients, add the exponents.

Note that $9.6075 \times 10^{15} \approx 10 \times 10^{15} = 10^{16}$.

For our purposes we round the distance light travels in a year to 10^{16} m. This unit is called a *light-year,* and it is used to measure astronomical distances.

(b) The distance from earth to the star Spica (in Virgo) is 2.2×10^{18} m. How many light-years is the star Spica away from earth?

We divide the distance (in meters) by the number of meters in 1 light-year.

$$\frac{2.2 \times 10^{18}}{10^{16}} = 2.2 \times 10^{18-16}$$
$$= 2.2 \times 10^2 = 220 \text{ light-years}$$

CHECK YOURSELF 18

The farthest object that can be seen with the unaided eye is the Andromeda galaxy. This galaxy is 2.3×10^{22} m from earth. What is this distance in light-years?

CHECK YOURSELF ANSWERS

1. (1) $(3z)^3$; (2) x^4.

2. (1) $(5b)^{11}$; (2) $(-3)^7$; (3) 10^{20}; (4) $(xy)^5$.

3. (1) $8a^5b^5$; (2) $6x^7y$; (3) $-6s^5t^5$; (4) $20d^7f^7$.

4. (1) y^7; (2) x; (3) $-5r^2$; (4) $7a^5b^4$; (5) 10^8.

5. (1) 1; (2) 1; (3) 8; (4) -7.

6. (1) $\dfrac{1}{a^{10}}$; (2) $\dfrac{1}{2^4} = \dfrac{1}{16}$; (3) $\dfrac{1}{(-4)^2} = \dfrac{1}{16}$; (4) $\dfrac{4}{25}$.

7. (1) $\dfrac{3}{w^4}$; (2) $\dfrac{10}{x^5}$; (3) $\dfrac{1}{(2y)^4} = \dfrac{1}{16y^4}$; (4) $\dfrac{-5}{t^2}$.

8. (1) x^4; (2) $3^3 = 27$; (3) $\dfrac{2a^2}{3}$; (4) $\dfrac{d^7}{c^5}$.

9. (1) x^4; (2) $y^{-4} = \dfrac{1}{y^4}$; (3) a^4.

10. (1) b^{28}; (2) 10^9; (3) b^{11}.

11. (1) $y^{-12} = \dfrac{1}{y^{12}}$; (2) p^{10}; (3) $w^{-30} = \dfrac{1}{w^{30}}$.

12. (1) a^7b^7; (2) $64p^3$; (3) $9m^8n^4$; (4) $\dfrac{y^8}{x^{20}}$; (5) $\dfrac{b^4}{9a^{10}}$.

13. (1) $\dfrac{m^{12}}{n^4}$; (2) $\dfrac{27t^6}{s^9}$; (3) $\dfrac{1}{x^{15}y^6}$; (4) $\dfrac{q^4p^8}{9}$.

14. (1) $\dfrac{25}{r^8}$; (2) $\dfrac{b^9}{a^{12}}$.

15. (1) $243y^5$; (2) $3a^3$; (3) $5xy^3$.

16. (1) x^8; (2) $\dfrac{3}{4ab^5}$; (3) $\dfrac{z^{24}y^3}{x^{15}}$.

17. (1) 2.12×10^{17}; (2) 5.6×10^6; (3) 7.9×10^{-4}; (4) 7×10^{-7}.

18. 2,300,000 light-years.

Name _____

Date _____

Exercises

ANSWERS

Build Your Skills

1. _____

Simplify each of the following expressions.

2. _____

1. $x^4 \cdot x^5$

2. $p^4 \cdot p^7$

3. _____

3. $y^5 \cdot y^4 \cdot y^3$

4. $z^2 \cdot z^3 \cdot z^4 \cdot z^5$

4. _____

5. _____

5. $3^5 \cdot 3^0$

6. $(-2)^7(-2)^4$

6. _____

7. $(-5)^2(-5)^3(-5)^5$

8. $6^5 \cdot 6^4 \cdot 6^3 \cdot 6^0$

7. _____

8. _____

9. $3 \cdot s^4 \cdot s^3 \cdot s^4$

10. $5 \cdot a^6 \cdot a^3 \cdot a^4$

9. _____

11. x^{-5}

12. 3^{-3}

10. _____

11. _____

13. 5^{-2}

14. y^{-8}

12. _____

15. $(-5)^{-2}$

16. $(-3)^{-3}$

13. _____

14. _____

17. $(-2)^{-3}$

18. $(-2)^{-4}$

15. _____

16. _____

19. $\left(\dfrac{2}{3}\right)^{-3}$

20. $\left(\dfrac{3}{4}\right)^{-2}$

17. _____

18. _____

21. $3x^{-2}$

22. $4w^{-3}$

19. _____

20. _____

21. _____

22. _____

ANSWERS

23. _____   **23.** $-5a^{-4}$ **24.** $(-2b)^{-4}$

24. _____   **25.** $(-3x)^{-2}$ **26.** $-5x^{-2}$

25. _____

26. _____   **27.** $\dfrac{1}{x^{-3}}$ **28.** $\dfrac{1}{m^{-5}}$

27. _____

28. _____   **29.** $\dfrac{1}{2^{-3}}$ **30.** $\dfrac{1}{5^{-2}}$

29. _____

30. _____

31. _____   **31.** $\dfrac{2}{5x^{-3}}$ **32.** $\dfrac{3}{4w^{-4}}$

32. _____

33. _____   **33.** $\dfrac{x^{-3}}{y^{-4}}$ **34.** $\dfrac{m^{-5}}{n^{-3}}$

34. _____

35. _____   Use the product rule of exponents together with the commutative and associative properties to simplify the following products.

36. _____   **35.** $(a^2b^3)(a^4b^2)$ **36.** $(p^4q)(p^2q^3)$

37. _____   **37.** $(x^3y^2)(x^4y^2)(x^2y^3)$ **38.** $(r^2s^3)(r^3s)(r^4s^0)$

38. _____   **39.** $(2x^4)(3x^3)(-4x^3)$ **40.** $(2m^3)(-3m)(-4m^4)$

39. _____

40. _____   **41.** $(5a^2)(3a^3)(a^0)(-2a^3)$ **42.** $(4s^2)(2s)(s^2)(2s^3)$

41. _____   **43.** $(5ab^3)(2a^2b)(3ab)$ **44.** $(-3xy)(5x^2y)(-2x^3y^0)$

42. _____

43. _____

44. _____

ANSWERS

45. _____

46. _____

47. _____

48. _____

49. _____

50. _____

51. _____

52. _____

53. _____

54. _____

55. _____

56. _____

57. _____

58. _____

59. _____

60. _____

61. _____

62. _____

63. _____

64. _____

65. _____

66. _____

45. $(ab^2c)(a^3b^5c)(a^4bc)$

46. $(rst)(r^8s^3t^6)(r^2st)(rst^4)$

47. $x^5 \cdot x^{-3}$

48. $y^{-4} \cdot y^5$

49. $a^{-9} \cdot a^6$

50. $w^{-5} \cdot w^3$

51. $z^{-2} \cdot z^{-8}$

52. $b^{-7} \cdot b^{-1}$

53. $a^{-5} \cdot a^5$

54. $x^4 \cdot x^{-4}$

Use the quotient rule of exponents to simplify each expression.

55. $\dfrac{x^{10}}{x^7}$

56. $\dfrac{b^{23}}{b^{18}}$

57. $\dfrac{x^7y^{11}}{x^4y^3}$

58. $\dfrac{a^5b^9}{ab^4}$

59. $\dfrac{a^5b^4c^2}{ab^2c^0}$

60. $\dfrac{x^8y^6z^4}{x^3yz^0}$

61. $\dfrac{21s^4t^5}{7st^2}$

62. $\dfrac{48w^6z^6}{12w^3z}$

63. $\dfrac{(2x+1)^9}{(2x+1)^5}$

64. $\dfrac{(3y-4)^7}{(3y-4)^6}$

65. $\dfrac{x^{-5}}{x^{-2}}$

66. $\dfrac{m^{-3}}{m^{-6}}$

ANSWERS

Use the first three properties of exponents to simplify each of the following.

67. _____

67. $(x^5)^3$

68. $(w^4)^6$

68. _____

69. $(2x^3)(x^2)^4$

70. $(p^4)(3p^3)^2$

69. _____

70. _____

71. $(3a^4)(a^3)(a^2)$

72. $(5y^2)(2y)(y^5)$

71. _____

73. $(x^4y)(x^2)^3(y^3)^0$

74. $(r^4)^2(r^2s)(s^3)^2$

72. _____

75. $(ab^2c)(a^4)^4(b^2)^3(c^3)^4$

76. $(p^2qr^2)(p^2)(q^3)^2(r^2)^0$

73. _____

74. _____

77. $(w^5)^{-3}$

78. $(x^{-2})^{-3}$

75. _____

79. $(b^{-4})^{-2}$

80. $(a^0b^{-4})^3$

76. _____

81. $(x^5y^{-3})^2$

82. $(p^{-3}q^2)^{-2}$

77. _____

78. _____

83. $(m^{-4}n^{-2})^{-3}$

84. $(3x^{-2}y^{-2})^3$

79. _____

80. _____

85. $(2r^{-3}s^0)^{-5}$

86. $\left(\dfrac{a^{-3}}{b^{-2}}\right)^2$

81. _____

82. _____

87. $\left(\dfrac{w^{-2}}{z^{-4}}\right)^3$

88. $\left(\dfrac{x^{-3}}{y^2}\right)^{-3}$

83. _____

84. _____

85. _____

86. _____

87. _____

88. _____

ANSWERS

89. _____

90. _____

91. _____

92. _____

93. _____

94. _____

95. _____

96. _____

97. _____

98. _____

99. _____

100. _____

101. _____

102. _____

103. _____

104. _____

105. _____

106. _____

107. _____

108. _____

109. _____

89. $\left(\dfrac{m^{-4}}{n^{-2}}\right)^{-2}$

90. $(3x^{-4})^2(2x^2)$

91. $(4y^{-2})^2(3y^{-4})$

Simplify each expression.

92. $(2a^5)^4(a^3)^2$

93. $(3b^2)^3(b^2)^4(b^2)$

94. $(2x^3)^3(3x^3)^2$

95. $(2 \times 10^4)^2 \cdot (1 \times 10^3)^4$

96. $(a^2b^3)^4(ab^3)^0$

97. $(xy^5z)^4(xyz^2)^8(x^6yz)^5$

98. $(a^2b^2c^2)^0(ab^2c)^2(a^3bc^2)$

99. $(3a^2)(5a^2)^2$

100. $(2a^3)^2(a^0)^5$

101. $(2a^3)^4(3a^5)^2$

102. $(3x^3)^2(2x^4)^5$

103. $\left(\dfrac{3a^6}{2b^9}\right)^3$

104. $\left(\dfrac{x^8}{y^6}\right)\left(\dfrac{2y^9}{x^3}\right)$

105. $(-7a^2b)(-3a^5b^6)^4$

106. $(2x^6y)(-5x^2y^5)^3$

107. $-a^3(3a^4)(5a^0)^2$

108. $\left(\dfrac{2w^5z^3}{3x^3y^9}\right)\left(\dfrac{x^5y^4}{w^4z^0}\right)^2$

109. $(2a^2b^{-3})(3a^{-4}b^{-2})$

ANSWERS

110. _____

110. $(-5m^{-2}n^{-4})(2m^5n^0)$

111. $\dfrac{(y^{-3})^{-2}(y^2)^{-4}}{y^{-3}}$

111. _____

112. $\dfrac{6p^3q^{-4}}{24p^{-2}q^{-2}}$

113. $\dfrac{15x^{-3}y^2z^{-4}}{20x^{-4}y^{-3}z^2}$

112. _____

114. $\dfrac{24p^{-5}q^{-3}r^2}{36p^{-2}q^3r^{-2}}$

115. $\left(\dfrac{x^{-5}y^{-7}}{x^0y^{-4}}\right)^3$

113. _____

116. $\left(\dfrac{xy^3w^{-4}}{x^{-3}y^{-2}w^2}\right)^{-2}$

117. $\left(\dfrac{a^{-2}b^2}{a^3b^{-2}}\right)^{-2}\left(\dfrac{a^{-4}b^2}{a^{-2}b^{-2}}\right)^2$

114. _____

115. _____

118. $\left(\dfrac{p^{-3}q^3}{p^{-4}q^2}\right)^3\left(\dfrac{p^{-2}q^{-2}}{pq^4}\right)^{-1}$

116. _____

Express each number in scientific notation.

119. The distance from the earth to the sun: 93,000,000 mi

117. _____

120. The diameter of a grain of sand: 0.000021 m

118. _____

121. The diameter of the sun: 130,000,000,000 cm

119. _____

122. The number of molecules in 22.4 L of a gas: 602,000,000,000,000,000,000,000 (Avogadro's number)

120. _____

121. _____

122. _____

ANSWERS

123. _____

123. The mass of the sun is approximately 1.98×10^{30} kilograms (kg). If this were written in standard or decimal form, how many zeros would follow the digit 8?

124. _____

124. Scientists estimate the mass of our galaxy to be 2.95×10^{41} kg. If this number were written in standard or decimal form, how many zeros would follow the digit 5?

125. _____

125. Archimedes estimated the universe to be 2.3×10^{19} millimeters (mm) in diameter. If this number were written in standard or decimal form, how many zeros would follow the digit 3?

126. _____

Write each of the following numbers in standard notation.

127. _____

126. 8×10^{-3} **127.** 7.5×10^{-6}

128. _____

128. 2.8×10^{-5} **129.** 5.21×10^{-4}

Write each of the following numbers in scientific notation.

129. _____

130. 0.0005   **131.** 0.000003

130. _____

132. 0.00037   **133.** 0.000051

Compute each of the following, using scientific notation, and write your answer in that form.

131. _____

134. $(4 \times 10^{-3})(2 \times 10^{-5})$ **135.** $(1.5 \times 10^{-6})(4 \times 10^{2})$

132. _____

133. _____

134. _____

135. _____

ANSWERS

136. _____

136. $\dfrac{9 \times 10^3}{3 \times 10^{-2}}$

137. $\dfrac{7.5 \times 10^{-4}}{1.5 \times 10^2}$

137. _____

138. Scientists now estimate the diameter of the observable universe to be 1.3×10^{29} mm. If this number were written in standard or decimal form, how many zeros would follow the digit 3?

138. _____

In the expressions below, perform the indicated calculations. Write your result in scientific notation.

139. $(2 \times 10^5)(4 \times 10^4)$

140. $(2.5 \times 10^7)(3 \times 10^5)$

139. _____

141. $\dfrac{6 \times 10^9}{3 \times 10^7}$

142. $\dfrac{4.5 \times 10^{12}}{1.5 \times 10^7}$

140. _____

143. $\dfrac{(3.3 \times 10^{15})(6 \times 10^{15})}{(1.1 \times 10^8)(3 \times 10^6)}$

144. $\dfrac{(6 \times 10^{12})(3.2 \times 10^8)}{(1.6 \times 10^7)(3 \times 10^2)}$

141. _____

145. Megrez, the nearest of the Big Dipper stars, is 6.6×10^{17} m from the planet Earth. Approximately how long does it take light, traveling at 10^{16} m/year, to travel from Megrez to earth?

142. _____

146. Alkaid, the most distant star in the Big Dipper, is 2.1×10^{18} m from earth. Approximately how long does it take light to travel from Alkaid to earth?

143. _____

144. _____

145. _____

146. _____

ANSWERS

Simplify each of the following expressions.

147. _____ **147.** $x^{2n} \cdot x^{3n}$

148. $a^{n+1} \cdot a^{3n}$

149. $\dfrac{w^{n+3}}{w^{n+1}}$

150. $\dfrac{r^{n-4}}{r^{n-1}}$

148. _____

151. $(y^n)^{3n}$

152. $(p^{n+1})^n$

149. _____ **153.** $\dfrac{(a^{2n})(a^{n+2})}{a^{3n}}$

154. $\dfrac{(x^n)(x^{3n+5})}{x^{4n}}$

150. _____

151. _____

ANSWERS

1. x^9　**3.** y^{12}　**5.** 3^5　**7.** $(-5)^{10}$　**9.** $3s^{11}$　**11.** $\dfrac{1}{x^5}$　**13.** $\dfrac{1}{25}$　**15.** $\dfrac{1}{25}$

17. $-\dfrac{1}{8}$　**19.** $\dfrac{27}{8}$　**21.** $\dfrac{3}{x^2}$　**23.** $\dfrac{-5}{a^4}$　**25.** $\dfrac{1}{9x^2}$　**27.** x^3　**29.** 8　**31.** $\dfrac{2x^3}{5}$

152. _____ **33.** $\dfrac{y^4}{x^3}$　**35.** a^6b^5　**37.** x^9y^7　**39.** $-24x^{10}$　**41.** $-30a^8$　**43.** $30a^4b^5$　**45.** $a^8b^8c^3$

47. x^2　**49.** $\dfrac{1}{a^3}$　**51.** $\dfrac{1}{z^{10}}$　**53.** 1　**55.** x^3　**57.** x^3y^8　**59.** $a^4b^2c^2$　**61.** $3s^3t^3$

63. $(2x+1)^4$　**65.** $\dfrac{1}{x^3}$　**67.** x^{15}　**69.** $2x^{11}$　**71.** $3a^9$　**73.** $x^{10}y$　**75.** $a^{17}b^8c^{13}$

153. _____ **77.** $\dfrac{1}{w^{15}}$　**79.** b^8　**81.** $\dfrac{x^{10}}{y^6}$　**83.** $m^{12}n^6$　**85.** $\dfrac{r^{15}}{32}$　**87.** $\dfrac{z^{12}}{w^6}$　**89.** $\dfrac{m^8}{n^4}$　**91.** $\dfrac{48}{y^8}$

93. $27b^{16}$　**95.** 4×10^{20}　**97.** $x^{42}y^{33}z^{25}$　**99.** $75a^6$　**101.** $144a^{22}$　**103.** $\dfrac{27a^{18}}{8b^{27}}$

105. $-567a^{22}b^{25}$　**107.** $-75a^7$　**109.** $\dfrac{6}{a^2b^5}$　**111.** y　**113.** $\dfrac{3xy^5}{4z^6}$　**115.** $\dfrac{1}{x^{15}y^9}$

117. a^6　**119.** 9.3×10^7　**121.** 1.3×10^{11}　**123.** 28　**125.** 18　**127.** 0.0000075

129. 0.000521　**131.** 3×10^{-6}　**133.** 5.1×10^{-5}　**135.** 6×10^{-4}　**137.** 5×10^{-6}

139. 8×10^9　**141.** 2×10^2　**143.** 6×10^{16}　**145.** 66 years　**147.** x^{5n}　**149.** w^2

154. _____ **151.** y^{3n^2}　**153.** a^2

Rational Exponents

OBJECTIVES
1. To define the meaning of a rational exponent
2. To simplify expressions involving rational exponents

In this section, we use the concept of roots to develop a new notation, using exponents that will provide an alternate way of writing these roots.

That new notation will involve *rational numbers as exponents*. To start the development, we will extend all the previous properties of exponents to include rational exponents.

Given that extension, suppose that

$$a = 4^{1/2} \tag{1}$$

Squaring both sides of the equation yields

$$a^2 = (4^{1/2})^2$$

or

We will see that the property $(x^m)^n = x^{mn}$ holds for rational numbers m and n.

$$a^2 = 4^{(1/2)(2)}$$
$$a^2 = 4^1$$
$$a^2 = 4 \tag{2}$$

From Equation (2) we see that a is the number whose square is 4; that is, a is the principal square root of 4. Using our earlier notation, we can write

$$a = \sqrt{4}$$

But from (1)

$$a = 4^{1/2}$$

and to be consistent, we must have

$4^{1/2}$ indicates the principal *square root* of 4.

$$4^{1/2} = \sqrt{4}$$

This argument can be repeated for any exponent of the form $\dfrac{1}{n}$, so it seems reasonable to make the following definition.

If a is any real number and n is a positive integer $(n > 1)$, then

$$a^{1/n} = \sqrt[n]{a}$$

We restrict a so that a is nonnegative when n is even.

In words, $a^{1/n}$ indicates the principal nth root of a.

The following example illustrates the use of rational exponents to represent roots.

Example 1*

Write each expression in radical form and then simplify.

$27^{1/3}$ is the *cube root* of 27.

(a) $25^{1/2} = \sqrt{25} = 5$
(b) $27^{1/3} = \sqrt[3]{27} = 3$
(c) $-36^{1/2} = -\sqrt{36} = -6$
(d) $(-36)^{1/2} = \sqrt{-36}$ is not a real number.

$32^{1/5}$ is the *fifth root* of 32.

(e) $32^{1/5} = \sqrt[5]{32} = 2$

CHECK YOURSELF 1

Write each expression in radical form and simplify.

1. $8^{1/3}$ **2.** $-64^{1/2}$ **3.** $81^{1/4}$

We are now ready to extend our exponent notation to allow *any* rational exponent, again assuming that our previous exponent properties must still be valid. Note that

This is because

$\dfrac{m}{n} = (m)\left(\dfrac{1}{n}\right) = \left(\dfrac{1}{n}\right)(m)$

$a^{m/n} = (a^{1/n})^m = (a^m)^{1/n}$

From our earlier work, we know that $a^{1/n} = \sqrt[n]{a}$, and combining this with the above observation, we offer the following definition for $a^{m/n}$.

The two radical forms for $a^{m/n}$ are equivalent, and the choice of which form to use generally depends on whether we are evaluating numerical expressions or rewriting expressions containing variables in radical form.

> For any real number a and positive integers m and n with $n > 1$,
>
> $a^{m/n} = (\sqrt[n]{a})^m = \sqrt[n]{a^m}$

This new extension of our rational exponent notation is applied in the following example.

Example 2

Simplify each expression.

(a) $9^{3/2} = (\sqrt{9})^3$
$\phantom{9^{3/2}} = 3^3 = 27$

(b) $\left(\dfrac{16}{81}\right)^{3/4} = \left(\sqrt[4]{\dfrac{16}{81}}\right)^3$
$\phantom{\left(\dfrac{16}{81}\right)^{3/4}} = \left(\dfrac{2}{3}\right)^3 = \dfrac{8}{27}$

*A screen is used to indicate an expression that is being simplified.

(c) $(-8)^{2/3} = (\sqrt[3]{-8})^2$
$= (-2)^2 = 4$

This illustrates why we use $(\sqrt[n]{a})^m$ for $a^{m/n}$ when evaluating numerical expressions. The numbers involved will be smaller and easier to work with.

Note In (a) we could also have evaluated the expression as

$9^{3/2} = \sqrt{9^3} = \sqrt{729}$
$= 27$

CHECK YOURSELF 2

Simplify each expression.

1. $16^{3/4}$ **2.** $\left(\dfrac{8}{27}\right)^{2/3}$ **3.** $(-32)^{3/5}$

Now we want to extend our rational exponent notation. Using the definition of negative exponents, we can write

$a^{-m/n} = \dfrac{1}{a^{m/n}}$

The following example illustrates the use of negative rational exponents.

Example 3

Simplify each expression.

(a) $16^{-1/2} = \dfrac{1}{16^{1/2}} = \dfrac{1}{4}$

(b) $27^{-2/3} = \dfrac{1}{27^{2/3}} = \dfrac{1}{(\sqrt[3]{27})^2} = \dfrac{1}{3^2} = \dfrac{1}{9}$

CHECK YOURSELF 3

Simplify each expression.

1. $16^{-1/4}$ **2.** $81^{-3/4}$

Calculators can be used to evaluate expressions that contain rational exponents by using the $\boxed{y^x}$ key and the parentheses keys.

Example 4

Using a scientific calculator, evaluate each of the following. Round all answers to three decimal places.

(a) $45^{2/5}$

Enter 45 and press the $\boxed{y^x}$ key. Then use the following keystrokes:

$\boxed{(} \; 2 \; \boxed{\div} \; 5 \; \boxed{)}$

Press $\boxed{=}$, and the display will read 4.584426407. Rounded to three decimal places, the result is 4.584.

(b) $38^{-2/3}$

Enter 38 and press the $\boxed{y^x}$ key. Then use the following keystrokes:

The $\boxed{+/-}$ key changes the sign of the exponent to minus.

$\boxed{(} \; 2 \; \boxed{\div} \; 3 \; \boxed{+/-} \; \boxed{)}$

Press $\boxed{=}$, and the display will read 0.088473037. Rounded to three decimal places, the result is 0.088.

CHECK YOURSELF 4

Evaluate each of the following by using a scientific calculator. Round each answer to three decimal places.

1. $23^{3/5}$ **2.** $18^{-4/7}$

As we mentioned earlier, we assume that all our previous exponent properties will continue to hold for rational exponents. Those properties are restated here for reference.

PROPERTIES OF EXPONENTS

For any nonzero real numbers a and b and rational numbers m and n,

1. $a^m \cdot a^n = a^{m+n}$

2. $\dfrac{a^m}{a^n} = a^{m-n}$

3. $(a^m)^n = a^{mn}$

4. $(ab)^m = a^m b^m$

5. $\left(\dfrac{a}{b}\right)^m = \dfrac{a^m}{b^m}$

We restrict a and b to being nonnegative real numbers when m or n indicates an even root.

The following example illustrates the use of our extended properties to simplify expressions involving rational exponents. Here we assume that all variables represent positive real numbers.

Example 5

Simplify each expression.

Property 1—add the exponents.

(a) $x^{2/3} \cdot x^{1/2} = x^{2/3+1/2}$
$= x^{4/6+3/6} = x^{7/6}$

Property 2—subtract the exponents.

(b) $\dfrac{w^{3/4}}{w^{1/2}} = w^{3/4-1/2}$

$= w^{3/4-2/4} = w^{1/4}$

Property 3—multiply the exponents.

(c) $(a^{2/3})^{3/4} = a^{(2/3)(3/4)}$
$= a^{1/2}$

CHECK YOURSELF 5

Simplify each expression.

1. $z^{3/4} \cdot z^{1/2}$

2. $\dfrac{x^{5/6}}{x^{1/3}}$

3. $(b^{5/6})^{2/5}$

As you would expect from your previous experience with exponents, simplifying expressions often involves using several exponent properties.

Example 6

Simplify each expression.

(a) $(x^{2/3} \cdot y^{5/6})^{3/2}$
$= (x^{2/3})^{3/2} \cdot (y^{5/6})^{3/2}$ Property 4
$= x^{(2/3)(3/2)} \cdot y^{(5/6)(3/2)} = xy^{5/4}$ Property 3

(b) $\left(\dfrac{r^{-1/2}}{s^{1/3}}\right)^6 = \dfrac{(r^{-1/2})^6}{(s^{1/3})^6}$ Property 5

$= \dfrac{r^{-3}}{s^2} = \dfrac{1}{r^3 s^2}$ Property 3

We simplify *inside the parentheses* as the first step.

(c) $\left(\dfrac{4a^{-2/3} \cdot b^2}{a^{1/3} \cdot b^{-4}}\right)^{1/2} = \left(\dfrac{4b^2 \cdot b^4}{a^{1/3} \cdot a^{2/3}}\right)^{1/2} = \left(\dfrac{4b^6}{a}\right)^{1/2}$

$= \dfrac{(4b^6)^{1/2}}{a^{1/2}} = \dfrac{4^{1/2}(b^6)^{1/2}}{a^{1/2}}$

$= \dfrac{2b^3}{a^{1/2}}$

CHECK YOURSELF 6

Simplify each expression.

1. $(a^{3/4} \cdot b^{1/2})^{2/3}$

2. $\left(\dfrac{w^{1/2}}{z^{-1/4}}\right)^4$

3. $\left(\dfrac{8x^{-3/4}y}{x^{1/4} \cdot y^{-5}}\right)^{1/3}$

Note: Here we use $a^{m/n} = \sqrt[n]{a^m}$, which is generally the preferred form in this situation.

We can also use the relationships between rational exponents and radicals to write expressions involving rational exponents as radicals and vice versa.

Example 7

Write each expression in radical form.

(a) $a^{3/5} = \sqrt[5]{a^3}$

(b) $(mn)^{3/4} = \sqrt[4]{(mn)^3}$
$= \sqrt[4]{m^3 n^3}$

Note that the exponent applies *only* to the variable y.

(c) $2y^{5/6} = 2\sqrt[6]{y^5}$

Now the exponent applies to $2y$ because of the parentheses.

(d) $(2y)^{5/6} = \sqrt[6]{(2y)^5}$
$= \sqrt[6]{32y^5}$

CHECK YOURSELF 7

Write each expression in radical form.

1. $(ab)^{2/3}$ **2.** $3x^{3/4}$ **3.** $(3x)^{3/4}$

Example 8

Using rational exponents, write each expression and simplify.

(a) $\sqrt[3]{5x} = (5x)^{1/3}$

(b) $\sqrt{9a^2b^4} = (9a^2b^4)^{1/2}$
$= 9^{1/2}(a^2)^{1/2}(b^4)^{1/2} = 3ab^2$

(c) $\sqrt[4]{16w^{12}z^8} = (16w^{12}z^8)^{1/4}$
$= 16^{1/4}(w^{12})^{1/4}(z^8)^{1/4} = 2w^3z^2$

CHECK YOURSELF 8

Using rational exponents, write each expression and simplify.

1. $\sqrt{7a}$ **2.** $\sqrt[3]{27p^6q^9}$ **3.** $\sqrt[4]{81x^8y^{16}}$

CHECK YOURSELF ANSWERS

1. (1) 2; (2) -8; (3) 3.   **2.** (1) 8; (2) $\dfrac{4}{9}$; (3) -8.

3. (1) $\dfrac{1}{2}$; (2) $\dfrac{1}{27}$.   **4.** (1) 6.562; (2) 0.192.

5. (1) $z^{5/4}$; (2) $x^{1/2}$; (3) $b^{1/3}$.   **6.** (1) $a^{1/2}b^{1/3}$; (2) w^2z; (3) $\dfrac{2y^2}{x^{1/3}}$.

7. (1) $\sqrt[3]{a^2b^2}$; (2) $3\sqrt[4]{x^3}$; (3) $\sqrt[4]{27x^3}$.

8. (1) $(7a)^{1/2}$; (2) $3p^2q^3$; (3) $3x^2y^4$.

Name _____

Date _____

Exercises

ANSWERS

Build Your Skills

1. _____

Use the definition of $a^{1/n}$ to evaluate each of the following expressions.

2. _____

   1. $36^{1/2}$ **2.** $100^{1/2}$

3. _____

   3. $-25^{1/2}$ **4.** $(-64)^{1/2}$

4. _____

5. _____

   5. $(-49)^{1/2}$ **6.** $-49^{1/2}$

6. _____

   7. $27^{1/3}$ **8.** $(-64)^{1/3}$

7. _____

8. _____

   9. $81^{1/4}$ **10.** $-32^{1/5}$

9. _____

10. _____

   11. $\left(\dfrac{4}{9}\right)^{1/2}$ **12.** $\left(\dfrac{27}{8}\right)^{1/3}$

11. _____

12. _____

Use the definition of $a^{m/n}$ to evaluate each of the following expressions.

13. _____

   13. $27^{2/3}$ **14.** $16^{3/2}$

14. _____

   15. $(-8)^{4/3}$ **16.** $125^{2/3}$

15. _____

16. _____

   17. $32^{2/5}$ **18.** $-81^{3/4}$

17. _____

   19. $81^{3/2}$ **20.** $(-243)^{3/5}$

18. _____

19. _____

   21. $\left(\dfrac{8}{27}\right)^{2/3}$ **22.** $\left(\dfrac{9}{4}\right)^{3/2}$

20. _____

21. _____

22. _____

ANSWERS

Use the definition of $a^{-m/n}$ to evaluate each of the following expressions.

23. _____

24. _____

25. _____

26. _____

27. _____

28. _____

29. _____

30. _____

31. _____

32. _____

33. _____

34. _____

35. _____

36. _____

37. _____

38. _____

39. _____

40. _____

41. _____

42. _____

43. _____

44. _____

23. $25^{-1/2}$

24. $27^{-1/3}$

25. $81^{-1/4}$

26. $121^{-1/2}$

27. $9^{-3/2}$

28. $16^{-3/4}$

29. $64^{-5/6}$

30. $16^{-3/2}$

31. $\left(\dfrac{4}{25}\right)^{-1/2}$

32. $\left(\dfrac{27}{8}\right)^{-2/3}$

Use the properties of exponents to simplify each expression. Assume all variables represent positive real numbers.

33. $x^{1/2} \cdot x^{1/2}$

34. $a^{2/3} \cdot a^{1/3}$

35. $y^{3/5} \cdot y^{1/5}$

36. $m^{1/4} \cdot m^{5/4}$

37. $b^{2/3} \cdot b^{3/2}$

38. $p^{5/6} \cdot p^{2/3}$

39. $\dfrac{x^{2/3}}{x^{1/3}}$

40. $\dfrac{a^{5/6}}{a^{1/6}}$

41. $\dfrac{s^{7/5}}{s^{2/5}}$

42. $\dfrac{z^{9/2}}{z^{3/2}}$

43. $\dfrac{w^{5/4}}{w^{1/2}}$

44. $\dfrac{b^{7/6}}{b^{2/3}}$

ANSWERS

45. _____

46. _____

47. _____

48. _____

49. _____

50. _____

51. _____

52. _____

53. _____

54. _____

55. _____

56. _____

57. _____

58. _____

59. _____

60. _____

61. _____

62. _____

63. _____

64. _____

65. _____

66. _____

45. $(x^{3/4})^{4/3}$

46. $(y^{4/3})^{3/4}$

47. $(a^{2/5})^{3/2}$

48. $(p^{3/4})^{2/3}$

49. $(y^{-3/4})^8$

50. $(w^{-2/3})^6$

51. $(a^{2/3} \cdot b^{3/2})^6$

52. $(p^{3/4} \cdot q^{5/2})^4$

53. $(2x^{1/5} \cdot y^{3/5})^5$

54. $(3m^{3/4} \cdot n^{5/4})^4$

55. $(s^{3/4} \cdot t^{1/4})^{4/3}$

56. $(x^{5/2} \cdot y^{5/7})^{2/5}$

57. $(8p^{3/2} \cdot q^{5/2})^{2/3}$

58. $(16a^{1/3} \cdot b^{2/3})^{3/4}$

59. $(x^{3/5} \cdot y^{3/4} \cdot z^{3/2})^{2/3}$

60. $(p^{5/6} \cdot q^{2/3} \cdot r^{5/3})^{3/5}$

61. $\dfrac{a^{5/6} \cdot b^{3/4}}{a^{1/3} \cdot b^{1/2}}$

62. $\dfrac{x^{2/3} \cdot y^{3/4}}{x^{1/2} \cdot y^{1/2}}$

63. $\dfrac{(r^{-1} \cdot s^{1/2})^3}{r \cdot s^{-1/2}}$

64. $\dfrac{(w^{-2} \cdot z^{-1/4})^6}{w^{-8} z^{1/2}}$

65. $\left(\dfrac{x^{12}}{y^8}\right)^{1/4}$

66. $\left(\dfrac{p^9}{q^6}\right)^{1/3}$

ANSWERS

67. _____

68. _____

69. _____

70. _____

71. _____

72. _____

73. _____

74. _____

75. _____

76. _____

77. _____

78. _____

79. _____

80. _____

67. $\left(\dfrac{m^{-1/4}}{n^{1/2}} \right)^4$

68. $\left(\dfrac{r^{1/5}}{s^{-1/2}} \right)^{10}$

69. $\left(\dfrac{r^{-1/2} \cdot s^{3/4}}{t^{1/4}} \right)^4$

70. $\left(\dfrac{a^{1/3} \cdot b^{-1/6}}{c^{-1/6}} \right)^6$

71. $\left(\dfrac{8x^3 \cdot y^{-6}}{z^{-9}} \right)^{1/3}$

72. $\left(\dfrac{16p^{-4} \cdot q^6}{r^2} \right)^{-1/2}$

73. $\left(\dfrac{16m^{-3/5} \cdot n^2}{m^{1/5} \cdot n^{-2}} \right)^{1/4}$

74. $\left(\dfrac{27x^{5/6} \cdot y^{-4/3}}{x^{-7/6} \cdot y^{5/3}} \right)^{1/3}$

75. $\left(\dfrac{x^{3/2} \cdot y^{1/2}}{z^2} \right)^{1/2} \left(\dfrac{x^{3/4} \cdot y^{3/2}}{z^{-3}} \right)^{1/3}$

76. $\left(\dfrac{p^{1/2} \cdot q^{4/3}}{r^{-4}} \right)^{3/4} \left(\dfrac{p^{15/8} \cdot q^{-3}}{r^6} \right)^{1/3}$

Write each of the following expressions in radical form. Do not simplify.

77. $a^{3/4}$

78. $m^{5/6}$

79. $2x^{2/3}$

80. $3m^{-2/5}$

211

ANSWERS

81. _____

82. _____

83. _____

84. _____

85. _____

86. _____

87. _____

88. _____

89. _____

90. _____

91. _____

92. _____

93. _____

94. _____

a. _____

b. _____

c. _____

d. _____

e. _____

f. _____

g. _____

h. _____

81. $3x^{2/5}$

83. $(3x)^{2/5}$

82. $2y^{-3/4}$

84. $(2y)^{-3/4}$

Write each of the following expressions, using rational exponents, and simplify where necessary.

85. $\sqrt{7a}$

86. $\sqrt{25w^4}$

87. $\sqrt[3]{8m^6n^9}$

88. $\sqrt[5]{32r^{10}s^{13}}$

Evaluate each of the following, using a scientific calculator. Round each answer to three decimal places.

89. $46^{3/5}$

90. $23^{2/7}$

91. $12^{-2/5}$

92. $36^{-3/4}$

93. $23^{3/8}$

94. $17^{5/6}$

Skillscan (Multiplication of Polynomials and Special Products)

Multiply.

a. $2x(3 + 5x)$

b. $(-3x)(2 - 5x)$

c. $(3 + 2x)(3 - x)$

d. $(3 - 4w)(5 - 2w)$

e. $(7 - 2a)(7 + 2a)$

f. $(5 + 3m)(5 - 3m)$

g. $(5 + y)^2$

h. $(4 - 3r)^2$

ANSWERS

1. 6 **3.** -5 **5.** Not a real number **7.** 3 **9.** 3 **11.** $\frac{2}{3}$ **13.** 9 **15.** 16

17. 4 **19.** 729 **21.** $\frac{4}{9}$ **23.** $\frac{1}{5}$ **25.** $\frac{1}{3}$ **27.** $\frac{1}{27}$ **29.** $\frac{1}{32}$ **31.** $\frac{5}{2}$ **33.** x

35. $y^{4/5}$ **37.** $b^{13/6}$ **39.** $x^{1/3}$ **41.** s **43.** $w^{3/4}$ **45.** x **47.** $a^{3/5}$ **49.** $\frac{1}{y^6}$

51. a^4b^9 **53.** $32xy^3$ **55.** $st^{1/3}$ **57.** $4pq^{5/3}$ **59.** $x^{2/5}y^{1/2}z$ **61.** $a^{1/2}b^{1/4}$ **63.** $\frac{s^2}{r^4}$

65. $\frac{x^3}{y^2}$ **67.** $\frac{1}{mn^2}$ **69.** $\frac{s^3}{r^2t}$ **71.** $\frac{2xz^3}{y^2}$ **73.** $\frac{2n}{m^{1/5}}$ **75.** $xy^{3/4}$ **77.** $\sqrt[4]{a^3}$

79. $2\sqrt[3]{x^2}$ **81.** $3\sqrt[5]{x^2}$ **83.** $\sqrt[5]{9x^2}$ **85.** $(7a)^{1/2}$ **87.** $2m^2n^3$ **89.** 9.946 **91.** 0.370

93. 3.241 **a.** $6x + 10x^2$ **b.** $-6x + 15x^2$ **c.** $9 + 3x - 2x^2$ **d.** $15 - 26w + 8w^2$

e. $49 - 4a^2$ **f.** $25 - 9m^2$ **g.** $25 + 10y + y^2$ **h.** $16 - 24r + 9r^2$

Polynomials—Addition and Subtraction

OBJECTIVES

1. To use the language of polynomials
2. To add and subtract polynomials

Much of our work with the properties of real numbers can be extended to an important class of algebraic expressions called *polynomials*.

First, we offer some definitions.

A *term* is an indicated product or quotient of numbers and one or more variable factors.

Example 1

$5x^2$, 7, $4xy$, and $\dfrac{9}{x}$ are all terms. $3x^2 + 2y$ is *not* a term; it is a sum of two terms, $3x^2$ and $2y$.

CHECK YOURSELF 1

Which of the following are terms?

1. $4x^3$ **2.** $\dfrac{8}{x}$ **3.** $2 - 3x$ **4.** $5x^2y^2$

Some terms are given special names. For instance,

A *monomial* is a term in which only *whole numbers* can appear as exponents.

The set of *whole numbers* consists of the natural numbers and 0; so in a monomial, the allowable exponents are 0, 1, 2, 3, and so on.

Now $4x$, -12, $3ab$, and $5m^3n$ are all monomials. But $\dfrac{9}{x}$ and $5\sqrt{m}$ are *not* monomials because they do not involve whole number exponents $\left(\text{here the exponents are } -1 \text{ and } \dfrac{1}{2}\right)$.

We often refer to the numerical coefficients as the *coefficients* for convenience.

The numerical factor in each monomial is called the *numerical coefficient*. For the monomials in the preceding paragraph, 4, -12, 3, and 5 are the numerical coefficients.

A polynomial is then a sum of *several terms* which are monomials. That's what the prefix "poly" means.

> A *polynomial* is a monomial or any finite sum (or difference) of monomials.

The expressions

$$5x^2 + 2x \qquad 3m^3 \qquad \text{and} \qquad 5a^2 + 3ab - 2b^2 + 4$$

are all polynomials.

Certain polynomials occur often enough that they are given special names according to the number of terms that they have.

The prefix "mono" means 1, "bi" means 2, and "tri" means 3.

A polynomial with one term is a *monomial*. A polynomial with two terms is a *binomial*. A polynomial with three terms is called a *trinomial*.

Example 2

Which of the following are polynomials? Classify the polynomials as monomial, binomial, or trinomial.

(a) $5x^2y$
(b) $3m + 5n$
(c) $4a^3 + 3a - 2$
(d) $5y^2 - \dfrac{2}{x}$

Solution

(a) $5x^2y$ is a monomial.
(b) $3m + 5n$ is a binomial.
(c) $4a^3 + 3a - 2$ trinomial.

Remember that

$$\frac{1}{x} = x^{-1}$$

(d) $5y^2 - \dfrac{2}{x}$ is not a polynomial since the exponent on x is -1.

CHECK YOURSELF 2

Which of the following are polynomials? Classify the polynomials as monomials, binomials, or trinomials.

1. $5x^2 - 6x$
2. $8x^5$
3. $5x^3 - 3xy + 7y^2$
4. $9x - \dfrac{3}{x}$

It is also useful to classify polynomials by their *degree*.

> The *degree* of a monomial is the sum of the exponents of the variable factors.

Example 3

(a) $5x^2$ has degree 2.
(b) $7n^5$ has degree 5.
(c) $4a^2b^4$ has degree 6. (The sum of the powers, 2 and 4, is 6.)
(d) 9 has degree 0 (because $9 = 9 \cdot 1 = 9x^0$).

CHECK YOURSELF 3

Give the degree of each monomial.

1. $4x^2$ **2.** $7x^3y^2$ **3.** $8p^2s$ **4.** 5

> The *degree* of a polynomial is that of the term with the highest degree.

Example 4

(a) $7x^3 - 5x^2 + 5$ has degree 3.
(b) $5y^7 - 3y^2 + 5y - 7$ has degree 7.
(c) $4a^2b^3 - 5ab^2$ has degree 5.

Polynomials such as those in Example 4a and b are called *polynomials in one variable,* and they are usually written in descending form so that the power of the variable decreases from left to right. In that case, the coefficient of the first term is called the *leading coefficient.*

CHECK YOURSELF 4

Give the degree of each polynomial. For those polynomials in one variable, write in descending form and give the leading coefficient.

1. $7x^4 - 5xy + 2$ **2.** 5
3. $4x^2 - 7x^3 - 8x + 5$

Before we consider the operations of addition and subtraction of polynomials, let's first review two concepts. Two terms that have exactly the same variable or literal factors are called *like* terms.

Example 5

Identify whether each group of terms are like terms.

(a) $5x$ and $-3x$ are like terms.
(b) $4x^2y$ and $-x^2y$ are like terms.
(c) $-2ab^2$ and $5a^2b$ are not like terms.

CHECK YOURSELF 5

Identify whether each pair of terms are like terms.

1. $2ab$ and $-7ab$ **2.** $3xy$ and $-2xy^2$ **3.** $-x^2y^3$ and $3x^2y^3$

Recall the distributive property from our coverage of the real numbers.

> **DISTRIBUTIVE PROPERTY**
>
> For any real numbers a, b, and c,
>
> $a(b + c) = ab + ac$

The distributive property also applies to polynomials. Like terms can always be combined by applying the distributive property. That property can also be extended to combine more than two like terms.

Example 6*

Combine like terms.

(a) $7x + 5x = (7 + 5)x = 12x$

(b) $4a^2b - 2a^2b = (4 - 2)a^2b = 2a^2b$

(c) $9m^3 - 5m^3 + 7m^3 = (9 - 5 + 7)m^3 = 11m^3$

CHECK YOURSELF 6

Combine like terms.

1. $7p^2q - 8p^2q$ **2.** $3xy^3 + 5xy^3 - 7xy^3$

Example 7

(a) Add $5x^2 + 3x + 7$ and $4x^2 - 5x - 2$.

Using a horizontal format, write

$(5x^2 + 3x + 7) + (4x^2 - 5x - 2)$

$= (5x^2 + 4x^2) + (3x - 5x) + (7 - 2)$ Commutative and associative properties

$= 9x^2 - 2x + 5$

The second step of regrouping like terms will become unnecessary with practice. You can learn to mentally combine like terms from the original problem.

*A screen is used to indicate an expression that is being simplified.

(b) Add $4x^3 - 2x$ and $3x^2 + 5x$.

Write

$$(4x^3 - 2x) + (3x^2 + 5x) = 4x^3 + 3x^2 + (-2x + 5x)$$
$$= 4x^3 + 3x^2 + 3x$$

(c) Add $x^3 + 2x^2y - 3xy^2 + y^3$ and $4x^3 - 2x^2y - y^3$.

Write

$$(x^3 + 2x^2y - 3xy^2 + y^3) + (4x^3 - 2x^2y - y^3)$$
$$= (x^3 + 4x^3) + (2x^2y - 2x^2y) + (-3xy^2) + (y^3 - y^3)$$
$$= 5x^3 - 3xy^2$$

CHECK YOURSELF 7

Add each of the following polynomials.

1. $5x^2 - 3x + 4$ and $-7x^2 + 3x - 4$ **2.** $5x^3 - 4x$ and $8x^2 + 6x$
3. $5x^3 - 3xy^2 + 2x^2y - y^3$ and $-3x^3 - xy^2 - 2x^2y + y^3$

Subtraction of polynomials proceeds in a similar fashion. We view the subtraction of a quantity as adding the opposite of that quantity.

For polynomials, we use the facts that:

Both statements are just applications of the distributive property. This shows us that the *opposite* of $a + b$ is $-a - b$ and the *opposite of a − b* is $-a + b$.

DISTRIBUTION OF THE NEGATIVE

$-(a + b) = -a - b$

and

$-(a - b) = -a + b$

We can now go on to subtracting polynomials.

Example 8

(a) Subtract $4x^2 + 5x$ from $7x^2 - 2x$.

Using the horizontal format, write

$$(7x^2 - 2x) - (4x^2 + 5x)$$
$$= 7x^2 - 2x - 4x^2 - 5x$$

Note the sign changes.

$$= 3x^2 - 7x$$

The second polynomial is subtracted from the first.

(b) Find the difference of $4y^2 - 2y + 3$ and $5y^2 - 2y + 7$.

Write

$(4y^2 - 2y + 3) - (5y^2 - 2y + 7)$
$= 4y^2 - 2y + 3 - 5y^2 + 2y - 7$ Note the sign changes.

$= -y^2 - 4$

(c) Find the difference of $6x^3y - 3xy^2 + 5x^2y^2$ and $2x^3y - 2xy^2 - 3x^2y^2$.

Write

$(6x^3y - 3xy^2 + 5x^2y^2) - (2x^3y - 2xy^2 - 3x^2y^2)$
$= 6x^3y - 3xy^2 + 5x^2y^2 - 2x^3y + 2xy^2 + 3x^2y^2$
$= 4x^3y - xy^2 + 8xy^2$

CHECK YOURSELF 8

1. Subtract $3a^2 - 5a$ from $2a^2 + 7a$.
2. Find the difference of $8y^2 - 6y - 10$ and $-7y^2 - 6y + 8$.

We have used parentheses as signs of grouping in subtracting polynomials. Other signs of grouping—brackets [ ] and braces { }—are also used in algebra. If one set of grouping symbols is contained within another, we use our earlier rules to remove the *innermost grouping symbol first*. Then work outward.

Example 9

(a) Simplify $3x - 3[5 - (2x - 4)]$.

        Remove the parentheses first.
$3x - 3[5 - (2x - 4)]$
$= 3x - 3[5 - 2x + 4]$ Combine the like terms inside the brackets.
$= 3x - 3[-2x + 9]$ Distribute -3.
$= 3x + 6x - 27$
$= 9x - 27$

(b) Simplify $(4x + 3) - [(2x + 3) - (4x - 7)]$.

Both signs inside the brackets change.

$(4x + 3) - [(2x + 3) - (4x - 7)]$ Remove the parentheses *inside* the brackets.
$= (4x + 3) - [2x + 3 - 4x + 7] = (4x + 3) - [-2x + 10]$
$= 4x + 3 + 2x - 10$
$= 6x - 7$

CHECK YOURSELF 9

Simplify $(7a - b) - [-(3a + 2b) - (5a - 3b)]$.

Many applications of polynomials involve finding the value of a polynomial for a given value of the variable. This is called *evaluating* the polynomial.

Example 10

(*a*) Find the value of $3x^3 - 2x^2 + 5x - 6$ when $x = 2$.

Start by substituting 2 for x in the given polynomial. When $x = 2$, we have

Keep in mind the order of operations. Evaluate the powers, multiply, then add or subtract.

$$
\begin{aligned}
3(2)^3 - 2(2)^2 + 5(2) - 6 &= 3(8) - 2(4) + 5(2) - 6 \\
&= 24 - 8 + 10 - 6 \\
&= 20
\end{aligned}
$$

(*b*) Evaluate the polynomial given in part *a* if $x = -3$.

When $x = -3$, the polynomial becomes

<CAUTION>

Be careful of the signs here!

$(-3)^3 = (-3)(-3)(-3)$
$ = -27$
$(-3)^2 = (-3)(-3) = 9$

$$
\begin{aligned}
3(-3)^3 - 2(-3)^2 + 5(-3) - 6 &= 3(-27) - 2(9) + 5(-3) - 6 \\
&= -81 - 18 - 15 - 6 \\
&= -120
\end{aligned}
$$

CHECK YOURSELF 10

Evaluate the polynomial (1) for $x = 3$ and (2) for $x = -2$.

$$2x^3 - 6x^2 + 7x - 8$$

Some Special Notation

Suppose we want to refer to a particular polynomial in x. It is useful in algebra to use letters to name the polynomial in the following fashion:

$P(x)$ is read "P of x," not "P times x."

$$P(x) = x^3 - 4x^2 + 5x - 6$$

or

$$Q(x) = 4x^4 - 7x^3 + 9$$

This notation allows us a very useful shorthand to indicate the numerical value of the polynomial for a given value of the variable. For instance, suppose we want the value of the polynomial $P(x)$ when x has the value of 2. We can simply write

Simply replace x with 2 in $P(x)$ to find $P(2)$—this is read "P of 2."

$$P(2) = (2)^3 - 4(2)^2 + 5(2) - 6$$
$$= 8 - 4(4) + 5(2) - 6$$
$$= 8 - 16 + 10 - 6$$
$$= -4$$

The statement

$P(2) = -4$

says that the value of the polynomial P, when $x = 2$, is -4.

To find the value of $Q(x)$ when $x = -2$, we write

$$Q(-2) = 4(-2)^4 - 7(-2)^3 + 9$$
$$= 4(16) - 7(-8) + 9$$
$$= 64 + 56 + 9$$
$$= 129$$

Example 11

If $T(x) = -3x^3 + 2x^2 - 3x + 8$, find $T(-1)$.

$$T(-1) = -3(-1)^3 + 2(-1)^2 - 3(-1) + 8$$
$$= -3(-1) + 2(1) - 3(-1) + 8$$
$$= 3 + 2 + 3 + 8$$
$$= 16$$

CHECK YOURSELF 11

If $R(x) = 2x^3 - 4x^2 + 7x - 7$, find each of the following.

1. $R(3)$ **2.** $R(-3)$

CHECK YOURSELF ANSWERS

1. (1) Term; (2) term; (3) not a term; (4) term.
2. Binomial; (2) monomial; (3) trinomial; (4) not a polynomial.
3. (1) 2; (2) 5; (3) 3; (4) 0.
4. (1) 4; (2) 0; (3) 3.
5. (1) Like terms; (2) not like terms; (3) like terms.
6. (1) $-p^2q$; (2) xy^3.
7. (1) $-2x^2$; (2) $5x^3 + 8x^2 + 2x$; (3) $2x^3 - 4xy^2$.
8. (1) $-a^2 + 12a$; (2) $15y^2 - 18$.
9. $15a - 2b$.
10. (1) 13; (2) -62.
11. (1) 32; (2) -118.

Name _____

Date _____

Exercises

ANSWERS

1. _____

2. _____

3. _____

4. _____

5. _____

6. _____

7. _____

8. _____

9. _____

10. _____

11. _____

12. _____

13. _____

14. _____

15. _____

16. _____

17. _____

18. _____

19. _____

20. _____

21. _____

22. _____

23. _____

24. _____

25. _____

26. _____

Build Your Skills

Identify each of the following as a monomial, binomial, or trinomial. Give the degree of each polynomial.

1. $4x - 3$

2. -5

3. $4y^3$

4. $5x^7 - 3$

5. $4x^6 + 2x - 5$

6. $w^2 - 2w^4 + 3$

7. $5 - 2a$

8. x^2y^3z

9. $2m^2n^3 + 3m^2n$

10. $5a^3b - 3a^2b + 7ab$

Add each of the following polynomials.

11. $5a - 3$ and $4a + 7$

12. $7x^2 + 3x$ and $5x^2 - 7x$

13. $5m^2 + 3mn$ and $4mn + 2n^2$

14. $9x^2y - 2xy$ and $3xy + 5xy^2$

15. $8x^2 - 3xy + 5y^2$ and $9x^2 - 5xy - 8y^2$

16. $6r^2 - 5rs - 2s^2$ and $-8r^2 + 6rs + 2s^2$

17. $8x - 3$, $4x - 3$, and $-2x + 5$

18. $-3a^2 + 4a + 2$, $5a - 2$, and $-7a^2 - 5$

Subtract each of the following polynomials.

19. $5x - 3$ from $7x + 10$

20. $8a - 7$ from $5a - 12$

21. $-5y^2 - 2y$ from $7y^2 + 3y$

22. $-3r^2 - 3r$ from $-10r^2 + 3r$

23. $5x^2 - 3x - 2$ from $8x^2 - 5x - 7$

24. $7y^3 - 3y^2 + 7y$ from $5y^3 - 2y^2 - 8y$

25. $8a^2 - 7a$ from $5a^2 + 5$

26. $9z^2 - 3$ from $5z^2 - 7z$

ANSWERS

Perform the indicated operations.

27. _____

28. _____

29. _____

30. _____

31. _____

32. _____

33. _____

34. _____

35. _____

36. _____

37. _____

38. _____

39. _____

40. _____

41. _____

42. _____

43. _____

44. _____

45. _____

46. _____

47. _____

48. _____

49. _____

50. _____

51. _____

52. _____

27. $(2x - 3) + (4x - 7) - (2x - 3)$

28. $(5a - 2) - (2a + 3) + (7a - 7)$

29. $(5x^2 - 2x + 7) - (2x^2 + 3x + 1) - (4x^2 + 2x + 3)$

30. $(8m^2 - 8m + 5) + (3m^2 + 2m - 7) - (m^2 - 6m + 4)$

31. $(8x^2 - 3) + (5x^2 + 7x) - (7x - 8)$

32. $(9r^2 + 7) - (5r^2 - 8r) - (4r^2 + 3)$

Simplify each of the following expressions by removing the innermost grouping symbol and working outward.

33. $x - [5x - (x - 3)]$

34. $m^2 - [7m^2 - (m^2 + 7)]$

35. $(2x - 3) - [x - (2x + 7)]$

36. $(3y^2 + 5y) - [y^2 - (2y^2 - 3y)]$

37. $2x - \{3x + 2[x - 2(x - 3)]\}$

38. $3r - \{5r - 2[r - 3(r + 4)]\}$

Evaluate each polynomial for the indicated value of the variable.

39. $4x^2 - 2x - 5$ for $x = 5$

40. $8x^2 + 4x + 2$ for $x = -3$

41. $5x^2 - 6x - 2$ for $x = 4$

42. $2x^2 - 4x + 5$ for $x = -2$

43. $3x^3 - 7x^2 + 6x - 8$ for $x = 3$

44. $2x^3 - 5x^2 - 3x + 8$ for $x = -3$

45. $x^3 - 5x^2 + 7$ for $x = 2$

46. $x^4 + 4x^3 + 3$ for $x = -2$

If $P(x) = 3x^3 - 2x^2 + 5x - 3$ and $Q(x) = -x^2 + x - 2$, find the following.

47. $P(2)$

48. $P(-3)$

49. $P(0)$

50. $Q(1)$

51. $Q(3)$

52. $Q(-2)$

ANSWERS

a. ________

b. ________

c. ________

d. ________

e. ________

f. ________

g. ________

h. ________

Skillscan (Integral Exponents and Scientific Notation)

Perform the indicated operations.

a. $(2x^3)(3x^2)$

b. $(-3y^3)(2y^5)$

c. $(4m^2n^3)(8mn^2)$

d. $(-3a^3b^3)(-7a^2b^5)$

e. $\dfrac{15w^3}{5w}$

f. $\dfrac{-24x^5}{3x^4}$

g. $\dfrac{30x^3y^5}{-6x^2y}$

h. $\dfrac{49p^5q^2}{7p^4q}$

ANSWERS

1. Binomial, 1 **3.** Monomial, 3 **5.** Trinomial, 6 **7.** Binomial, 1 **9.** Binomial, 5 **11.** $9a + 4$ **13.** $5m^2 + 7mn + 2n^2$ **15.** $17x^2 - 8xy - 3y^2$ **17.** $10x - 1$ **19.** $2x + 13$ **21.** $12y^2 + 5y$ **23.** $3x^2 - 2x - 5$ **25.** $-3a^2 + 7a + 5$ **27.** $4x - 7$ **29.** $-x^2 - 7x + 3$ **31.** $13x^2 + 5$ **33.** $-3x - 3$ **35.** $3x + 4$ **37.** $x - 12$ **39.** 85 **41.** 54 **43.** 28 **45.** -5 **47.** 23 **49.** -3 **a.** $6x^5$ **b.** $-6y^8$ **c.** $32m^3n^5$ **d.** $21a^5b^8$ **e.** $3w^2$ **f.** $-8x$ **g.** $-5xy^4$ **h.** $7pq$

Multiplication of Polynomials and Special Products

OBJECTIVES
1. To multiply polynomials
2. To square a binomial
3. To find a product of binomials as a difference of squares

In our coverage of integral exponents and scientific notation, we state the first exponent law and use that law to multiply monomials.

Example 1*

Remember: $a^m a^n = a^{m+n}$

Multiply.

Note the use of the commutative and associative properties to "regroup" and "reorder" the factors.

$$(8x^2y)(4x^3y^4) = (8 \cdot 4)(x^{2+3})(y^{1+4})$$

Add exponents.

Multiply.

$$= 32x^5y^5$$

CHECK YOURSELF 1

Multiply.

1. $(4a^3b)(9a^3b^2)$ **2.** $(-5m^3n)(7mn^5)$

We want now to extend the process to multiplying other polynomials. The distributive property is the key. The simplest case is the product of a monomial and a polynomial.

Example 2

Multiply $3x^2$ and $5x^3 - 3x^2 + 4$.

$$3x^2(5x^3 - 3x^2 + 4)$$

Now distribute $3x^2$ over the terms of the trinomial:

$$3x^2(5x^3 - 3x^2 + 4)$$
$$= (3x^2)(5x^3) + (3x^2)(-3x^2) + (3x^2)(4)$$
$$= 15x^5 - 9x^4 + 12x^2$$

*A screen is used to indicate an expression that is being simplified.

CHECK YOURSELF 2

Multiply.

1. $4a^3(2a^2 - 3a)$ **2.** $-5x^2(x^4 + 2x + 3)$

The distributive property is also used to multiply a polynomial by a polynomial. To consider the patterns, let's start with the product of two binomials.

Example 3

Multiply $x + 3$ and $2x + 5$.

$(x + 3)(2x + 5)$

We distribute $x + 3$ over the sum $2x + 5$. So

$(x + 3)(2x + 5)$

Apply the distributive property *again*.

$= (x + 3)(2x) + (x + 3)(5)$
$= (x)(2x) + (3)(2x) + (x)(5) + (3)(5)$
$= 2x^2 + 6x + 5x + 15$
$= 2x^2 + 11x + 15$

Notice that this ensures that each term in the first polynomial is multiplied by each term in the second polynomial.

CHECK YOURSELF 3

Use the distributive property to multiply.

$(2x - 4)(3x + 7)$

Finding the product of two binomials is one of the most common forms of multiplication in algebra. Fortunately a convenient pattern emerges that will allow us to write these products directly. Let's consider another product.

We are given the product

$(3x + 2)(2x - 7)$

This time we distribute $2x - 7$ over the sum $3x + 2$:

The second factor is being distributed over the first.

$$(3x + 2)(2x - 7)$$
$$= 3x(2x - 7) + 2(2x - 7)$$
$$= (3x)(2x) + (3x)(-7) + (2)(2x) + (2)(-7)$$
$$= 6x^2 - 21x + 4x - 14$$

Before we combine the second and third terms, let's look at the process in more detail.

1. $6x^2$ is the product of the *first* terms of the binomials:

$$(3x)(2x) = 6x^2$$
$$(3x + 2)(2x - 7)$$

2. $-21x$ is the product of the *outer* terms of the binomials:

$$(3x)(-7) = -21x$$
$$(3x + 2)(2x - 7)$$

3. $4x$ is the product of the *inner* terms of the binomials:

$$(2)(2x) = 4x$$
$$(3x + 2)(2x - 7)$$

4. -14 is the product of the *last* terms of the binomials:

$$(2)(-7) = -14$$
$$(3x + 2)(2x - 7)$$

So $(3x + 2)(2x - 7)$ is

$$6x^2 - 21x + 4x - 14 \qquad \text{or} \qquad 6x^2 - 17x - 14$$

Of course, it is called FOIL to help you remember the pattern: First, Outer, Inner, Last.

This shortened process is called the *FOIL method* for multiplying binomials, and it should allow you to find such products quickly and easily.

Example 4

Use the FOIL method to multiply the binomials.

(*a*) $(2x - 3)(5x + 2)$
$$= 10x^2 + 4x - 15x - 6$$
$$\quad\ \ \text{F} \quad\ \text{O} \quad\ \text{I} \quad\ \text{L}$$
$$= 10x^2 - 11x - 6$$

(*b*) $(3m - 7n)(5m - 9n)$
$$= 15m^2 - 27mn - 35mn + 63n^2$$
$$\quad\ \ \text{F} \quad\ \ \text{O} \quad\ \ \ \text{I} \quad\ \ \ \text{L}$$
$$= 15m^2 - 62mn + 63n^2$$

When possible, you can combine the *outer* and *inner* terms mentally and write the product directly.

(c) $(8a^3 - b)(3a^3 + 2b)$

$\quad = 24a^6 + 16a^3b - 3a^3b - 2b^2$

$\quad = 24a^6 + 13a^3b - 2b^2$

Here the outer and inner terms *cannot* be combined.

(d) $(5x^2 - y)(3x + 2y^2)$

$\quad = 15x^3 + 10x^2y^2 - 3xy - 2y^3$

CHECK YOURSELF 4

Use the FOIL method to multiply.

1. $(5x - 3y)(3x + 7y)$

2. $(5r^2 + 2s)(3r + s^2)$

Certain products occur frequently enough in algebra that it is worth learning special formulas for dealing with them. Consider these products of two equal binomial factors.

$a^2 + 2ab + b^2$ and
$a^2 - 2ab + b^2$

are called *perfect-square trinomials*.

$(a + b)^2 = (a + b)(a + b)$

$\quad = a^2 + 2ab + b^2 \qquad\qquad (1)$

$(a - b)^2 = (a - b)(a - b)$

$\quad = a^2 - 2ab + b^2 \qquad\qquad (2)$

We can summarize these statements as follows:

SQUARING A BINOMIAL

The square of a binomial is the sum of (1) the square of the first term, (2) twice the product of the two terms, and (3) the square of the last term.

$(a + b)^2 = a^2 + 2ab + b^2$

and

$(a - b)^2 = a^2 - 2ab + b^2$

Example 5

Find each of the following binomial squares.

Be sure to write out the expansion in detail.

(a) $(x + 5)^2 = x^2 + 2(x)(5) + 5^2$

Square of first term   Twice the product of the two terms   Square of last term

$\quad = x^2 + 10x + 25$

(b) $(2a - 7)^2 = (2a)^2 - 2(2a)(7) + (-7)^2$
$$= 4a^2 - 28a + 49$$

<CAUTION>

Be Careful! A very common mistake in squaring binomials is to forget the middle term!

$(y + 7)^2$ is not equal to $y^2 + (7)^2$

The correct square is $y^2 + 14y + 49$.

$(b - 6)^2$ is not equal to $b^2 - (6)^2$

The correct square is $b^2 - 12b + 36$. The square of a binomial is *always* a trinomial.

CHECK YOURSELF 5

Find each of the following binomial squares.

1. $(x + 8)^2$ **2.** $(3x - 5)^2$

Another special product involves binomials that differ only in sign. It will be extremely important in your work on factoring. Consider the following:

$(a + b)(a - b) = a^2 - ab + ab + b^2$
$$= a^2 - b^2$$

> **PRODUCT OF BINOMIALS DIFFERING IN SIGN**
>
> $(a + b)(a - b) = a^2 - b^2$
>
> In words, the product of two binomials that differ only in the signs of their second terms is the difference of the squares of the two terms of the binomials.

Example 6

Multiply.

<CAUTION>

The entire term $2x$ is squared, not just the x.

(a) $(x - 3)(x + 3) = x^2 - (3)^2$
$$= x^2 - 9$$

(b) $(2x - 3y)(2x + 3y) = (2x)^2 - (3y)^2$
$$= 4x^2 - 9y^2$$

(c) $(5a + 4b^2)(5a - 4b^2) = (5a)^2 - (4b)^2$
$$= 25a^2 - 16b^2$$

CHECK YOURSELF 6

Find each of the following products.

1. $(y + 5)(y - 5)$ **2.** $(2x - 3)(2x + 3)$
3. $(4r + 5s^2)(4r - 5s^2)$

Multiplication of binomials is almost always done by the FOIL method or by one of our special product formulas. However, if one (or both) of the factors involves three or more terms, it is often easier to use a vertical format similar to that used in the multiplication of whole numbers. The following example illustrates.

This format ensures that each term of one polynomial multiplies each term of the other.

Example 7

Multiply $3x^3 - 2x^2 + 5$ and $3x + 2$.

Multiply each term of $3x^3 - 2x^2 + 5$ by 2.

Step 1
$$
\begin{array}{r}
3x^3 - 2x^2 + 5 \\
3x + 2 \\
\hline
6x^3 - 4x^2 + 10
\end{array}
$$

Multiply each term of $3x^3 - 2x^2 + 5$ by $3x$.

Note how we align like terms in the partial products.

Step 2
$$
\begin{array}{r}
3x^3 - 2x^2 + 5 \\
3x + 2 \\
\hline
6x^3 - 4x^2 + 10 \\
9x^4 - 6x^3 + 15x
\end{array}
$$

Add the partial products.

Step 3
$$
\begin{array}{r}
3x^3 - 2x^2 + 5 \\
3x + 2 \\
\hline
6x^3 - 4x^2 + 10 \\
9x^4 - 6x^3 + 15x \\
\hline
9x^4 - 4x^2 + 15x + 10
\end{array}
$$

CHECK YOURSELF 7

Find the following product, using the vertical method.

$$(4x^3 - 6x + 7)(3x - 2)$$

A horizontal approach to the multiplication of Example 7 is also possible by the distributive property. As we see below, we distribute $3x$ over the trinomial and then the 2.

Example 8

Multiply $(3x + 2)(3x^3 - 2x^2 + 5)$, using a horizontal format.

Again this ensures that each term of one polynomial multiplies each term of the other.

Step 1

$$(3x + 2)(3x^3 - 2x^2 + 5)$$

Step 2

$$= \underbrace{9x^4 - 6x^3 + 15x}_{\text{Step 1}} + \underbrace{6x^3 - 4x^2 + 10}_{\text{Step 2}}$$

Combine like terms, and write the product in descending form.

$$= 9x^4 - 4x^2 + 15x + 10$$

CHECK YOURSELF 8

Find the product of Check Yourself 7, using a horizontal format.

Multiplication sometimes involves the product of more than two polynomials. In such cases, the associative property of multiplication allows us to choose the order of multiplication that we find easiest. Generally we choose to start with the product of binomials. The following example illustrates.

Example 9

Find the products.

Find the product $(x + 3)(x - 3)$. Then distribute x as the last step.

(a) $x(x + 3)(x - 3) = x(x^2 - 9)$
$$= x^3 - 9x$$

Find the product of the binomials.

Distribute $2x$.

(b) $2x(x + 3)(2x - 1) = 2x(2x^2 + 5x - 3)$
$$= 4x^3 + 10x^2 - 6x$$

CHECK YOURSELF 9

Find each of the following products.

1. $m(2m + 3)(2m - 3)$ **2.** $3a(2a + 5)(a - 3)$

CHECK YOURSELF ANSWERS

1. (1) $36a^6b^3$; (2) $-35m^4n^6$.

2. (1) $8a^5 - 12a^4$; (2) $-5x^6 - 10x^3 - 15x^2$.

3. $6x^2 + 2x - 28$.

4. (1) $15x^2 + 26xy - 21y^2$; (2) $15r^3 + 5r^2s^2 + 6rs + 2s^3$.

5. (1) $x^2 + 16x + 64$; (2) $9x^2 - 30x + 25$.

6. (1) $y^2 - 25$; (2) $4x^2 - 9$; (3) $16r^2 - 25s^4$.

7. $12x^4 - 8x^3 - 18x^2 + 33x - 14$.

8. $12x^4 - 8x^3 - 18x^2 + 33x - 14$.

9. (1) $4m^3 - 9m$; (2) $6a^3 - 3a^2 - 45a$.

Name _____

Date _____

Exercises

ANSWERS

Build Your Skills

1. _____

Multiply each of the following polynomials.

2. _____

1. $(4x)(5y)$

2. $(-3m)(5n)$

3. _____

3. $(6x^2)(-3x^3)$

4. $(5y^4)(3y^2)$

4. _____

5. $(5r^2s)(6r^3s^4)$

6. $(-8a^2b^5)(-3a^3b^2)$

5. _____

6. _____

7. $3x(2x^2 - 3x)$

8. $-5c(2c^2 - d^2)$

7. _____

9. $5a^2(a^2 - 3a + 1)$

10. $3p^2(2p^3 + 5p^2 - p)$

8. _____

11. $5x^2y^3(x^2 - 3xy + y^2)$

12. $4m^3n(8m^2n - 2mn + 5mn^2)$

9. _____

10. _____

13. $-2ab(a^2 - ab + 3ab^2 + b^3)$

14. $4cd(2c^3 - 3c^2d + 5cd^2 - d^3)$

11. _____

Multiply, using the FOIL method.

12. _____

15. $(x + y)(x + 3y)$

16. $(a - 3b)(a - 5b)$

13. _____

17. $(m - 2n)(m + 7n)$

18. $(p + 7q)(p - 3q)$

14. _____

19. $(5a - 7b)(5a - 9b)$

20. $(3r - 5s)(7r + 2s)$

15. _____

16. _____

17. _____

18. _____

19. _____

20. _____

233

ANSWERS

21. _____

22. _____

23. _____

24. _____

25. _____

26. _____

27. _____

28. _____

29. _____

30. _____

31. _____

32. _____

33. _____

34. _____

35. _____

36. _____

37. _____

38. _____

39. _____

40. _____

41. _____

42. _____

21. $(7c - 5d)(3c - 4d)$ **22.** $(9w + 7v)(3w - 2v)$

23. $(5x^2 - 2y)(3x + 2y^2)$ **24.** $(6s^2 - 5t^2)(3s^2 - 2t)$

Multiply, using the special product formulas.

25. $(x + 5)^2$ **26.** $(y - 7)^2$

27. $(2a - 3)^2$ **28.** $(5s + 3)^2$

29. $(4c - 3d)^2$ **30.** $(7r - 5s)^2$

31. $(4x + 3y^2)^2$ **32.** $(3p^3 - 7q)^2$

33. $(x - 3y)(x + 3y)$ **34.** $(x + 5y)(x - 5y)$

35. $(2p - 3q)(2p + 3q)$ **36.** $(5c + 3d)(5c - 3d)$

37. $(4a^2 + 3b)(4a^2 - 3b)$ **38.** $(7u - 6w^2)(7u + 6w^2)$

Multiply, using the vertical format.

39. $(3x - y)(x^2 + 3xy - y^2)$ **40.** $(5a + b)(a^2 - 3ab + b^2)$

41. $(x - 2y)(x^2 + 2xy + 4y^2)$ **42.** $(m + 3n)(m^2 - 3mn + 9n^2)$

ANSWERS

Multiply each of the following polynomials.

43. _____

43. $x(x - 3)(x + 1)$

44. $a(a - 4)(a - 2)$

45. $2x(x - 3y)(x + 4y)$

46. $y^2(2y + 1)(2y + 3)$

44. _____

Skillscan

45. _____

List all the factors for each of the following integers.

a. 10

b. 18

46. _____

c. 25

d. 23

e. 28

f. 52

a. _____

g. 100

h. 72

b. _____

c. _____

d. _____

e. _____

f. _____

ANSWERS

1. $20xy$ 3. $-18x^5$ 5. $30r^5s^5$ 7. $6x^3 - 9x^2$ 9. $5a^4 - 15a^3 + 5a^2$
11. $5x^4y^3 - 15x^3y^4 + 5x^2y^5$ 13. $-2a^3b + 2a^2b^2 - 6a^2b^3 - 2ab^4$ 15. $x^2 + 4xy + 3y^2$
17. $m^2 + 5mn - 14n^2$ 19. $25a^2 - 80ab + 63b^2$ 21. $21c^2 - 43cd + 20d^2$

g. _____

23. $15x^3 + 10x^2y^2 - 6xy - 4y^3$ 25. $x^2 + 10x + 25$ 27. $4a^2 - 12a + 9$
29. $16c^2 - 24cd + 9d^2$ 31. $16x^2 + 24xy^2 + 9y^4$ 33. $x^2 - 9y^2$ 35. $4p^2 - 9q^2$
37. $16a^4 - 9b^2$ 39. $3x^3 + 8x^2y - 6xy^2 + y^3$ 41. $x^3 - 8y^3$ 43. $x^3 - 2x^2 - 3x$
45. $2x^3 + 2x^2y - 24xy^2$ a. 1, 2, 5, 10   b. 1, 2, 3, 6, 9, 18   c. 1, 5, 25   d. 1, 23
e. 1, 2, 4, 7, 14, 28   f. 1, 2, 4, 13, 26, 52   g. 1, 2, 4, 5, 10, 20, 25, 50, 100

h. _____

h. 1, 2, 3, 4, 6, 8, 9, 12, 18, 24, 36, 72

Common Factors and Factoring by Grouping

OBJECTIVES
1. To remove the greatest common factor (GCF) of a polynomial
2. To factor by grouping

When the integers 3 and 5 are multiplied, the product is 15. We call 3 and 5 the *factors* of 15.

Recall that a prime number is any integer greater than 1 that has only itself and 1 as factors. Writing

$$15 = 3 \cdot 5$$

as a product of prime factors is called the *completely factored form* for 15.

Writing $3 \cdot 5 = 15$ indicates multiplication, but when we write $15 = 3 \cdot 5$, we say we have *factored* 15. In general, factoring is the reverse of multiplication. We can extend this idea to algebra.

From the section on multiplying polynomials and special products, we know that

$$(2x + 3)(x - 2) = 2x^2 - x - 6$$

Our work here will involve starting with $2x^2 - x - 6$ and finding the factors $2x + 3$ and $x - 2$. As in arithmetic, this is called *factoring,* and here it means writing a polynomial as a product of other polynomials.

In fact, we will see that factoring out the GCF is the *first method* to try in any of the factoring problems we will discuss.

Let's start with the simplest method, *factoring out* (or removing) *the greatest common factor*.

> The *greatest common factor* (GCF) of a polynomial is the monomial with the highest degree and the largest numerical coefficient that is a factor of each term of the polynomial.

Once the GCF is found, we apply the distributive property to write the original polynomial as a product of the GCF and the polynomial formed by dividing each term by that GCF. The following examples illustrate.

Example 1*

(*a*) Factor $4x^3 - 12x$.

4 is the GCF of the numerical coefficients, and the highest common power of *x* is 1, so the GCF of $4x^3 - 12x$ is $4x$.

Note that the numerical coefficient of the GCF is 4 and the variable factor is x (the highest power common to each term). So

$$4x^3 - 12x = 4x \cdot x^2 - 4x \cdot 3$$
$$= 4x(x^2 - 3)$$

Here 6 is the GCF of the numerical coefficients, the highest common power of *a* is 2, and the highest common power of *b* is 2.

(*b*) Factor $6a^3b^2 - 12a^2b^3 + 24a^4b^4$.

Here the GCF is $6a^2b^2$, and we can write

$$6a^3b^2 - 12a^2b^3 + 24a^4b^4$$
$$= 6a^2b^2 \cdot a - 6a^2b^2 \cdot 2b + 6a^2b^2 \cdot 4a^2b^2$$
$$= 6a^2b^2(a - 2b + 4a^2b^2)$$

*A screen is used to indicate an expression that is being simplified.

236

(c) Factor $8m^4n^2 - 16m^2n^2 + 24mn^3 - 32mn^4$.

Here the GCF is $8mn^2$, and we have

$$8m^4n^2 - 16m^2n^2 + 24mn^3 - 32mn^4$$
$$= 8mn^2 \cdot m^3 - 8mn^2 \cdot 2m + 8mn^2 \cdot 3n - 8mn^2 \cdot 4n^2$$
$$= 8mn^2(m^3 - 2m + 3n - 4n^2)$$

Notice that in Example 1b it is also true that

$$6a^3b^2 - 12a^2b^3 + 24a^4b^4 = 3ab(2a^2b - 4ab^2 + 8a^3b^3)$$

However, this is not in *completely factored form* since we agree that this means factoring out the GCF (that monomial with the largest possible coefficient and degree). In this case we must remove $6a^2b^2$.

CHECK YOURSELF 1

Write each of the following in completely factored form.

1. $7x^3y - 21x^2y^2 + 28xy^3$
2. $15m^4n^4 - 5mn^3 + 20mn^2 - 25m^2n^2$

The following example shows a related factoring method that is used in the remainder of this section as we discuss *factoring by grouping*. It is sometimes possible to factor a binomial as the GCF.

Example 2

(a) Factor $3x(x + y) + 2(x + y)$.

We see that *the binomial* $x + y$ is a common factor and can be removed:

Because of the commutative property, the factors can be written in either order.

$$3x(x + y) + 2(x + y)$$
$$= (x + y) \cdot 3x + (x + y) \cdot 2$$
$$= (x + y)(3x + 2)$$

(b) Factor $3x^2(x - y) + 6x(x - y) + 9(x - y)$.

We note that here the GCF is $3(x - y)$. Factoring as before, we have

$$3(x - y)(x^2 + 2x + 3)$$

CHECK YOURSELF 2

Completely factor each of the polynomials.

1. $7a(a - 2b) + 3(a - 2b)$
2. $4x^2(x + y) - 8x(x + y) - 16(x + y)$

If the terms of a polynomial have no common factor (other than 1), we can sometimes use a technique called *factoring by grouping*. The following example illustrates this technique.

Example 3

Suppose we want to factor the polynomial

You will note that our example has *four terms*. That is the clue for trying the grouping method.

$$ax - ay + bx - by$$

As you can see, the polynomial has no common factors. However, look at what happens if we separate the polynomial into *two groups of two terms*.

$$ax - ay + bx - by$$
$$= \underbrace{ax - ay}_{(1)} \quad \underbrace{+ \ bx - by}_{(2)}$$

Now *each* group has a common factor, and we can write the polynomial as

$$a(x - y) + b(x - y)$$

In this form we can see that $x - y$ is the GCF, and factoring out $x - y$, we get

$$a(x - y) + b(x - y) = (x - y)(a + b)$$

CHECK YOURSELF 3

Use the grouping method to factor.

$$x^2 - 2xy + 3x - 6y$$

Be particularly careful of your treatment of algebraic signs in applying the method of grouping. Look at our next example.

Example 4

Factor $2x^3 - 3x^2 - 6x + 9$.

We group the polynomial as follows.

Note that $9 = (-3)(-3)$.

$$\underbrace{2x^3 - 3x^2}_{(1)} \quad \underbrace{- \ 6x + 9}_{(2)}$$

Remove the common factor of -3 from the second two terms.

$$= x^2(2x - 3) - 3(2x - 3)$$
$$= (2x - 3)(x^2 - 3)$$

CHECK YOURSELF 4

Factor by grouping.

$3y^3 + 2y^2 - 6y - 4$

It may also be necessary to change the order of the terms as they are grouped. Look at the following example.

Example 5

Factor $x^2 - 6yz + 2xy - 3xz$.

Grouping the terms as before, we have

$$\underbrace{x^2 - 6yz}_{(1)} + \underbrace{2xy - 3xz}_{(2)}$$

Do you see that we have accomplished nothing because there are no common factors in the first group?

We can, however, rearrange the terms to write the original polynomial as

$$\underbrace{x^2 + 2xy}_{(1)} - \underbrace{3xz - 6yz}_{(2)}$$
$$= x(x + 2y) - 3z(x + 2y) \qquad \text{We can now remove the common factor}$$
$$= (x + 2y)(x - 3z) \qquad \qquad \text{of } x + 2y \text{ in group (1) and group (2).}$$

Note It is often true that the grouping can be done in more than one way. The factored form will be the same.

CHECK YOURSELF 5

We can write the polynomial of Example 5 as

$x^2 - 3xz + 2xy - 6yz$

Factor, and verify that the factored form is the same in either case.

CHECK YOURSELF ANSWERS

1. (1) $7xy(x^2 - 3xy + 4y^2)$; (2) $5mn^2(3m^3n^2 - n + 4 - 5m)$.
2. (1) $(a - 2b)(7a + 3)$; (2) $4(x + y)(x^2 - 2x - 4)$.
3. $(x - 2y)(x + 3)$.　　　**4.** $(3y + 2)(y^2 - 2)$.　　　**5.** $(x - 3z)(x + 2y)$.

Name _____

Date _____

Exercises

Build Your Skills

1. _____

Completely factor each of the following polynomials.

2. _____

1. $6x + 9y$ **2.** $7a - 21b$

3. _____

3. $4x^2 - 12x$ **4.** $5a^2 + 25a$

4. _____

5. $18m^2n + 27mn^2$ **6.** $24c^2d^3 - 30c^3d^2$

5. _____

7. $9x^2 - 6x + 3$ **8.** $8y^2 + 12y - 4$

6. _____

9. $5x^3 - 15x^2 + 25x$ **10.** $28r^3 - 21r^2 + 7r$

7. _____

11. $12m^3n - 6mn + 18mn^2$ **12.** $18w^2z + 27wz - 36wz^2$

8. _____

13. $4a^3b^2 - 8a^2b + 12ab^2 - 4ab$ **14.** $9r^2s^3 + 27r^3s^2 - 6r^2s^2 + 3rs$

9. _____

15. $x(y - z) + 3(y - z)$ **16.** $2a(c - d) - b(c - d)$

10. _____

17. $3(m - n) + 5(m - n)^2$ **18.** $4(r + 2s) - 3(r + 2s)^2$

11. _____

12. _____

13. _____

14. _____

15. _____

16. _____

17. _____

18. _____

ANSWERS

19. _____   **19.** $5x^2(x - y) - 10x(x - y) + 15(x - y)$

20. _____   **20.** $7a^2(a + 2b) + 21a(a + 2b) - 14(a + 2b)$

21. _____   Factor each of the following polynomials by grouping.

21. $ab - ac + b^2 - bc$ **22.** $ax + 2a + bx + 2b$

22. _____

23. $6r^2 + 12rs - r - 2s$ **24.** $2mn - 4m^2 + 3n - 6m$

23. _____

25. $ab^2 - 2b^2 + 3a - 6$ **26.** $r^2s^2 - 3s^2 - 2r^2 + 6$

24. _____

27. $16a^3 - 4a^2b^2 - 4ab + b^3$ **28.** $2x^3 + 10x^2y - 7x - 35y$

25. _____

29. $3x^2 - 2xy + 3x - 2y$ **30.** $xy - 5y^2 - x + 5y$

26. _____

Factor each of the following polynomials by grouping. *Hint:* Consider a rearrangement of terms.

27. _____   **31.** $x^2 - 10y - 5xy + 2x$ **32.** $a^2 - 12b + 3ab - 4a$

28. _____   **33.** $m^2 - 6n^3 + 2mn^2 - 3mn$ **34.** $r^2 - 3rs^2 - 12s^3 + 4rs$

29. _____

30. _____

31. _____

32. _____

33. _____

34. _____

ANSWERS

Skillscan (Multiplication of Polynomials and Special Products)

a. _____

Multiply.

a. $(x - 2)(x + 2)$

b. $(2a + 3)(2a - 3)$

b. _____

c. $(5m + n)(5m - n)$

d. $(3c - 5d^2)(3c + 5d^2)$

c. _____

e. $(x + 1)(x^2 - x + 1)$

f. $(w - 2)(w^2 + 2w + 4)$

d. _____

g. $(a - b)(a^2 + ab + b^2)$

h. $(2p + q)(4p^2 - 2pq + q^2)$

e. _____

f. _____

g. _____

h. _____

ANSWERS

1. $3(2x + 3y)$ **3.** $4x(x - 3)$ **5.** $9mn(2m + 3n)$ **7.** $3(3x^2 - 2x + 1)$
9. $5x(x^2 - 3x + 5)$ **11.** $6mn(2m^2 - 1 + 3n)$ **13.** $4ab(a^2b - 2a + 3b - 1)$
15. $(y - z)(x + 3)$ **17.** $(m - n)(3 + 5m - 5n)$ **19.** $5(x - y)(x^2 - 2x + 3)$
21. $(b - c)(a + b)$ **23.** $(r + 2s)(6r - 1)$ **25.** $(a - 2)(b^2 + 3)$ **27.** $(4a - b^2)(4a^2 - b)$
29. $(3x - 2y)(x + 1)$ **31.** $(x + 2)(x - 5y)$ **33.** $(m - 3n)(m + 2n^2)$ **a.** $x^2 - 4$
b. $4a^2 - 9$ **c.** $25m^2 - n^2$ **d.** $9c^2 - 25d^4$ **e.** $x^3 + 1$ **f.** $w^3 - 8$ **g.** $a^3 - b^3$
h. $8p^3 + q^3$

Factoring Special Polynomials

OBJECTIVES

1. To factor the difference of two squares
2. To factor the sum and difference of two cubes

We continue our work on factoring with a discussion of factoring polynomials with special forms. Certain patterns occur frequently enough that it is worth developing special techniques to work with them.

In our coverage of multiplication of polynomials and special products, we look at some special products in multiplication. Now let's look at those patterns from a factoring standpoint. Remember that

The product of the sum and difference of two terms gives the *difference of two squares*.

$$(a + b)(a - b) = a^2 - b^2$$

Now to use the same formula in factoring, we can write the following:

> **THE DIFFERENCE OF TWO SQUARES**
>
> $$a^2 - b^2 = (a + b)(a - b) \qquad (1)$$

Formula (1) is easy to apply in factoring. It is just a matter of recognizing a binomial as the difference of two squares.

Example 1*

Note that our example has two terms—a clue to try factoring as the difference of two squares.

We are looking for perfect squares—the exponents must be multiples of 2 and the coefficients perfect squares—1, 4, 9, 16, and so on.

(a) Factor $x^2 - 25$.

$$x^2 - 25 = (x)^2 - (5)^2$$
$$= (x + 5)(x - 5)$$

(b) Factor $9a^2 - 16$.

$$9a^2 - 16 = (3a)^2 - (4)^2$$
$$= (3a + 4)(3a - 4)$$

(c) Factor $25m^4 - 49n^2$.

$$25m^4 - 49n^2 = (5m^2)^2 - (7n)^2$$
$$= (5m^2 + 7n)(5m^2 - 7n)$$

Note In Example 1 we factored the difference of two squares. What about the sum of two squares, such as

$$x^2 + 25$$

*A screen is used to indicate an expression that is being simplified.

In general, it is *not possible* to factor (using real numbers) a sum of two squares. So

$$(x^2 + 25) \neq (x + 5)(x + 5)$$

CHECK YOURSELF 1

Factor each of the following binomials.

1. $y^2 - 36$ **2.** $25m^2 - n^2$ **3.** $16a^4 - 9b^2$

Note that factoring out a common factor should always be considered your first step. Then other techniques may be obvious. Consider the following example.

Example 2

Factor $a^3 - 16ab^2$.

First note the common factor of a. Removing that factor, we have

$$a^3 - 16ab^2 = a(a^2 - 16b^2)$$

We now see that the binomial factor is a difference of squares, and we can continue to factor as before. So

$$a^2 - 16ab^2 = a(a + 4b)(a - 4b)$$

CHECK YOURSELF 2

Factor $2x^3 - 18xy^2$.

You may also have to apply the difference-of-squares formula *more than once* to completely factor a polynomial.

Example 3

Factor $m^4 - 81n^4$.

$$m^4 - 81n^4 = (m^2 + 9n^2)(m^2 - 9n^2)$$

Do you see that we are not done in this case? Since $m^2 - 9n^2$ is still factorable, we can continue to write

Note: The other binomial factor is $m^2 + 9n^2$, a *sum of two squares*. It cannot be factored further.

$$m^4 - 81n^4 = (m^2 + 9n^2)(m + 3n)(m - 3n)$$

in completely factored form.

CHECK YOURSELF 3

Factor $x^4 - 16y^4$.

Two additional formulas are available for factoring certain binomials.

THE SUM AND DIFFERENCE OF TWO CUBES

$$a^3 + b^3 = (a + b)(a^2 - ab + b^2) \qquad (2)$$
$$a^3 - b^3 = (a - b)(a^2 + ab + b^2) \qquad (3)$$

See Exercises 49 and 50 at the end of this section.

Of course, you can use multiplication to verify both formulas. The use of the formulas is quite similar to the use of the difference-of-squares formula we saw earlier.

Example 4

We are now looking for perfect cubes—the exponents must be multiples of 3 and the coefficients perfect cubes—1, 8, 27, 64, and so on.

(a) Factor $x^3 + 27$

$$x^3 + 27 = (x)^3 + (3)^3$$

The first term is the cube of x, and the second is the cube of 3, so we can apply Equation (2). Letting $a = x$ and $b = 3$, we have

$$x^3 + 27 = (x + 3)(x^2 - 3x + 9)$$

Note again that our example has *two terms*—this leads us to consider the sum or difference of two cubes as a factoring method.

(b) Factor $8w^3 - 27z^3$.

$$8w^3 - 27z^3 = (2w)^3 - (3z)^3 \qquad \text{This is a difference of cubes, so use formula (3).}$$
$$= (2w - 3z)[(2w)^2 + (2w)(3z) + (3z)^2]$$
$$= (2w - 3z)(4w^2 + 6wz + 9z^2)$$

(c) Factor $5a^3b - 40b^4$.

Again, looking for a *common factor* should be your first step.

First, note the common factor of $5b$. So

$$5a^3b - 40b^4 = 5b(a^3 - 8b^3) \qquad \text{The binomial is the difference of cubes.}$$
$$= 5b(a - 2b)(a^2 + 2ab + 4b^2)$$

Remember to write the GCF as a part of the final factored form.

CHECK YOURSELF 4

Factor completely.

1. $27x^3 + 8y^3$

2. $3a^4 - 24ab^3$

CHECK YOURSELF ANSWERS

1. (1) $(y + 6)(y - 6)$; (2) $(5m + n)(5m - n)$; (3) $(4a^2 + 3b)(4a^2 - 3b)$.
2. $2x(x + 3y)(x - 3y)$.   **3.** $(x^2 + 4y^2)(x + 2y)(x - 2y)$.
4. (1) $(3x + 2y)(9x^2 - 6xy + 4y^2)$; (2) $3a(a - 2b)(a^2 + 2ab + 4b^2)$.

Name _____

Date _____

Exercises

ANSWERS

Build Your Skills

1. _____

Factor each binomial completely.

2. _____

1. $x^2 - 49$ **2.** $m^2 - 64$

3. _____

4. _____

3. $a^2 - 81$ **4.** $b^2 - 36$

5. _____

5. $9p^2 - 1$ **6.** $4x^2 - 9$

6. _____

7. _____

7. $25a^2 - 16$ **8.** $16m^2 - 49$

8. _____

9. _____

9. $x^2y^2 - 25$ **10.** $m^2n^2 - 9$

10. _____

11. _____

11. $4c^2 - 25d^2$ **12.** $9a^2 - 49b^2$

12. _____

13. _____

13. $49p^2 - 64q^2$ **14.** $25x^2 - 36y^2$

14. _____

15. $x^4 - 16y^2$ **16.** $a^2 - 25b^4$

15. _____

16. _____

17. $a^3 - 4ab^2$ **18.** $9p^2q - q^3$

17. _____

18. _____

19. $2b^2c - 18c^3$ **20.** $3r^3 - 27rs^2$

19. _____

20. _____

21. $a^4 - 16b^4$ **22.** $81x^4 - y^4$

21. _____

22. _____

23. $x^3 + 64$ **24.** $y^3 - 8$

23. _____

25. $m^3 - 125$ **26.** $b^3 + 27$

24. _____

25. _____

26. _____

ANSWERS

27. _____

28. _____

29. _____

30. _____

31. _____

32. _____

33. _____

34. _____

35. _____

36. _____

37. _____

38. _____

39. _____

40. _____

41. _____

42. _____

43. _____

44. _____

45. _____

46. _____

47. _____

48. _____

27. $a^3b^3 - 27$

28. $p^3q^3 - 64$

29. $8w^3 + z^3$

30. $c^3 - 27d^3$

31. $r^3 - 64s^3$

32. $125x^3 + y^3$

33. $8x^3 - 27y^3$

34. $64m^3 - 27n^3$

35. $8x^3 + y^6$

36. $m^6 - 27n^3$

37. $4x^3 - 32y^3$

38. $3a^3 + 81b^3$

39. $5m^4 + 40mn^3$

40. $2p^3q - 54q^4$

Factor each polynomial completely. *Hint:* Try factoring by grouping as your first step.

41. $x^3 + 3x^2 - 4x - 12$

42. $a^3 - 5a^2 - 9a + 45$

43. $8x^3 + 12x^2 - 2x - 3$

44. $18b^3 - 9b^2 - 2b + 1$

45. $9a^3 + 27a^2 - 4a - 12$

46. $4m^3 + 12m^2 - 25m - 75$

47. $x^4 - x^3y + xy^3 - y^4$

48. $a^4 + a^3b - 8ab^3 - 8b^4$

ANSWERS

49. _____

49. Verify the formula for factoring the sum of two cubes by finding the product $(a + b)(a^2 - ab + b^2)$.

50. _____

50. Verify the formula for factoring the difference of two cubes by finding the product $(a - b)(a^2 + ab + b^2)$.

Skillscan (Multiplication of Polynomials and Special Products)

a. _____

Multiply.

a. $(x - 3)(x + 5)$ **b.** $(m + 5)(m + 8)$

b. _____

c. $(2a - 3)(a - 5)$ **d.** $(3d + 2)(2d - 5)$

e. $(5w + 3z)(w - z)$ **f.** $(7c - d)(3c + 2d)$

c. _____

g. $m(3m - 2)(m + 1)$ **h.** $2y(y - 3)(2y - 7)$

d. _____

e. _____

f. _____

ANSWERS

1. $(x + 7)(x - 7)$ **3.** $(a + 9)(a - 9)$ **5.** $(3p + 1)(3p - 1)$ **7.** $(5a + 4)(5a - 4)$
9. $(xy + 5)(xy - 5)$ **11.** $(2c + 5d)(2c - 5d)$ **13.** $(7p + 8q)(7p - 8q)$
15. $(x^2 + 4y)(x^2 - 4y)$ **17.** $a(a + 2b)(a - 2b)$ **19.** $2c(b + 3c)(b - 3c)$
21. $(a^2 + 4b^2)(a + 2b)(a - 2b)$ **23.** $(x + 4)(x^2 - 4x + 16)$ **25.** $(m - 5)(m^2 + 5m + 25)$
27. $(ab - 3)(a^2b^2 + 3ab + 9)$ **29.** $(2w + z)(4w^2 - 2wz + z^2)$ **31.** $(r - 4s)(r^2 + 4rs + 16s^2)$

g. _____

33. $(2x - 3y)(4x^2 + 6xy + 9y^2)$ **35.** $(2x + y^2)(4x^2 - 2xy^2 + y^4)$
37. $4(x - 2y)(x^2 + 2xy + 4y^2)$ **39.** $5m(m + 2n)(m^2 - 2mn + 4n^2)$ **41.** $(x + 3)(x + 2)(x - 2)$
43. $(2x + 3)(2x + 1)(2x - 1)$ **45.** $(a + 3)(3a + 2)(3a - 2)$ **47.** $(x - y)(x + y)(x^2 - xy + y^2)$
49. $a^3 + b^3$ **a.** $x^2 + 2x - 15$ **b.** $m^2 + 13m + 40$ **c.** $2a^2 - 13a + 15$

h. _____

d. $6d^2 - 11d - 10$ **e.** $5w^2 - 2wz - 3z^2$ **f.** $21c^2 + 11cd - 2d^2$ **g.** $3m^3 + m^2 - 2m$
h. $4y^3 - 26y^2 + 42y$

Factoring Trinomials

OBJECTIVE
To factor trinomials

The product of two binomials may be a trinomial of the form

$$ax^2 + bx + c$$

This suggests that some trinomials may be factored as the product of two binomials. And, in fact, factoring trinomials in this way is probably the most common type of factoring that you will encounter in algebra. One process for factoring a trinomial into a product of two binomials is called *trial and error*.

Let's introduce the factoring technique with an example from multiplication. Consider

$$(x + 3)(x + 4) = x^2 + 4x + 3x + 12$$
$$= x^2 + 7x + 12$$

Product of first terms, x and x

Sum of inner and outer products, $3x$ and $4x$

Product of last terms, 3 and 4

To reverse the multiplication process to one of factoring, we see that the product of the *first* terms of the binomial factors is the *first* term of the given trinomial, the product of the *last* terms of the binomial factors is the *last* term of the trinomial, and the *middle* term of the trinomial must equal the sum of the *outer* and *inner* terms of those factors. That leads us to the following sign patterns in factoring a trinomial.

FACTORING TRINOMIALS		Factoring Sign Pattern
$x^2 + bx + c$	Both signs are positive.	$(x + \quad)(x + \quad)$
$x^2 - bx + c$	The constant is positive, and the x coefficient is negative.	$(x - \quad)(x - \quad)$
$x^2 + bx - c$ or $x^2 - bx - c$	The constant is negative.	$(x + \quad)(x - \quad)$

Given the above information let's work through an example.

Example 1

Factor $x^2 + 7x + 10$.

The desired sign pattern is

$$(x + \quad)(x + \quad)$$

From the constant, 10, and the x coefficient of our original trinomial, 7, for the second terms of the binomial factors, we want two numbers whose product is 10 and whose sum is 7.

Consider the following:

With practice, you will do much of this work mentally. We show the factors and their sums here, and in later examples, to emphasize the process.

Factors of 10	*Sum*
1, 10	11
2, 5	7

We can see that the correct factorization is

Note: To check, multiply the factors by using the method in our coverage of multiplication of polynomials and special products.

$$x^2 + 7x + 10 = (x + 2)(x + 5)$$

CHECK YOURSELF 1

Factor $x^2 + 8x + 15$.

The next example shows how to factor a polynomial with a positive constant term and a negative middle term.

Example 2

Factor $x^2 - 9x + 14$.

Do you see that the sign pattern must be as follows?

$$(x - \quad)(x - \quad)$$

We then want two factors of 14 whose sum is -9.

Here we use two negative factors of 14 since the coefficient of the x term is negative while the constant is positive.

Factors of 14	*Sum*
$-1, -14$	-15
$-2, -7$	-9

Since the desired middle term is $-9x$, the correct factors are

$$x^2 - 9x + 14 = (x - 2)(x - 7)$$

CHECK YOURSELF 2

Factor $x^2 - 12x + 32$.

Let's turn now to applying our factoring technique to a trinomial whose constant term is negative. Consider the following example.

Example 3

Factor $x^2 + 4x - 12$.

In this case, the sign pattern is

Since the constant is now negative, the signs in the binomial factors must be *opposite*.

$(x - \quad)(x + \quad)$

Here we want two numbers whose product is -12 and whose sum is 4. Again let's look at the possible factors:

Factors of -12	Sum
$1, -12$	-11
$-1, 12$	11
$3, -4$	-1
$-3, 4$	1
$2, -6$	-4
$-2, 6$	4

From the information above, we see that the correct factors are

$$x^2 + 4x - 12 = (x - 2)(x + 6)$$

CHECK YOURSELF 3

Factor $x^2 - 7x - 18$.

Thus far we have considered only trinomials of the form $x^2 + bx + c$. Suppose that the leading coefficient is *not* 1. In general, to factor the trinomial $ax^2 + bx + c$ (with $a \neq 1$), we must consider binomial factors of the form

$(\quad x + \quad)(\quad x + \quad)$

where one or both of the coefficients of x in the binomial factors are greater than 1. Again, let's look at a multiplication example for some clues to the technique. Consider

$$(2x + 3)(3x + 5) = 6x^2 + 19x + 15$$

Product of $2x$ and $3x$ Sum of outer and inner Product of 3 and 5
products, $10x$ and $9x$

Now, to reverse the process to factoring, we can proceed as in the following example.

Example 4

To factor $5x^2 + 9x + 4$, we must have the pattern

Both binomials must have positive signs. Why?

$$(\quad x + \quad)(\quad x + \quad) \qquad \text{This product must be 4.}$$

This product must be 5.

Factors of 5   *Factors of 4*

1, 5   1, 4
              2, 2

Therefore, the possible binomial factors are

The sum of the outer and inner products must be $9x$.

$(x + 1)(5x + 4)$
$(x + 4)(5x + 1)$
$(x + 2)(5x + 2)$

Checking the middle terms of each product, we see that the proper factorization is

$$5x^2 + 9x + 4 = (x + 1)(5x + 4)$$

CHECK YOURSELF 4

Factor $6x^2 - 17x + 7$.

The sign patterns remain the same when the leading coefficient is not 1. Look at the following example involving a trinomial with a negative constant.

Example 5*

Factor $6x^2 + 7x - 3$.

The sign patterns are

*A screen is used to indicate an expression that is being simplified.

$$(\ x + \ \ )(\ x - \ \ )$$

Factors of 6   *Factors of −3*

1, 6   1, −3

2, 3   −1, 3

There are eight possible binomial factors:

Again, as the number of factors for the first coefficient and the constant increase, the number of possible factors becomes larger. Can we reduce the search? One clue: If the trinomial has no common factors (other than 1), then a binomial factor can have no common factor. This means that $6x - 3$, $6x + 3$, $3x - 3$, and $3x + 3$ need not be considered. They are shown here to completely illustrate the possibilities.

Factors	Middle Term $(I + O)$
$(x + 1)(6x - 3)$	$6x - 3x = 3x$
$(x - 1)(6x + 3)$	$-6x + 3x = -3x$
$(x + 3)(6x - 1)$	$18x - x = 17x$
$(x - 3)(6x + 1)$	$-18x + x = -17x$
$(2x + 1)(3x - 3)$	$3x - 6x = -3x$
$(2x - 1)(3x + 3)$	$-3x + 6x = 3x$
$(3x + 1)(2x - 3)$	$2x - 9x = -7x$
$(3x - 1)(2x + 3)$	$-2x + 9x = 7x$

Again, checking the middle terms, we find the correct factors:

$$6x^2 + 7x - 3 = (3x - 1)(2x + 3)$$

Factoring certain trinomials in more than one variable involves similar techniques, as is illustrated below.

CHECK YOURSELF 5

Factor $10x^2 - 7x - 12$.

Example 6

Factor $4x^2 - 16xy + 7y^2$.

From the first term of the trinomial we see that possible first terms for our binomial factors are $4x$ and x or $2x$ and $2x$. The last term of the trinomial tells us that the only choices for the last terms of our binomial factors are y and $7y$. So given the sign of the middle and last terms, the only possible factors are

Find the middle term of each product.

Factors	Middle Term
$(4x - 7y)(x - y)$	$-7xy - 4xy = -11xy$
$(4x - y)(x - 7y)$	$-xy - 28xy = -29xy$
$(2x - 7y)(2x - y)$	$-14xy - 2xy = -16xy$

From the middle term of our original trinomial we see that $2x - 7y$ and $2x - y$ are the correct factors.

CHECK YOURSELF 6

Factor $6a^2 + 11ab - 10b^2$.

Recall our earlier comment that the *first step* in any factoring problem is to remove any existing common factors. As before, it may be necessary to combine common-term factoring with other methods (such as factoring a trinomial into a product of binomials) to completely factor a polynomial. Look at the following example.

Example 7

(*a*) Factor $2x^2 - 16x + 30$.

First note the common factor of 2. So we can write

"Remove" the common factor of 2.

$$2x^2 - 16x + 30 = 2(x^2 - 8x + 15)$$

Now, as the second step, examine the trinomial factor. By our earlier methods we know that

$$x^2 - 8x + 15 = (x - 3)(x - 5)$$

and we have

$$2x^2 - 16x + 30 = 2(x - 3)(x - 5)$$

in completely factored form.

(*b*) Factor $6x^3 + 15x^2y - 9xy^2$.

As before, note the common factor of $3x$ in each term of the trinomial. Removing that common factor, we have

$$6x^3 + 15x^2y - 9xy^2 = 3x(2x^2 + 5xy - 3y^2)$$

Again, considering the trinomial factor, we see that $2x^2 + 5xy - 3y^2$ has factors of $2x - y$ and $x + 3y$. And our original trinomial becomes

$$3x(2x - y)(x + 3y)$$

in completely factored form.

CHECK YOURSELF 7

Factor each of the following.

1. $9x^2 - 39x + 36$ **2.** $24a^3 + 4a^2b - 8ab^2$

Consider the trinomial $x^2 + 8x + 16$. Using the methods developed in this section, we can factor this trinomial as follows:

$$x^2 + 8x + 16 = (x + 4)(x + 4) = (x + 4)^2$$

Note that the final result is the square of a binomial. We say that $x^2 + 8x + 16$ is a *perfect-square trinomial*.

The *trial-and-error* process can be used to factor a perfect-square trinomial, but a faster technique is possible if we can recognize a trinomial as a perfect square.

A trinomial is a perfect square if

1. The first and third terms are squares such as a^2 and b^2.
2. The middle term is $2ab$.
3. The signs of the first and third terms are positive.

The patterns for factoring a perfect-square trinomial are as follows:

PERFECT-SQUARE TRINOMIALS

$$a^2 + 2ab + b^2 = (a + b)^2$$
$$a^2 - 2ab + b^2 = (a - b)^2$$

Example 8

(a) Factor $x^2 - 10x + 25$.

The sign of the middle term in the trinomial matches the sign in the binomial.

$$\begin{aligned} x^2 - 10x + 25 &= (x)^2 - 2(5)(x) + (5)^2 \\ &= (x - 5)(x - 5) \\ &= (x - 5)^2 \end{aligned}$$

(b) Factor $9x^2 + 24x + 16$.

$$\begin{aligned} 9x^2 + 24x + 16 &= (3x)^2 + 2(3x)(4) + (4)^2 \\ &= (3x + 4)^2 \end{aligned}$$

CHECK YOURSELF 8

Factor.

1. $4x^2 - 20x + 25$ 　　　　　　　　**2.** $16x^2 + 24x + 9$

One Final Note When factoring, we require that all coefficients be integers. Given this restriction, not all polynomials are factorable over the integers. The following illustrates.

To factor $x^2 - 9x + 12$, we know that the only possible binomial factors (using integers as coefficients) are

$(x - 1)(x - 12)$
$(x - 2)(x - 6)$
$(x - 3)(x - 4)$

You can easily verify that *none* of these pairs gives the correct middle term of $-9x$. We then say that the original trinomial is not factorable by using integers as coefficients.

CHECK YOURSELF ANSWERS

1. $(x + 3)(x + 5)$. **2.** $(x - 4)(x - 8)$. **3.** $(x - 9)(x + 2)$.
4. $(2x - 1)(3x - 7)$. **5.** $(2x - 3)(5x + 4)$.
6. $(3a - 2b)(2a + 5b)$.
7. (1) $3(x - 3)(3x - 4)$; (2) $4a(3a + 2b)(2a - b)$.
8. (1) $(2x - 5)^2$; (2) $(4x + 3)^2$.

PART A.

Factor each of these trinomials completely.

1. $x^2 + 7x + 12$ 2. $a^2 + 9a + 20$ 3. $b^2 - 9b + 8$

4. $m^2 - 11m + 10$ 5. $y^2 - 15y + 50$ 6. $x^2 - 13x + 40$

7. $m^2 + 7m - 30$ 8. $a^2 - 7a - 18$ 9. $x^2 - 10x + 24$

10. $r^2 + 13r - 30$ 11. $a^2 - 7a - 44$ 12. $y^2 - 15y - 54$

13. $x^2 + 8xy + 15y^2$ 14. $a^2 - 9ab + 20b^2$ 15. $m^2 - 16mn + 55n^2$

16. $p^2 - 9pq - 22q^2$ 17. $3x^2 + 11x - 20$ 18. $2b^2 + 9b - 18$

19. $5x^2 + 18x - 8$ 20. $3m^2 - 20m - 7$ 21. $12y^2 + 23y + 5$

22. $8x^2 + 30x + 7$ 23. $4x^2 + 20x + 25$ 24. $9x^2 - 24x + 16$

25. $5a^2 + 19a - 30$ 26. $3p^2 + 17p - 28$ 27. $5b^2 + 24b - 36$

28. $3a^2 - 14a - 24$ 29. $10x^2 - 7x - 12$ 30. $6y^2 + 5y - 21$

31. $16y^2 + 40y + 25$ 32. $18x^2 + 45x + 7$ 33. $7r^2 - 17rs + 6s^2$

34. $5a^2 + 17ab - 12b^2$ 35. $8x^2 - 30xy + 7y^2$

36. $8c^2 - 14cd - 15d^2$ 37. $3x^2 - 24x + 45$

38. $2a^2 + 10a - 28$ 39. $2n^2 - 26n + 72$ 40. $3y^2 + 39y + 120$

41. $6x^3 - 31x^2 + 5x$ 42. $8a^3 + 25a^2 + 3a$ 43. $5b^3 + 14b^2 - 24b$

44. $3x^4 + 17x^3 - 28x^2$ 45. $3m^3 - 15m^2n - 18mn^2$

PART B.

Factor Completely:

1. $2x^2 + 6x$ 2. $y^2 + y$

3. $3y^2 + 2y$ 4. $a^3x^2 + a^2x$

5. $y^2 + 5y + 6$ 6. $y^2 - 5y + 6$

7. $m^2 - 3m + 2$

8. $t^2 - 7t + 6$

9. $x^2 - 9x + 14$

10. $x^2 + 9x + 14$

11. $y^2 + 8y + 12$

12. $p^2 - 6p - 7$

13. $x^2 - 7x + 12$

14. $a^2 + 6a + 5$

15. $p^2 + 7pq + 6q^2$

16. $m^2 + 8mn + 7n^2$

17. $x^2 + 9xy - 10y^2$

18. $x^2 - 5xy - 36y^2$

19. $2p^2q - 10pq - 72q$

20. $x^2 - y^2$

21. $2r^2 - 2s^2$

22. $3y^2 - 27$

23. $x^2 - 36$

24. $4p^2 - 100$

25. $2y^2 - 2r^2$

26. $a^2 + 2a + 1$

27. $b^2 - 2b + 1$

28. $x^2 + 6x + 9$

29. $y^2 - 4y + 4$

30. $t^2 + 8t + 16$

31. $p^2 - 12p + 36$

32. $-2y^2 + 12y - 18$

33. $6x^2 + 12x + 6$

34. $3x^2 - 12x + 12$

35. $2x^2 + 10x + 12$

36. $3x^2 - 18x - 21$

37. $2x^2y + 12xy + 18y$

38. $4m^2n + 28mn - 32n$

Factor by first removing the leading coefficient:

39. $\dfrac{1}{5}x^2 + \dfrac{2}{5}x - \dfrac{3}{5}$

40. $\dfrac{1}{2}x^2 + 3x + 4$

41. $\dfrac{1}{2}x^2 + x + \dfrac{1}{2}$

42. $-\dfrac{1}{3}x^2 + \dfrac{2}{3}x - \dfrac{1}{3}$

43. $\dfrac{1}{4}x^2 + 2x + 4$

44. $-\dfrac{1}{2}x^2 + 4x - 8$

Answers

Part A.

1. $(x + 3)(x + 4)$ 3. $(b - 8)(b - 1)$ 5. $(y - 10)(y - 5)$ 7. $(m + 10)(m - 3)$
9. $(x - 6)(x - 4)$ 11. $(a - 11)(a + 4)$ 13. $(x + 3y)(x + 5y)$ 15. $(m - 11n)(m - 5n)$
17. $(3x - 4)(x + 5)$ 19. $(5x - 2)(x + 4)$ 21. $(3y + 5)(4y + 1)$ 23. $(2x + 5)^2$
25. $(5a - 6)(a + 5)$ 27. $(5b - 6)(b + 6)$ 29. $(2x - 3)(5x + 4)$ 31. $(4y + 5)^2$
33. $(7r - 3s)(r - 2s)$ 35. $(4x - y)(2x - 7y)$ 37. $3(x - 5)(x - 3)$ 39. $2(n - 4)(n - 9)$
41. $x(6x - 1)(x - 5)$ 43. $b(b + 4)(5b - 6)$ 45. $3m(m - 6n)(m + n)$

259

PART B.

1. $2x(x+3)$ 2. $y(y+1)$ 3. $y(3y+2)$
4. $a^2x(ax+1)$ 5. $(y+2)(y+3)$ 6. $(y-3)(y-2)$
7. $(m-2)(m-1)$ 8. $(t-6)(t-1)$ 9. $(x-7)(x-2)$
10. $(x+7)(x+2)$ 11. $(y+6)(y+2)$ 13. $(x-4)(x-3)$
14. $(a+5)(a+1)$ 15. $(p+6q)(p+q)$ 16. $(m+7n)(m+n)$
17. $(x+10y)(x-y)$ 18. $(x-9y)(x+4y)$ 19. $2q(p-9)(p+4)$
20. $(x+y)(x-y)$ 21. $2(r+s)(r-s)$ 22. $3(y+3)(y-3)$
23. $(x+6)(x-6)$ 24. $4(p+5)(p-5)$ 25. $2(y+r)(y-r)$
26. $(a+1)^2$ 27. $(b-1)^2$ 28. $(x+3)^2$
29. $(y-2)^2$ 30. $(t+4)^2$ 31. $(p-6)^2$
32. $-2(y-3)^2$ 33. $6(x+1)^2$ 34. $3(x-2)^2$
35. $2(x+3)(x+2)$ 36. $3(x-7)(x+1)$ 37. $2y(x+3)^2$

38. $4n(m+8)(m-1)$ 39. $\frac{1}{5}(x+3)(x-1)$ 40. $\frac{1}{2}(x+4)(x+2)$

41. $\frac{1}{2}(x+1)^2$ 42. $-\frac{1}{3}(x-1)^2$ 43. $\frac{1}{4}(x+4)^2$

44. $-\frac{1}{2}(x-4)^2$

Simplification of Rational Expressions

OBJECTIVE
To simplify a rational expression

Our work in this section will expand your experience with algebraic expressions to include algebraic fractions or *rational expressions.*

Fortunately, you will observe many parallels to your previous work with arithmetic fractions.

First, let's define what we mean by a rational expression. In our coverage of the real numbers, we define a rational number as the ratio of two integers. Similarly, a rational expression can be written as the ratio of two polynomials, where the denominator cannot have the value 0.

Again, the word "rational" comes from "ratio."

A *rational expression* is the ratio of two polynomials. It can be written as

$$\frac{P}{Q}$$ where P and Q are polynomials and Q cannot have the value 0

The expressions

$$\frac{x-3}{x+1} \qquad \frac{x^2+5}{x-3} \qquad \text{and} \qquad \frac{x^2-2x}{x^2+3x+1}$$

are all rational expressions. The restriction that the denominator of the expressions not be 0 means that certain values for the variable may have to be excluded. This is because division by 0 is undefined.

Example 1

(*a*) For what values of x is the following expression undefined?

$$\frac{x}{x-5}$$

To answer this question, we must find where the denominator is 0. Set

$$x - 5 = 0$$

or

$$x = 5$$

A fraction is undefined when its denominator is equal to 0.

Note that when $x = 5$, $\dfrac{x}{x-5}$

becomes $\dfrac{5}{5-5}$, or $\dfrac{5}{0}$.

The expression $\dfrac{x}{x-5}$ is undefined for $x = 5$.

(*b*) For what values of X is the following expression undefined?

$$\frac{3}{x + 5}$$

Again, set the denominator equal to 0:

$$x + 5 = 0$$

or

$$x = -5$$

The expression $\dfrac{3}{x + 5}$ is undefined for $x = -5$.

CHECK YOURSELF 1

For what values of the variable are the following expressions undefined?

1. $\dfrac{1}{r + 7}$ **2.** $\dfrac{5}{2x - 9}$

Scientific calculators are often used to evaluate rational expressions for values of the variable. The *parentheses keys* help in this process.

Example 2*

Using a scientific calculator, evaluate the following expressions for the given value of the variable.

(*a*) $\dfrac{3x}{2x - 5}$ for $x = 4$

Enter the expression in your calculator as follows:

$$3 \; \boxed{\times} \; 4 \; \boxed{\div} \; \boxed{(\!(} \; 2 \; \boxed{\times} \; 4 \; \boxed{-} \; 5 \; \boxed{)\!)} \; \boxed{=}$$

The display will read the value 4.

(*b*) $\dfrac{2x + 7}{4x - 11}$ for $x = 4$

Enter the expression as follows:

$$\boxed{(\!(} \; 2 \; \boxed{\times} \; 4 \; \boxed{+} \; 7 \; \boxed{)\!)} \; \boxed{\div} \; \boxed{(\!(} \; 4 \; \boxed{\times} \; 4 \; \boxed{-} \; 11 \; \boxed{)\!)} \; \boxed{=}$$

The display will read the value 3.

*A screen is used to indicate an expression that is being simplified.

<CAUTION>

Be sure to use the parenthesis key before the 2 and after the 5.

CHECK YOURSELF 2

Using a scientific calculator, evaluate each of the following.

1. $\dfrac{5x}{3x-2}$ for $x = 4$ 　　　　　　**2.** $\dfrac{2x+9}{3x-4}$ for $x = 3$

Generally, we want to write rational expressions in the simplest possible form. To begin our discussion of simplifying rational expressions, let's review for a moment. As we pointed out above, there are many parallels to your work with arithmetic fractions. Recall that

We multiply by $\dfrac{2}{2}$, or 1.

$$\frac{3}{5} = \frac{3 \cdot 2}{5 \cdot 2} = \frac{6}{10}$$

so

$$\frac{3}{5} \quad \text{and} \quad \frac{6}{10}$$

name equivalent fractions. In a similar fashion,

Divide numerator and denominator by the common factor of 5.

$$\frac{10}{15} = \frac{5 \cdot 2}{5 \cdot 3} = \frac{2}{3}$$

We use the fact that $\dfrac{5}{5} = 1$.

so

$$\frac{10}{15} \quad \text{and} \quad \frac{2}{3}$$

name equivalent fractions.

We can always multiply or divide the numerator and denominator of a fraction by the same nonzero number. The same pattern is true in algebra.

FUNDAMENTAL PRINCIPLE OF RATIONAL EXPRESSIONS

For polynomials P, Q, and R,

$$\frac{P}{Q} = \frac{PR}{QR} \qquad Q \neq 0, R \neq 0$$

This principle can be used in two ways. We can multiply or divide the numerator and denominator of a rational expression by the same nonzero polynomial. The result will always be an expression that is equivalent to the original one.

In simplifying arithmetic fractions, we used this principle to divide the numerator and denominator by all common factors. With arithmetic fractions,

In fact, you will see that most of the methods of this chapter depend on factoring polynomials.

those common factors are generally easy to recognize. Given rational expressions where the numerator and denominator are polynomials, we must determine those factors as our first step. The most important tools for simplifying expressions are the factoring techniques found in our coverage of polynomial expressions.

Example 3

We find the common factors 4, x, and y in the numerator and denominator.

We divide the numerator and denominator by the common factor $4xy$. Note that

$$\frac{4xy}{4xy} = 1$$

Simplify each rational expression. Assume denominators are not 0.

(a) $\dfrac{4x^2y}{12xy^2} = \dfrac{4xy \cdot x}{4xy \cdot 3y}$

$\qquad\qquad = \dfrac{x}{3y}$

Factor the numerator and the denominator.

(b) $\dfrac{3x - 6}{x^2 - 4} = \dfrac{3(x - 2)}{(x + 2)(x - 2)}$

We can now divide the numerator and denominator by the common factor $x - 2$:

We have *divided* the numerator and denominator by the common factor $x - 2$. Again note that

$$\frac{x - 2}{x - 2} = 1$$

$$\frac{3(x - 2)}{(x + 2)(x - 2)} = \frac{3}{x + 2}$$

and the rational expression is in simplest form.

Be Careful! Given the expression

$$\frac{x + 2}{x + 3}$$

◁CAUTION▷

Pick any value other than 0 for the variable x, and substitute. You will quickly see that

$$\frac{x + 2}{x + 3} \neq \frac{2}{3}$$

students are often tempted to divide by the variable x, as in

$$\frac{x + 2}{x + 3} = \frac{2}{3}$$

This is not a valid operation. We can only divide by common *factors,* and in the expression above the variable x is a *term* in both the numerator and the denominator. The numerator and denominator of a rational expression must be factored *before* dividing out common factors.

$$\frac{x + 2}{x + 3}$$

is in its simplest possible form.

CHECK YOURSELF 3

Simplify each expression.

1. $\dfrac{36a^3b}{9ab^2}$

2. $\dfrac{x^2 - 25}{4x + 20}$

264

The same techniques are used when trinomials need to be factored. Here are some further examples that illustrate the simplification of rational expressions.

Example 4

Simplify each rational expression.

Divide by the common factor $x + 1$, using the fact that

$$\frac{x + 1}{x + 1} = 1$$

where $x \neq -1$.

(a) $\dfrac{5x^2 - 5}{x^2 - 4x - 5} = \dfrac{5(x - 1)(x + 1)}{(x - 5)(x + 1)}$

$$= \dfrac{5(x - 1)}{x - 5}$$

(b) $\dfrac{2x^2 + x - 6}{2x^2 - x - 3} = \dfrac{(x + 2)(2x - 3)}{(x + 1)(2x - 3)}$

$$= \dfrac{x + 2}{x + 1}$$

Here we factor by grouping in the numerator and use the sum of cubes in the denominator. Note that

$$x^3 + 2x^2 - 3x - 6$$
$$= x^2(x + 2) - 3(x + 2)$$
$$= (x + 2)(x^2 - 3)$$

(c) $\dfrac{x^3 + 2x^2 - 3x - 6}{x^3 + 8} = \dfrac{(x + 2)(x^2 - 3)}{(x + 2)(x^2 - 2x + 4)} = \dfrac{x^2 - 3}{x^2 - 2x + 4}$.

CHECK YOURSELF 4

Simplify each rational expression.

1. $\dfrac{x^2 - 5x + 6}{3x^2 - 6x}$

2. $\dfrac{3x^2 + 14x - 5}{3x^2 + 2x - 1}$

Simplifying certain algebraic expressions involves recognizing a particular pattern. Verify for yourself that

$$3 - 9 = -(9 - 3)$$

Note that

$$\frac{a - b}{a - b} = 1$$

but

$$\frac{a - b}{b - a} = -1$$

where $a \neq b$.

In general, it is true that

$$a - b = -(-a + b) = -(b - a)$$

or, by dividing both sides of the equation by $b - a$,

$$\frac{a - b}{b - a} = \frac{-(b - a)}{b - a} = -1$$

The following examples make use of this result.

Example 5

Note:

$$\frac{x-2}{2-x} = -1$$

Simplify each rational expression.

(a) $\dfrac{2x-4}{4-x^2} = \dfrac{2\overset{-1}{\cancel{(x-2)}}}{(2+x)\cancel{(2-x)}}$

$\qquad = \dfrac{2(-1)}{2+x} = \dfrac{-2}{2+x}$

(b) $\dfrac{9-x^2}{x^2+2x-15} = \dfrac{(3+x)\overset{-1}{\cancel{(3-x)}}}{(x+5)\cancel{(x-3)}}$

$\qquad = \dfrac{(3+x)(-1)}{x+5}$

$\qquad = \dfrac{-x-3}{x+5}$

CHECK YOURSELF 5

Simplify each rational expression.

1. $\dfrac{5x-20}{16-x^2}$

2. $\dfrac{x^2-6x-27}{81-x^2}$

The following algorithm will summarize our work with simplifying rational expressions.

SIMPLIFYING RATIONAL EXPRESSIONS

1. Completely factor both the numerator and the denominator of the expression.
2. Divide the numerator and denominator by *all* common factors.
3. The resulting expression will be in simplest form.

CHECK YOURSELF ANSWERS

1. (1) $r = -7$; (2) $x = \dfrac{9}{2}$.

2. (1) 2; (2) 3.

3. (1) $\dfrac{4a^2}{b}$; (2) $\dfrac{x-5}{4}$.

4. (1) $\dfrac{x-3}{3x}$; (2) $\dfrac{x+5}{x+1}$.

5. (1) $\dfrac{-5}{x+4}$; (2) $\dfrac{-x-3}{x+9}$.

Name _____

Date _____

Exercises

ANSWERS

Build Your Skills

1. _____

For what values of the variable are each of the following rational expressions undefined?

2. _____

1. $\dfrac{x}{x-5}$ 2. $\dfrac{y}{y+7}$

3. _____

3. $\dfrac{x+5}{3}$ 4. $\dfrac{a-6}{4}$

4. _____

5. _____

5. $\dfrac{2m-3}{2m-1}$ 6. $\dfrac{3x-2}{3x+1}$

6. _____

7. _____

7. $\dfrac{2x+5}{x}$ 8. $\dfrac{3c-7}{c}$

8. _____

9. $\dfrac{x(x+1)}{x+2}$ 10. $\dfrac{x+2}{3x-7}$

9. _____

10. _____

11. $\dfrac{4-x}{x}$ 12. $\dfrac{2a+7}{3x+\dfrac{1}{3}}$

11. _____

12. _____

Evaluate each of the following expressions, using a scientific calculator.

13. _____

13. $\dfrac{3x}{2x-1}$ for $x=2$ 14. $\dfrac{5x}{4x-3}$ for $x=2$

14. _____

15. $\dfrac{2x+3}{x+3}$ for $x=-6$ 16. $\dfrac{4x-7}{2x-1}$ for $x=-2$

15. _____

16. _____

ANSWERS

Simplify each of the following fractions. Assume denominators are not 0.

17. _____

18. _____

19. _____

20. _____

21. _____

22. _____

23. _____

24. _____

25. _____

26. _____

27. _____

28. _____

29. _____

30. _____

31. _____

32. _____

33. _____

34. _____

35. _____

36. _____

17. $\dfrac{14}{21}$

18. $\dfrac{45}{75}$

19. $\dfrac{4x^5}{6x^2}$

20. $\dfrac{25x^6}{20x^2}$

21. $\dfrac{10x^2y^5}{25xy^2}$

22. $\dfrac{18a^2b^3}{24a^4b^3}$

23. $\dfrac{-42x^3y}{14xy^3}$

24. $\dfrac{-15x^3y^3}{-20xy^2}$

25. $\dfrac{28a^5b^3c^2}{84a^2bc^4}$

26. $\dfrac{-52p^5q^3r^2}{39p^3q^5r^2}$

Simplify each of the following rational expressions.

27. $\dfrac{6x - 24}{x^2 - 16}$

28. $\dfrac{x^2 - 25}{3x - 15}$

29. $\dfrac{x^2 + 2x + 1}{6x + 6}$

30. $\dfrac{5y^2 - 10y}{y^2 + y - 6}$

31. $\dfrac{x^2 - 5x - 14}{x^2 - 49}$

32. $\dfrac{2m^2 + 11m - 21}{4m^2 - 9}$

33. $\dfrac{3b^2 - 14b - 5}{b - 5}$

34. $\dfrac{a^2 - 9b^2}{a^2 + 8ab + 15b^2}$

35. $\dfrac{2y^2 + 3yz - 5z^2}{2y^2 + 11yz + 15z^2}$

36. $\dfrac{6x^2 - x - 2}{3x^2 - 5x + 2}$

ANSWERS

37. _____

38. _____

39. _____

40. _____

41. _____

42. _____

43. _____

44. _____

45. _____

46. _____

47. _____

48. _____

49. _____

50. _____

37. $\dfrac{x^3 - 64}{x^2 - 16}$

38. $\dfrac{r^2 - rs - 6s^2}{r^3 + 8s^3}$

39. $\dfrac{a^4 - 81}{a^2 + 5a + 6}$

40. $\dfrac{c^4 - 16}{c^2 - 3c - 10}$

41. $\dfrac{xy - 2x + 3y - 6}{x^2 + 8x + 15}$

42. $\dfrac{cd - 3c + 5d - 15}{d^2 - 7d + 12}$

43. $\dfrac{x^2 + 3x - 18}{x^3 - 3x^2 - 2x + 6}$

44. $\dfrac{y^2 + 2y - 35}{y^2 - 5y - 3y + 15}$

45. $\dfrac{2m - 10}{25 - m^2}$

46. $\dfrac{5x - 20}{16 - x^2}$

47. $\dfrac{49 - x^2}{2x^2 - 13x - 7}$

48. $\dfrac{2x^2 - 7x + 3}{9 - x^2}$

49. $\dfrac{2x^2 - 2xy + 3x - 3y}{y^2 - x^2}$

50. $\dfrac{6a^2 - 3ab + 4a - 2b}{b^2 - ab - 2a^2}$

ANSWERS

Skillscan

Perform the indicated operations.

a. _____

a. $\dfrac{2}{3} \cdot \dfrac{4}{5}$

b. $\dfrac{5}{6} \cdot \dfrac{4}{11}$

b. _____

c. $\dfrac{4}{7} \div \dfrac{8}{5}$

d. $\dfrac{1}{6} \div \dfrac{7}{9}$

c. _____

e. $\dfrac{5}{8} \cdot \dfrac{16}{15}$

f. $\dfrac{15}{21} \div \dfrac{10}{7}$

g. $\dfrac{15}{8} \cdot \dfrac{24}{25}$

h. $\dfrac{28}{16} \div \dfrac{21}{20}$

d. _____

e. _____

f. _____

ANSWERS

1. 5   **3.** Never undefined   **5.** $\dfrac{1}{2}$ **7.** 0   **9.** -2 **11.** 0   **13.** 2   **15.** 3

g. _____

17. $\dfrac{2}{3}$ **19.** $\dfrac{2x^3}{3}$ **21.** $\dfrac{2xy^3}{5}$ **23.** $\dfrac{-3x^2}{y^2}$ **25.** $\dfrac{a^3b^2}{3c^2}$ **27.** $\dfrac{6}{x+4}$ **29.** $\dfrac{x+1}{6}$

31. $\dfrac{x+2}{x+7}$ **33.** $3b+1$ **35.** $\dfrac{y-z}{y+3z}$ **37.** $\dfrac{x^2+4x+16}{x+4}$ **39.** $\dfrac{(a^2+9)(a-3)}{a+2}$

41. $\dfrac{y-2}{x+5}$ **43.** $\dfrac{x+6}{x^2-2}$ **45.** $\dfrac{-2}{m+5}$ **47.** $\dfrac{-x-7}{2x+1}$ **49.** $\dfrac{-2x-3}{x+y}$ **a.** $\dfrac{8}{15}$

h. _____

b. $\dfrac{10}{33}$ **c.** $\dfrac{5}{14}$ **d.** $\dfrac{3}{14}$ **e.** $\dfrac{2}{3}$ **f.** $\dfrac{1}{2}$ **g.** $\dfrac{9}{5}$ **h.** $\dfrac{5}{3}$

Multiplication and Division of Rational Expressions

OBJECTIVES
1. To multiply rational expressions
2. To divide rational expressions

Let's turn to an example from arithmetic to begin our discussion of multiplying rational expressions. In order to multiply two fractions, we must multiply the numerators and multiply the denominators. For instance,

$$\frac{2}{5} \cdot \frac{3}{7} = \frac{2 \cdot 3}{5 \cdot 7} = \frac{6}{35}$$

In algebra, the pattern is exactly the same.

For all problems with rational expressions, assume denominators are not 0.

MULTIPLYING RATIONAL EXPRESSIONS

For polynomials P, Q, R, and S,

$$\frac{P}{Q} \cdot \frac{R}{S} = \frac{PR}{QS} \qquad \text{where } Q \neq 0 \text{ and } S \neq 0$$

Example 1*

Multiply.

$$\frac{2x^3}{5y^2} \cdot \frac{10y}{3x^2} = \frac{20x^3y}{15x^2y^2} = \frac{5x^2y \cdot 4x}{5x^2y \cdot 3y} = \frac{4x}{3y} \qquad \text{We divide by the common factor } 5x^2y.$$

CHECK YOURSELF 1

Multiply.

$$\frac{9a^2b^3}{5ab^4} \cdot \frac{20ab^2}{27ab^3}$$

Generally, you will find it best to divide by any common factors before you multiply. The following example illustrates.

*A screen is used to indicate an expression that is being simplified.

Example 2

Multiply as indicated.

(a) $\dfrac{x}{x^2 - 3x} \cdot \dfrac{6x - 18}{9x}$ Factor.

$= \dfrac{x}{x(x - 3)} \cdot \dfrac{6(x - 3)}{9x}$ Divide by the common factors of 3, x, and $x - 3$.

$= \dfrac{2}{3x}$

(b) $\dfrac{x^2 - y^2}{5x^2 - 5xy} \cdot \dfrac{10xy}{x^2 + 2xy + y^2}$ Factor and divide by the common factors of 5, x, $x + y$, and $x - y$.

$= \dfrac{(x + y)(x - y)}{5x(x - y)} \cdot \dfrac{10xy}{(x + y)(x + y)}$

$= \dfrac{2y}{x + y}$

(c) $\dfrac{4}{x^2 - 2x} \cdot \dfrac{10x - 5x^2}{8x + 24}$

$= \dfrac{4}{x(x - 2)} \cdot \dfrac{5x(2 - x)}{8(x + 3)}$

$= \dfrac{-5}{2(x + 3)}$

Note that

$\dfrac{2 - x}{x - 2} = -1$

CHECK YOURSELF 2

Multiply as indicated.

1. $\dfrac{x^2 - 5x - 14}{4x^2} \cdot \dfrac{8x + 56}{x^2 - 49}$ 2. $\dfrac{x}{2x - 6} \cdot \dfrac{3x - x^2}{2}$

The following algorithm summarizes our work in multiplying rational expressions.

MULTIPLYING RATIONAL EXPRESSIONS

STEP 1   Write each numerator and denominator in completely factored form.

STEP 2   Divide by any common factors appearing in both a numerator and a denominator.

STEP 3   Multiply as needed to form the desired product.

In dividing rational expressions, you can again use your experience from arithmetic. Recall that

We invert the *divisor* (*the second fraction*) and multiply.

$$\frac{3}{5} \div \frac{2}{3} = \frac{3}{5} \cdot \frac{3}{2} = \frac{9}{10}$$

Once more, the pattern in algebra is identical.

DIVIDING RATIONAL EXPRESSIONS

For polynomials P, Q, R, and S,

$$\frac{P}{Q} \div \frac{R}{S} = \frac{P}{Q} \cdot \frac{S}{R} = \frac{PS}{QR}$$

where $Q \neq 0$, $R \neq 0$, and $S \neq 0$.

To divide rational expressions, invert the divisor and multiply as before. The following example illustrates.

Example 3

Divide as indicated.

Invert the divisor and multiply.

(a) $\dfrac{3x^2}{8x^3y} \div \dfrac{9x^2y^2}{4y^4} = \dfrac{3x^2}{8x^3y} \cdot \dfrac{4y^4}{9x^2y^2} = \dfrac{y}{6x^3}$

Be Careful: Invert the divisor, then factor.

(b) $\dfrac{2x^2 + 4xy}{9x - 18y} \div \dfrac{4x + 8y}{3x - 6y} = \dfrac{2x^2 + 4xy}{9x - 18y} \cdot \dfrac{3x - 6y}{4x + 8y}$

$$= \frac{\cancel{2}x(x + 2y)}{\underset{3}{\cancel{9}}(x - 2y)} \cdot \frac{\cancel{3}(x - 2y)}{\underset{2}{\cancel{4}}(x + 2y)} = \frac{x}{6}$$

(c) $\dfrac{2x^2 - x - 6}{4x^2 + 6x} \div \dfrac{x^2 - 4}{4x} = \dfrac{2x^2 - x - 6}{4x^2 + 6x} \cdot \dfrac{4x}{x^2 - 4}$

$$= \frac{(2x + 3)(x - 2)}{2x(2x + 3)} \cdot \frac{4x}{(x + 2)(x - 2)} = \frac{2}{x + 2}$$

CHECK YOURSELF 3

Divide and simplify.

1. $\dfrac{5xy}{7x^3} \div \dfrac{10y^2}{14x^3}$ 2. $\dfrac{3x - 9y}{2x + 10y} \div \dfrac{x^2 - 3xy}{4x^2 + 20xy}$

3. $\dfrac{x^2 - 9}{x^3 - 27} \div \dfrac{x^2 - 2x - 15}{2x^2 - 10x}$

Let's summarize our work in dividing fractions with an algorithm.

DIVIDING RATIONAL EXPRESSIONS

STEP 1   Invert the divisor (the *second* rational expression) to write the problem as one of multiplication

STEP 2   Proceed as in the algorithm for multiplication of rational expressions.

CHECK YOURSELF ANSWERS

1. $\dfrac{4a}{3b^2}$.

2. (1) $\dfrac{2(x+2)}{x^2}$; (2) $\dfrac{-x^2}{4}$.

3. (1) $\dfrac{x}{y}$; (2) 6; (3) $\dfrac{2x}{x^2 + 3x + 9}$.

Name _____

Date _____

Exercises

ANSWERS

Build Your Skills

1. _____

Multiply or divide as indicated. Express your result in simplest form.

2. _____

1. $\dfrac{x^2}{3} \cdot \dfrac{6x}{x^4}$

2. $\dfrac{-y^3}{10} \cdot \dfrac{15y}{y^6}$

3. _____

3. $\dfrac{a}{7a^3} \div \dfrac{a^2}{21}$

4. $\dfrac{p^5}{8} \div \dfrac{-p^2}{12p}$

4. _____

5. _____

5. $\dfrac{4xy^2}{15x^3} \cdot \dfrac{25xy}{16y^3}$

6. $\dfrac{3x^3y}{10xy^3} \cdot \dfrac{5xy^2}{-9xy^3}$

6. _____

7. _____

7. $\dfrac{8b^3}{15ab} \div \dfrac{2ab^2}{20ab^3}$

8. $\dfrac{4x^2y^2}{9x^3} \div \dfrac{-8y^2}{27xy}$

8. _____

9. _____

9. $\dfrac{m^3n}{2mn} \cdot \dfrac{6mn^2}{m^3n} \div \dfrac{3mn}{5m^2n}$

10. $\dfrac{4cd^2}{5cd} \cdot \dfrac{3c^3d}{2c^2d} \div \dfrac{9cd}{20cd^3}$

10. _____

11. $\dfrac{5x + 15}{3x} \cdot \dfrac{9x^2}{2x + 6}$

12. $\dfrac{a^2 - 3a}{5a} \cdot \dfrac{20a^2}{3a - 9}$

11. _____

12. _____

13. $\dfrac{3b - 15}{6b} \div \dfrac{4b - 20}{9b^2}$

14. $\dfrac{7m^2 + 28m}{4m} \div \dfrac{5m + 20}{12m^2}$

13. _____

14. _____

15. $\dfrac{x^2 - 3x - 10}{5x} \cdot \dfrac{15x^2}{3x - 15}$

16. $\dfrac{y^2 - 8y}{4y} \cdot \dfrac{12y^2}{y^2 - 64}$

15. _____

16. _____

ANSWERS

17. _____

18. _____

19. _____

20. _____

21. _____

22. _____

23. _____

24. _____

25. _____

26. _____

27. _____

28. _____

29. _____

30. _____

31. _____

32. _____

17. $\dfrac{c^2 + 2c - 8}{6c} \div \dfrac{5c + 20}{18c}$

18. $\dfrac{m^2 - 49}{5m} \div \dfrac{3m + 21}{20m^2}$

19. $\dfrac{x^2 - 2x - 8}{4x - 16} \cdot \dfrac{10x}{x^2 - 4}$

20. $\dfrac{y^2 + 7y + 10}{y^2 + 5y} \cdot \dfrac{2y}{y^2 - 4}$

21. $\dfrac{d^2 - 3d - 18}{16d - 96} \div \dfrac{d^2 - 9}{20d}$

22. $\dfrac{b^2 + 6b + 8}{b^2 + 4b} \div \dfrac{b^2 - 4}{2b}$

23. $\dfrac{2x^2 - x - 3}{3x^2 + 7x + 4} \cdot \dfrac{3x^2 - 11x - 20}{4x^2 - 9}$

24. $\dfrac{4p^2 - 1}{2p^2 - 9p - 5} \cdot \dfrac{3p^2 - 13p - 10}{9p^2 - 4}$

25. $\dfrac{a^2 - 9}{2a^2 - 6a} \div \dfrac{2a^2 + 5a - 3}{4a^2 - 1}$

26. $\dfrac{2x^2 - 5x - 7}{4x^2 - 9} \div \dfrac{5x^2 + 5x}{2x^2 + 3x}$

27. $\dfrac{2w - 6}{w^2 + 2w} \cdot \dfrac{3w}{3 - w}$

28. $\dfrac{3y - 15}{y^2 + 3y} \cdot \dfrac{4y}{5 - y}$

29. $\dfrac{a - 7}{2a + 6} \div \dfrac{21 - 3a}{a^2 + 3a}$

30. $\dfrac{x - 4}{x^2 + 2x} \div \dfrac{16 - 4x}{3x + 6}$

31. $\dfrac{x^2 - 9y^2}{2x^2 - xy - 15y^2} \cdot \dfrac{4x + 10y}{x^2 + 3xy}$

32. $\dfrac{2a^2 - 7ab - 15b^2}{2ab - 10b^2} \cdot \dfrac{2a^2 - 3ab}{4a^2 - 9b^2}$

ANSWERS

33. _____

33. $\dfrac{3m^2 - 5mn + 2n^2}{9m^2 - 4n^2} \div \dfrac{m^3 - m^2n}{9m^2 + 6mn}$

34. $\dfrac{2x^2y - 5xy^2}{4x^2 - 25y^2} \div \dfrac{4x^2 + 20xy}{2x^2 + 15xy + 25y^2}$

34. _____

35. $\dfrac{x^3 + 8}{x^2 - 4} \cdot \dfrac{5x - 10}{x^3 - 2x^2 + 4x}$

36. $\dfrac{a^3 - 27}{a^2 - 9} \div \dfrac{a^3 + 3a^2 + 9a}{3a^3 + 9a^2}$

35. _____

Skillscan

Perform the indicated operations.

36. _____

a. $\dfrac{7}{16} + \dfrac{3}{16}$

b. $\dfrac{5}{12} - \dfrac{1}{12}$

a. _____

c. $\dfrac{3}{4} + \dfrac{1}{2}$

d. $\dfrac{7}{10} - \dfrac{3}{5}$

b. _____

e. $\dfrac{5}{6} + \dfrac{3}{8}$

f. $\dfrac{7}{8} - \dfrac{3}{5}$

c. _____

g. $\dfrac{5}{12} + \dfrac{7}{16}$

h. $\dfrac{9}{10} - \dfrac{2}{15}$

d. _____

e. _____

f. _____

ANSWERS

g. _____

1. $\dfrac{2}{x}$ 3. $\dfrac{3}{a^4}$ 5. $\dfrac{5}{12x}$ 7. $\dfrac{16b^3}{3a}$ 9. $5mn$ 11. $\dfrac{15x}{2}$ 13. $\dfrac{9b}{8}$ 15. $x^2 + 2x$

17. $\dfrac{3(c - 2)}{5}$ 19. $\dfrac{5x}{2(x - 2)}$ 21. $\dfrac{5d}{4(d - 3)}$ 23. $\dfrac{x - 5}{2x + 3}$ 25. $\dfrac{2a + 1}{2a}$

27. $\dfrac{-6}{w + 2}$ 29. $\dfrac{-a}{6}$ 31. $\dfrac{2}{x}$ 33. $\dfrac{3}{m}$ 35. $\dfrac{5}{x}$ a. $\dfrac{5}{8}$ b. $\dfrac{1}{3}$ c. $\dfrac{5}{4}$ d. $\dfrac{1}{10}$

h. _____

e. $\dfrac{29}{24}$ f. $\dfrac{11}{40}$ g. $\dfrac{41}{48}$ h. $\dfrac{23}{30}$

Addition and Subtraction of Rational Expressions

OBJECTIVES
1. To add rational expressions
2. To subtract rational expressions

Adding or subtracting two arithmetic fractions with the same denominator is straightforward. The same is true in algebra. To add or subtract two rational expressions with the same denominator, we add or subtract their numerators and then write that sum or difference over the common denominator. In symbols:

ADDING OR SUBTRACTING RATIONAL EXPRESSIONS

$$\frac{P}{R} + \frac{Q}{R} = \frac{P+Q}{R}$$

and

$$\frac{P}{R} - \frac{Q}{R} = \frac{P-Q}{R}$$

where $R \neq 0$.

Example 1*

Perform the indicated operations.

Since we have common denominators, we simply perform the indicated operations on the numerators.

$$\frac{3}{2a^2} - \frac{1}{2a^2} + \frac{5}{2a^2} = \frac{3-1+5}{2a^2}$$
$$= \frac{7}{2a^2}$$

CHECK YOURSELF 1

Perform the indicated operations.

$$\frac{5}{3y^2} + \frac{4}{3y^2} - \frac{7}{3y^2}$$

The sum or difference of rational expressions should always be expressed in simplest form. Consider the following example.

*A screen is used to indicate an expression that is being simplified.

Example 2

Add or subtract as indicated.

(a) $\dfrac{5x}{x^2 - 9} + \dfrac{15}{x^2 - 9}$ Add the numerators.

$= \dfrac{5x + 15}{x^2 - 9}$

$= \dfrac{5(x + 3)}{(x - 3)(x + 3)} = \dfrac{5}{x - 3}$ Factor and divide by the common factor.

(b) $\dfrac{3x + y}{2x} - \dfrac{x - 3y}{2x} = \dfrac{(3x + y) - (x - 3y)}{2x}$ Be sure to *enclose the second numerator* in parentheses.
Remove the parentheses by *changing each sign.*

$= \dfrac{3x + y - x + 3y}{2x}$

$= \dfrac{2x + 4y}{2x} = \dfrac{2(x + 2y)}{2x}$ Factor and divide by the common factor of 2.

$= \dfrac{x + 2y}{x}$

CHECK YOURSELF 2

Perform the indicated operations.

1. $\dfrac{6a}{a^2 - 2a - 8} + \dfrac{12}{a^2 - 2a - 8}$ 2. $\dfrac{5x - y}{3y} - \dfrac{2x - 4y}{3y}$

Now, what if our rational expressions *do not* have common denominators? In that case, we must use the least common denominator (LCD). The *least common denominator* is the simplest polynomial that is divisible by each of the individual denominators. Each expression in the desired sum or difference is then "built up" to an equivalent expression having that LCD as a denominator. We can then add or subtract as before.

While in many cases we can find the LCD by inspection, we can state a procedure for finding the LCD that is similar to the one used in arithmetic.

Again we see the key role that factoring plays in the process of working with rational expressions.

FINDING THE LEAST COMMON DENOMINATOR

STEP 1 Write each of the denominators in completely factored form.

STEP 2 Write the LCD as the product of each prime factor to the highest power to which it appears in the factored form of any individual denominators.

The following example illustrates the procedure.

Example 3

Find the LCD for each of the following pairs of rational expressions.

(a) $\dfrac{3}{4x^2}$ and $\dfrac{5}{6xy}$

Factor the denominators.

You may very well be able to find this LCD by inspecting the numerical coefficients and the variable factors.

$4x^2 = 2^2 \cdot x^2$

$6xy = 2 \cdot 3 \cdot x \cdot y$

The LCD must have the factors

$2^2 \cdot 3 \cdot x^2 \cdot y$

and so $12x^2y$ is the desired LCD.

(b) $\dfrac{7}{x-3}$ and $\dfrac{2}{x+5}$

Here neither denominator can be factored. The LCD must have the factors $x - 3$ and $x + 5$. So the LCD is

It is generally best to leave the LCD in this factored form.

$(x - 3)(x + 5)$

CHECK YOURSELF 3

Find the LCD for the following pairs of rational expressions.

1. $\dfrac{3}{8a^3}$ and $\dfrac{5}{6a^2}$

2. $\dfrac{4}{x+7}$ and $\dfrac{3}{x-5}$

Let's see how factoring techniques are applied in the following example.

Example 4

Find the LCD for the following pairs of rational expressions.

(a) $\dfrac{2}{x^2-x-6}$ and $\dfrac{1}{x^2-9}$

Factoring, we have

$x^2 - x - 6 = (x + 2)(x - 3)$

and

$x^2 - 9 = (x + 3)(x - 3)$

The LCD of the given expressions is then

The LCD must contain *each* of the factors appearing in the original denominators.

$$(x + 2)(x - 3)(x + 3)$$

(b) $\dfrac{5}{x^2 - 4x + 4}$ and $\dfrac{3}{x^2 + 2x - 8}$

Again we factor:

$$x^2 - 4x + 4 = (x - 2)^2$$
$$x^2 + 2x - 8 = (x - 2)(x + 4)$$

The LCD must contain $(x - 2)^2$ as a factor since $x - 2$ appears *twice* as a factor in the first denominator.

The LCD is then

$$(x - 2)^2(x + 4)$$

CHECK YOURSELF 4

Find the LCD for the following pairs of rational expressions.

1. $\dfrac{3}{x^2 - 2x - 15}$ and $\dfrac{5}{x^2 - 25}$

2. $\dfrac{5}{y^2 + 6y + 9}$ and $\dfrac{3}{y^2 - y - 12}$

Let's look at some examples where the concept of the LCD is applied in adding or subtracting rational expressions.

Example 5

Add or subtract as indicated.

(a) $\dfrac{5}{4xy} + \dfrac{3}{2x^2}$

The LCD for $2x^2$ and $4xy$ is $4x^2y$. We rewrite each of the rational expressions with the LCD as a denominator.

Note that in each case we are multiplying by 1, $\dfrac{x}{x}$ in the first fraction and $\dfrac{2y}{2y}$ in the second fraction. That's why the resulting fractions are equivalent to the original ones.

$$\frac{5}{4xy} + \frac{3}{2x^2} = \frac{5 \cdot x}{4xy \cdot x} + \frac{3 \cdot 2y}{2x^2 \cdot 2y}$$

$$= \frac{5x}{4x^2y} + \frac{6y}{4x^2y} = \frac{5x + 6y}{4x^2y}$$

(b) $\dfrac{3}{a - 3} - \dfrac{2}{a}$

The LCD for a and $a - 3$ is $a(a - 3)$. We rewrite each of the rational expressions with that LCD as a denominator.

$$\frac{3}{a - 3} - \frac{2}{a}$$

$$= \frac{3a}{a(a - 3)} - \frac{2(a - 3)}{a(a - 3)}$$

Subtract the numerators.

$$= \frac{3a - 2(a - 3)}{a(a - 3)}$$

Remove the parentheses, and combine like terms.

$$= \frac{3a - 2a + 6}{a(a - 3)} = \frac{a + 6}{a(a - 3)}$$

CHECK YOURSELF 5

Perform the indicated operations.

1. $\dfrac{3}{2ab} + \dfrac{4}{5b^2}$

2. $\dfrac{5}{y + 2} - \dfrac{3}{y}$

Let's proceed to an example in which factoring will be required in forming the LCD.

Example 6

Add or subtract as indicated.

(a) $\dfrac{-5}{x^2 - 3x - 4} + \dfrac{8}{x^2 - 16}$

We first factor the two denominators.

$$x^2 - 3x - 4 = (x + 1)(x - 4)$$
$$x^2 - 16 = (x + 4)(x - 4)$$

We see that the LCD must be

$$(x + 1)(x + 4)(x - 4)$$

Again, rewriting the original expressions gives

We use the facts that

$\dfrac{x + 4}{x + 4} = 1$ and

$\dfrac{x + 1}{x + 1} = 1$

$$\frac{-5}{(x + 1)(x - 4)} + \frac{8}{(x - 4)(x + 4)}$$

$$= \frac{-5(x + 4)}{(x + 1)(x - 4)(x + 4)} + \frac{8(x + 1)}{(x - 4)(x + 4)(x + 1)}$$

Now add the numerators.

$$= \frac{-5(x + 4) + 8(x + 1)}{(x + 1)(x - 4)(x + 4)}$$

$$= \frac{-5x - 20 + 8x + 8}{(x + 1)(x - 4)(x + 4)}$$

Combine like terms in the numerator.

$$= \frac{3x - 12}{(x + 1)(x - 4)(x + 4)}$$

Factor and divide by the common factor of $x - 4$.

$$= \frac{3(x - 4)}{(x + 1)(x - 4)(x + 4)}$$

$$= \frac{3}{(x + 1)(x + 4)}$$

(b) $\dfrac{5}{x^2 - 5x + 6} - \dfrac{3}{4x - 12}$

Again factor the denominators.

$$x^2 - 5x + 6 = (x - 2)(x - 3)$$
$$4x - 12 = 4(x - 3)$$

The LCD is $4(x - 2)(x - 3)$, and proceeding as before, we have

$$\frac{5}{(x - 2)(x - 3)} - \frac{3}{4(x - 3)}$$

$$= \frac{5 \cdot 4}{4(x - 2)(x - 3)} - \frac{3(x - 2)}{4(x - 2)(x - 3)}$$

Simplify the numerator, and combine like terms.

$$= \frac{20 - 3(x - 2)}{4(x - 2)(x - 3)} = \frac{20 - 3x + 6}{4(x - 2)(x - 3)} = \frac{-3x + 26}{4(x - 2)(x - 3)}$$

CHECK YOURSELF 6

Add or subtract as indicated.

1. $\dfrac{-4}{x^2 - 4} + \dfrac{7}{x^2 - 3x - 10}$　　　　2. $\dfrac{5}{3x - 9} - \dfrac{2}{x^2 - 9}$

Our next example will look slightly different from those you have seen thus far, but the reasoning involved in performing the subtraction is exactly the same.

Example 7

Subtract

$$3 - \frac{5}{2x - 1}$$

To perform the subtraction, remember that 3 is equivalent to the fraction $\dfrac{3}{1}$, so

$$3 - \frac{5}{2x - 1} = \frac{3}{1} - \frac{5}{2x - 1}$$

The LCD for 1 and $2x - 1$ is just $2x - 1$. We now rewrite the first expression with that denominator:

$$3 - \frac{5}{2x - 1} = \frac{3(2x - 1)}{2x - 1} - \frac{5}{2x - 1}$$

$$= \frac{3(2x - 1) - 5}{2x - 1} = \frac{6x - 8}{2x - 1}$$

CHECK YOURSELF 7

Subtract.

$$\frac{4}{3x + 1} - 3$$

Our final example uses an observation from our coverage of simplification of rational expressions. Remember that

$$a - b = -(b - a)$$
$$= -1(b - a)$$

Let's see how this is used in adding rational expressions.

Example 8

Add

$$\frac{x^2}{x - 5} + \frac{3x + 10}{5 - x}$$

Your first thought might be to use a denominator of $(x - 5)(5 - x)$. However, we can simplify our work considerably by using the observation above. Multiply the numerator and denominator of the second fraction by -1:

Use

$$\frac{-1}{-1} = 1$$

Note that

$(-1)(5 - x) = x - 5$

The fractions now have a common denominator, and we can add as before.

$$\frac{x^2}{x - 5} + \frac{3x + 10}{5 - x}$$

$$= \frac{x^2}{x - 5} + \frac{(-1)(3x + 10)}{(-1)(5 - x)}$$

$$= \frac{x^2}{x - 5} + \frac{-3x - 10}{x - 5}$$

$$= \frac{x^2 - 3x - 10}{x - 5}$$

$$= \frac{(x + 2)(x - 5)}{x - 5}$$

$$= x + 2$$

CHECK YOURSELF 8

Add.

$$\frac{x^2}{x - 7} + \frac{10x - 21}{7 - x}$$

CHECK YOURSELF ANSWERS

1. $\dfrac{2}{3y^2}$.

2. (1) $\dfrac{6}{a - 4}$; (2) $\dfrac{x + y}{y}$.

3. (1) $24a^3$; (2) $(x + 7)(x - 5)$.

4. (1) $(x - 5)(x + 5)(x + 3)$; (2) $(y + 3)^2(y - 4)$.

5. (1) $\dfrac{8a + 15b}{10ab^2}$; (2) $\dfrac{2y - 6}{y(y + 2)}$.

6. (1) $\dfrac{3}{(x - 2)(x - 5)}$; (2) $\dfrac{5x + 9}{3(x + 3)(x - 3)}$.

7. $\dfrac{-9x + 1}{3x + 1}$.

8. $x - 3$.

Name _____

Date _____

Exercises

ANSWERS

Build Your Skills

1. _____

Perform the indicated operations. Express your results in simplest form.

2. _____

1. $\dfrac{7}{2x^2} + \dfrac{5}{2x^2}$

2. $\dfrac{11}{3b^3} - \dfrac{2}{3b^3}$

3. _____

3. $\dfrac{5}{3a + 7} + \dfrac{2}{3a + 7}$

4. $\dfrac{6}{5x + 3} - \dfrac{3}{5x + 3}$

4. _____

5. $\dfrac{2x}{x - 3} - \dfrac{6}{x - 3}$

6. $\dfrac{7w}{w + 3} + \dfrac{21}{w + 3}$

5. _____

6. _____

7. $\dfrac{y^2}{2y + 8} + \dfrac{3y - 4}{2y + 8}$

8. $\dfrac{x^2}{4x - 12} - \dfrac{9}{4x - 12}$

7. _____

9. $\dfrac{4m - 7}{m - 5} - \dfrac{2m + 3}{m - 5}$

10. $\dfrac{3b - 8}{b - 6} + \dfrac{b - 16}{b - 6}$

8. _____

9. _____

11. $\dfrac{x - 7}{x^2 - x - 6} + \dfrac{2x - 2}{x^2 - x - 6}$

12. $\dfrac{5x - 12}{x^2 - 8x + 15} - \dfrac{3x - 2}{x^2 - 8x + 15}$

10. _____

13. $\dfrac{5}{3x} + \dfrac{3}{2x}$

14. $\dfrac{4}{5w} - \dfrac{3}{4w}$

11. _____

12. _____

13. _____

14. _____

ANSWERS

15. _____

16. _____

17. _____

18. _____

19. _____

20. _____

21. _____

22. _____

23. _____

24. _____

25. _____

26. _____

27. _____

28. _____

15. $\dfrac{6}{a} + \dfrac{3}{a^2}$

16. $\dfrac{3}{p} - \dfrac{7}{p^2}$

17. $\dfrac{2}{m} - \dfrac{2}{n}$

18. $\dfrac{3}{x} + \dfrac{3}{y}$

19. $\dfrac{3}{4b^2} - \dfrac{5}{3b^3}$

20. $\dfrac{4}{5x^3} - \dfrac{3}{2x^2}$

21. $\dfrac{2}{a} - \dfrac{1}{a-2}$

22. $\dfrac{4}{c} + \dfrac{3}{c+1}$

23. $\dfrac{2}{x+1} + \dfrac{3}{x+2}$

24. $\dfrac{4}{y-1} + \dfrac{2}{y+3}$

25. $\dfrac{5}{y-3} - \dfrac{1}{y+1}$

26. $\dfrac{4}{x+5} - \dfrac{3}{x-1}$

27. $\dfrac{2w}{w-7} + \dfrac{w}{w-2}$

28. $\dfrac{3n}{n+5} + \dfrac{n}{n-4}$

ANSWERS

29. _____

30. _____

31. _____

32. _____

33. _____

34. _____

35. _____

36. _____

37. _____

38. _____

39. _____

40. _____

41. _____

42. _____

43. _____

44. _____

29. $\dfrac{3x}{3x-2} - \dfrac{2x}{2x+1}$

30. $\dfrac{5c}{5c-1} + \dfrac{2c}{2c-3}$

31. $\dfrac{6}{m-7} + \dfrac{2}{7-m}$

32. $\dfrac{5}{a-5} - \dfrac{3}{5-a}$

33. $\dfrac{3}{x^2-16} + \dfrac{2}{x-4}$

34. $\dfrac{5}{y^2+5y+6} + \dfrac{2}{y+2}$

35. $\dfrac{4m}{m^2-3m+2} - \dfrac{1}{m-2}$

36. $\dfrac{x}{x^2-1} - \dfrac{2}{x+1}$

37. $\dfrac{6y}{y^2-8y+15} + \dfrac{9}{y-3}$

38. $\dfrac{8a}{a^2-8a+12} + \dfrac{4}{a-2}$

39. $\dfrac{6x}{x^2-10x+24} - \dfrac{18}{x-6}$

40. $\dfrac{21p}{p^2-3p-10} - \dfrac{15}{p-5}$

41. $\dfrac{2}{z^2-4} + \dfrac{3}{z^2+2z-8}$

42. $\dfrac{5}{x^2-3x-10} + \dfrac{2}{x^2-25}$

43. $\dfrac{6w}{w^2-9} - \dfrac{5w}{w^2+w-6}$

44. $\dfrac{4b}{b^2+6b+5} + \dfrac{2b}{b^2-1}$

ANSWERS

Skillscan (Multiplication and Division of Rational Expressions)

a. _____

b. _____

c. _____

d. _____

e. _____

f. _____

g. _____

h. _____

Multiply.

a. $\dfrac{3}{10} \cdot 20$ b. $\dfrac{7}{12} \cdot 24$

c. $\dfrac{6}{a^2} \cdot a^2$ d. $\dfrac{9}{w^2} \cdot w^3$

e. $\dfrac{2}{mn} \cdot mn^2$ f. $\dfrac{3}{x^2} \cdot x^2 y^2$

g. $\dfrac{5}{rs} \cdot r^2 s^2$ h. $\dfrac{3}{a^2 b} \cdot a^2 b^2$

ANSWERS

1. $\dfrac{6}{x^2}$ 3. $\dfrac{7}{3a+7}$ 5. 2 7. $\dfrac{y-1}{2}$ 9. 2 11. $\dfrac{3}{x+2}$ 13. $\dfrac{19}{6x}$ 15. $\dfrac{3(2a+1)}{a^2}$

17. $\dfrac{2(n+m)}{mn}$ 19. $\dfrac{9b-20}{12b^3}$ 21. $\dfrac{a-4}{a(a-2)}$ 23. $\dfrac{5x+7}{(x+1)(x+2)}$ 25. $\dfrac{4(y+2)}{(y-3)(y+1)}$

27. $\dfrac{w(3w-11)}{(w-7)(w-2)}$ 29. $\dfrac{7x}{(3x-2)(2x+1)}$ 31. $\dfrac{4}{m-7}$ 33. $\dfrac{2x+11}{(x+4)(x-4)}$

35. $\dfrac{3m+1}{(m-1)(m-2)}$ 37. $\dfrac{15}{y-5}$ 39. $\dfrac{-12}{x-4}$ 41. $\dfrac{5z+14}{(z+2)(z-2)(z+4)}$

43. $\dfrac{w}{(w-3)(w-2)}$ a. 6 b. 14 c. 6 d. $9w$ e. $2n$ f. $3y^2$ g. $5rs$ h. $3b$

Complex Fractions

OBJECTIVE
To simplify complex fractions

Our work in this section deals with simplifying complex fractions. A complex fraction is a fraction that has a fraction in its numerator or denominator (or both).

Some examples are

$$\frac{\dfrac{5}{6}}{\dfrac{3}{4}} \qquad \frac{\dfrac{4}{x}}{\dfrac{3}{x+1}} \qquad \text{and} \qquad \frac{1+\dfrac{1}{x}}{1-\dfrac{1}{x}}$$

Fundamental principle:

$$\frac{P}{Q} = \frac{PR}{QR}$$

where $Q \neq 0$ and $R \neq 0$

Method 1 By the fundamental principle we can always multiply the numerator and denominator of a fraction by the same nonzero quantity. In simplifying a complex fraction, we multiply the numerator and denominator by the LCD of all fractions that appear within the complex fraction.

Here the denominators are 5 and 10, so we can write

Again we are multiplying by $\frac{10}{10}$, or 1.

$$\frac{\dfrac{3}{5}}{\dfrac{7}{10}} = \frac{\dfrac{3}{5} \cdot 10}{\dfrac{7}{10} \cdot 10} = \frac{6}{7}$$

Method 2 Our second approach interprets the complex fraction as indicating division and applies our earlier work in dividing fractions. The numerator and denominator of the complex fraction are written as single fractions. The division step follows.

Invert and multiply.

$$\frac{\dfrac{3}{5}}{\dfrac{7}{10}} = \frac{3}{5} \div \frac{7}{10} = \frac{3}{5} \cdot \frac{10}{7} = \frac{6}{7}$$

Which method is best? The answer depends on the expression you are trying to simplify. Both approaches are effective, and you should be familiar with both. With practice you will be able to tell which method may be easier to use in a particular situation.

Let's look at the same two methods applied to the simplification of an algebraic complex fraction.

Example 1*

Simplify

$$\frac{1 + \dfrac{2x}{y}}{2 - \dfrac{x}{y}}$$

Method 1 The LCD of 1, $\dfrac{2x}{y}$, 2, and $\dfrac{x}{y}$ is y. So we multiply the numerator and denominator by y:

Use $\dfrac{y}{y} = 1$

$$\frac{1 + \dfrac{2x}{y}}{2 - \dfrac{x}{y}} = \frac{\left(1 + \dfrac{2x}{y}\right) \cdot y}{\left(2 - \dfrac{x}{y}\right) \cdot y}$$ Distribute y over the numerator and denominator.

$$= \frac{1 \cdot y + \dfrac{2x}{y} \cdot y}{2 \cdot y - \dfrac{x}{y} \cdot y}$$ Simplify.

$$= \frac{y + 2x}{2y - x}$$

Method 2 In this approach we must *first work separately* in the numerator and denominator to form single fractions.

Make sure you understand the steps in forming a single fraction in the numerator and denominator.

$$\frac{1 + \dfrac{2x}{y}}{2 - \dfrac{x}{y}} = \frac{\dfrac{y + 2x}{y}}{\dfrac{2y - x}{y}}$$

Invert the divisor and multiply.

$$= \frac{y + 2x}{y} \cdot \frac{y}{2y - x}$$

$$= \frac{y + 2x}{2y - x}$$

CHECK YOURSELF 1

Simplify.

$$\frac{\dfrac{x}{y} - 1}{\dfrac{2x}{y} + 2}$$

*A screen is used to indicate an expression that is being simplified.

Again, simplifying a complex fraction means writing an equivalent simple fraction in lowest terms. The following example illustrates.

Example 2

Simplify

$$\frac{1 - \dfrac{2y}{x} + \dfrac{y^2}{x^2}}{1 - \dfrac{y^2}{x^2}}$$

We choose the first method of simplification in this case. The LCD of all the fractions that appear is x^2. So we multiply the numerator and denominator by x^2.

Distribute x^2 over the numerator and denominator, and simplify.

$$\frac{1 - \dfrac{2y}{x} + \dfrac{y^2}{x^2}}{1 - \dfrac{y^2}{x^2}} = \frac{\left(1 - \dfrac{2y}{x} + \dfrac{y^2}{x^2}\right) \cdot x^2}{\left(1 - \dfrac{y^2}{x^2}\right) \cdot x^2}$$

$$= \frac{x^2 - 2xy + y^2}{x^2 - y^2}$$

Factor the numerator and denominator, and divide by the common factor $x - y$.

$$= \frac{(x - y)(x - y)}{(x + y)(x - y)} = \frac{x - y}{x + y}$$

CHECK YOURSELF 2

Simplify.

$$\frac{1 + \dfrac{5}{x} + \dfrac{6}{x^2}}{1 - \dfrac{9}{x^2}}$$

We will illustrate the second method of simplification for purposes of comparison.

Example 3

Simplify

$$\frac{1 - \dfrac{1}{x + 2}}{x - \dfrac{2}{x - 1}}$$

Form single fractions in the numerator and denominator:

Again, take time to make sure you understand how the numerator and denominator are rewritten as single fractions.

Note Method 2 is probably the more efficient in this case. The LCD of the denominators would be $(x + 2)(x - 1)$, leading to a somewhat more complicated process if method 1 were used.

$$\frac{1 - \dfrac{1}{x + 2}}{x - \dfrac{2}{x - 1}} = \frac{\dfrac{x + 1}{x + 2}}{\dfrac{x^2 - x - 2}{x - 1}}$$

$$= \frac{x + 1}{x + 2} \cdot \frac{x - 1}{x^2 - x - 2}$$

$$= \frac{x + 1}{x + 2} \cdot \frac{x - 1}{(x - 2)(x + 1)}$$

$$= \frac{x - 1}{(x + 2)(x - 2)}$$

CHECK YOURSELF 3

Simplify.

$$\frac{2 + \dfrac{5}{x - 3}}{x - \dfrac{1}{2x + 1}}$$

The following algorithm summarizes our work with complex fractions.

SIMPLIFYING COMPLEX FRACTIONS

METHOD 1

1. Multiply the numerator and denominator of the complex fraction by the LCD of all the fractions that appear within the numerator and denominator.
2. Simplify the resulting rational expression, writing the expression in lowest terms.

METHOD 2

1. Write the numerator and denominator of the complex fraction as single fractions, if necessary.
2. Invert the denominator and multiply as before, writing the result in lowest terms.

CHECK YOURSELF ANSWERS

1. $\dfrac{x - y}{2x + 2y}$.   2. $\dfrac{x + 2}{x - 3}$.   3. $\dfrac{2x + 1}{(x - 3)(x + 1)}$.

Name _____

Date _____

Exercises

ANSWERS

Build Your Skills

1. _____

Simplify each of the following complex fractions.

2. _____

1. $\dfrac{\dfrac{2}{3}}{\dfrac{6}{8}}$

2. $\dfrac{\dfrac{5}{6}}{\dfrac{10}{15}}$

3. _____

3. $\dfrac{\dfrac{2}{3} + \dfrac{1}{2}}{\dfrac{3}{4} - \dfrac{1}{3}}$

4. $\dfrac{\dfrac{3}{4} + \dfrac{1}{2}}{\dfrac{7}{8} - \dfrac{1}{4}}$

4. _____

5. $\dfrac{2 + \dfrac{1}{3}}{3 - \dfrac{1}{5}}$

6. $\dfrac{1 + \dfrac{3}{4}}{2 - \dfrac{1}{8}}$

5. _____

6. _____

7. $\dfrac{\dfrac{x}{8}}{\dfrac{x^2}{4}}$

8. $\dfrac{\dfrac{a^2}{10}}{\dfrac{a^3}{15}}$

7. _____

9. $\dfrac{\dfrac{3}{m}}{\dfrac{6}{m^2}}$

10. $\dfrac{\dfrac{15}{x^2}}{\dfrac{20}{x^3}}$

8. _____

9. _____

10. _____

ANSWERS

11. _____

12. _____

13. _____

14. _____

15. _____

16. _____

17. _____

18. _____

19. _____

20. _____

21. _____

22. _____

11. $\dfrac{\dfrac{y+1}{y}}{\dfrac{y-1}{2y}}$

12. $\dfrac{\dfrac{x+3}{4x}}{\dfrac{x-3}{2x}}$

13. $\dfrac{\dfrac{a+2b}{3a}}{\dfrac{a^2+2ab}{9b}}$

14. $\dfrac{\dfrac{m-3n}{4m}}{\dfrac{m^2-3mn}{8n}}$

15. $\dfrac{\dfrac{x-2}{x^2-9}}{\dfrac{x^2-4}{x^2+3x}}$

16. $\dfrac{\dfrac{x+5}{x^2-6x}}{\dfrac{x^2-25}{x^2-36}}$

17. $\dfrac{2-\dfrac{1}{x}}{2+\dfrac{1}{x}}$

18. $\dfrac{3+\dfrac{1}{b}}{3-\dfrac{1}{b}}$

19. $\dfrac{\dfrac{1}{x}-\dfrac{1}{y}}{\dfrac{1}{xy}}$

20. $\dfrac{\dfrac{1}{ab}}{\dfrac{1}{a}+\dfrac{1}{b}}$

21. $\dfrac{\dfrac{x^2}{y^2}-1}{\dfrac{x}{y}+1}$

22. $\dfrac{\dfrac{m}{n}+2}{\dfrac{m^2}{n^2}-4}$

ANSWERS

23. _____

24. _____

25. _____

26. _____

27. _____

28. _____

29. _____

30. _____

31. _____

32. _____

33. _____

34. _____

23. $\dfrac{1 + \dfrac{3}{a} - \dfrac{4}{a^2}}{1 + \dfrac{2}{a} - \dfrac{3}{a^2}}$

24. $\dfrac{1 - \dfrac{2}{x} - \dfrac{8}{x^2}}{1 - \dfrac{1}{x} - \dfrac{6}{x^2}}$

25. $\dfrac{\dfrac{x^2}{y} + 2x + y}{\dfrac{1}{y^2} - \dfrac{1}{x^2}}$

26. $\dfrac{\dfrac{a}{b} + 1 - \dfrac{2b}{a}}{\dfrac{1}{b^2} - \dfrac{4}{a^2}}$

27. $\dfrac{1 + \dfrac{1}{x-1}}{1 - \dfrac{1}{x-1}}$

28. $\dfrac{2 - \dfrac{1}{m-2}}{2 + \dfrac{1}{m-2}}$

29. $\dfrac{1 - \dfrac{1}{y-1}}{y - \dfrac{8}{y+2}}$

30. $\dfrac{1 + \dfrac{1}{x+2}}{x - \dfrac{18}{x-3}}$

31. $\dfrac{\dfrac{1}{x-3} + \dfrac{1}{x+3}}{\dfrac{1}{x-3} - \dfrac{1}{x+3}}$

32. $\dfrac{\dfrac{2}{m-2} + \dfrac{1}{m-3}}{\dfrac{2}{m-2} - \dfrac{1}{m-3}}$

33. $\dfrac{\dfrac{x}{x+1} + \dfrac{1}{x-1}}{\dfrac{x}{x-1} - \dfrac{1}{x+1}}$

34. $\dfrac{\dfrac{y}{y-4} + \dfrac{1}{y+2}}{\dfrac{4}{y-4} - \dfrac{1}{y+2}}$

ANSWERS

35. _____

36. _____

37. _____

38. _____

39. _____

40. _____

35. $\dfrac{\dfrac{a+1}{a-1} - \dfrac{a-1}{a+1}}{\dfrac{a+1}{a-1} + \dfrac{a-1}{a+1}}$

36. $\dfrac{\dfrac{x+2}{x-2} - \dfrac{x-2}{x+2}}{\dfrac{x+2}{x-2} + \dfrac{x-2}{x+2}}$

37. $1 + \dfrac{1}{1 + \dfrac{1}{x}}$

38. $1 + \dfrac{1}{1 - \dfrac{1}{y}}$

39. $1 + \dfrac{1}{1 + \dfrac{1}{m-1}}$

40. $a - \dfrac{1}{1 - \dfrac{1}{a+1}}$

ANSWERS

1. $\dfrac{8}{9}$ 3. $\dfrac{14}{5}$ 5. $\dfrac{5}{6}$ 7. $\dfrac{1}{2x}$ 9. $\dfrac{m}{2}$ 11. $\dfrac{2(y+1)}{y-1}$ 13. $\dfrac{3b}{a^2}$

15. $\dfrac{x}{(x+2)(x-3)}$ 17. $\dfrac{2x-1}{2x+1}$ 19. $y-x$ 21. $\dfrac{x-y}{y}$ 23. $\dfrac{a+4}{a+3}$

25. $\dfrac{x^2y(x+y)}{x-y}$ 27. $\dfrac{x}{x-2}$ 29. $\dfrac{y+2}{(y-1)(y+4)}$ 31. $\dfrac{x}{3}$ 33. 1 35. $\dfrac{2a}{a^2+1}$

37. $\dfrac{2x+1}{x+1}$ 39. $\dfrac{2m-1}{m}$

Simplifying Rational Expressions

Rational expressions have the form

$\dfrac{x^2 - 5x}{x - 3}$ is a rational expression. The variable x cannot have the value 3.

$$\frac{P}{Q}$$ where P and Q are polynomials and Q cannot have the value 0

Fundamental Principle of Fractions   For polynomials P, Q, and R,

This uses the fact that

$$\frac{R}{R} = 1$$

where $R = 0$.

$$\frac{x^2 - 4}{x^2 - 2x - 8}$$

$$= \frac{(x - 2)(x - 2)}{(x - 4)(x \div 2)}$$

$$= \frac{x - 2}{x - 4}$$

$$\frac{P}{Q} = \frac{PR}{QR}$$ where $Q \neq 0$ and $R \neq 0$

This principle can be used in two ways. We can multiply or divide the numerator and denominator of a rational expression by the same nonzero polynomial.

Simplifying Rational Expressions   To simplify a rational expression, use the following algorithm.

1. Completely factor both the numerator and denominator of the expression.
2. Divide the numerator and denominator by *all* common factors.
3. The resulting expression will be in simplest form (or in lowest terms).

Multiplication and Division of Rational Expressions

Multiplying Rational Expressions   In symbols, the multiplication pattern is as follows: For polynomials P, Q, R, and S,

$$\frac{P}{Q} \cdot \frac{R}{S} = \frac{PR}{QS}$$

where $Q \neq 0$ and $S \neq 0$.

In practice, we apply the following algorithm to multiply two rational expressions.

$$\frac{2x - 6}{x^2 - 9} \cdot \frac{x^2 + 3x}{6x + 24}$$

$$= \frac{2(x - 3)}{(x - 3)(x \div 3)} \cdot \frac{x(x + 3)}{6(x + 4)}$$

$$= \frac{x}{3(x + 4)}$$

1. Write each numerator and denominator in completely factored form.
2. Divide by any common factors appearing in both a numerator and a denominator.
3. Multiply as needed to form the desired product.

Dividing Rational Expressions   In symbols, the division pattern is

$$\frac{P}{Q} \div \frac{R}{S} = \frac{P}{Q} \cdot \frac{S}{R} = \frac{PS}{QR}$$

where $Q \neq 0$, $R \neq 0$, and $S \neq 0$.

$$\frac{5y}{2y-8} \div \frac{10y^2}{y^2-y-12}$$

$$= \frac{5y}{2y-8} \cdot \frac{y^2-y-12}{10y^2}$$

$$= \frac{5y}{2(y-4)} \cdot \frac{(y-4)(y+3)}{10y^2}$$

$$= \frac{y+3}{4y}$$

To divide two rational expressions, you can apply the following algorithm.

1. Invert the divisor (the *second* rational expression) to write the problem as one of multiplication.

2. Proceed as in the algorithm for multiplication of rational expressions.

Adding and Subtracting Rational Expressions

To add or subtract rational expressions with the same denominator, add or subtract the numerator and then write that sum over the common denominator. The result should be written in lowest terms.

In symbols,

$$\frac{P}{R} + \frac{Q}{R} = \frac{P+Q}{R}$$

and

$$\frac{P}{R} - \frac{Q}{R} = \frac{P-Q}{R}$$

where $R \neq 0$.

$$\frac{5w}{w^2-16} - \frac{20}{w^2-16}$$

$$= \frac{5w-20}{w^2-16} =$$

$$\frac{5(w-4)}{(w+4)(w-4)}$$

$$= \frac{5}{w+4}$$

Least Common Denominator

The *least common denominator* (LCD) of a group of rational expressions is the simplest polynomial that is divisible by each of the individual denominators of the rational expressions. To find the LCD, you can use the following algorithm.

1. Write each of the denominators in completely factored form.

2. Write the LCD as the product of each prime factor, to the highest power to which it appears in the factored form of any of the denominators.

To find the LCD for

$$\frac{2}{x^2+2x+1} \quad \text{and} \quad \frac{3}{x^2+x}$$

write

$$x^2 + 2x + 1 = (x+1)(x+1)$$
$$x^2 + x = x(x+1)$$

The LCD is

$$x(x+1)(x+1)$$

$$\frac{2}{(x+1)^2} - \frac{3}{x(x+1)}$$

$$= \frac{2 \cdot x}{(x+1)^2 x} -$$

$$\frac{3(x+1)}{x(x+1)(x+1)}$$

$$= \frac{2x - 3(x+1)}{x(x+1)(x+1)}$$

$$= \frac{-x-3}{x(x+1)(x+1)}$$

Now to add or subtract rational expressions with different denominators, we first find the LCD by the procedure outlined above. We then rewrite each of the rational expressions with that LCD as a common denominator. Then we can add or subtract as before.

Complex Fractions

$$\text{Simplify } \dfrac{1 - \dfrac{2}{x}}{1 - \dfrac{4}{x^2}}.$$

Complex fractions are fractions that have a fraction in their numerator or denominator (or both).

There are two commonly used methods for simplifying complex fractions. They are outlined below.

Method 1:

$$= \frac{\left(1 - \dfrac{2}{x}\right)x^2}{\left(1 - \dfrac{4}{x^2}\right)x^2}$$

$$= \frac{x^2 - 2x}{x^2 - 4} = \frac{x(x - 2)}{(x + 2)(x - 2)}$$

$$= \frac{x}{x + 2}$$

Method 1

1. Multiply the numerator and denominator of the complex fraction by the LCD of all the fractions that appear within the numerator and denominator.
2. Simplify the resulting rational expression, writing the result in lowest terms.

Method 2:

$$= \frac{\dfrac{x - 2}{x}}{\dfrac{x^2 - 4}{x^2}}$$

$$= \frac{x - 2}{x} \cdot \frac{x^2}{x^2 - 4}$$

$$= \frac{x - 2}{x} \cdot \frac{x^2}{(x + 2)(x - 2)}$$

$$= \frac{x}{x + 2}$$

Method 2

1. Write the numerator and denominator of the complex fraction as single fractions, if necessary.
2. Then invert the denominator and multiply as before, writing the result in lowest terms.

This supplementary exercise set is provided to give you practice with each of the objectives of the chapter. Each exercise is keyed to the appropriate chapter section. The answers are provided in the instructor's manual that accompanies this text. Your instructor will provide guidelines on how to best use these exercises in your instructional program.

For what value of the variable will each of the following rational expressions be undefined?

1. $\dfrac{x}{2}$

2. $\dfrac{3}{y}$

3. $\dfrac{2}{x-5}$

4. $\dfrac{3x}{2x+5}$

Simplify each of the following rational expressions.

5. $\dfrac{18x^5}{24x^3}$

6. $\dfrac{15m^3n}{-5mn^2}$

7. $\dfrac{8y-64}{y-8}$

8. $\dfrac{5x-20}{x^2-16}$

9. $\dfrac{9-x^2}{x^2+2x-15}$

10. $\dfrac{3w^2+8w-35}{2w^2+13w+15}$

11. $\dfrac{6a^2-ab-b^2}{9a^2-b^2}$

12. $\dfrac{6w-3z}{8w^3-z^3}$

Multiply or divide as indicated. Express your results in simplest form.

13. $\dfrac{x^5}{24}\cdot\dfrac{20}{x^3}$

14. $\dfrac{a^3b}{4ab^2}\div\dfrac{ab}{12ab^2}$

15. $\dfrac{6y-18}{9y}\cdot\dfrac{10}{5y-15}$

16. $\dfrac{m^2-3m}{m^2-5m+6}\cdot\dfrac{m^2-4}{m^2+7m+10}$

17. $\dfrac{a^2 - 2a}{a^2 - 4} \div \dfrac{2a^2}{3a + 6}$

18. $\dfrac{r^2 + 2rs}{r^3 - r^2s} \div \dfrac{5r + 10s}{r^2 - 2rs + s^2}$

19. $\dfrac{x^2 - 2xy - 3y^2}{x^2 - xy - 2y^2} \cdot \dfrac{x^2 - 4y^2}{x^2 - 8xy + 15y^2}$

20. $\dfrac{w^3 + 3w^2 + 2w + 6}{w^4 - 4} \div (w^3 + 27)$

Perform the indicated operations. Express your results in simplified form.

21. $\dfrac{5x + 7}{x + 4} - \dfrac{2x - 5}{x + 4}$

22. $\dfrac{3}{4x^2} + \dfrac{5}{6x}$

23. $\dfrac{2}{x - 5} - \dfrac{1}{x}$

24. $\dfrac{2}{y + 5} + \dfrac{3}{y + 4}$

25. $\dfrac{2}{3m - 3} - \dfrac{5}{2m - 2}$

26. $\dfrac{7}{x - 3} - \dfrac{5}{3 - x}$

27. $\dfrac{5}{4x + 4} + \dfrac{5}{2x - 2}$

28. $\dfrac{2a}{a^2 - 9a + 20} + \dfrac{8}{a - 4}$

29. $\dfrac{2}{s - 1} - \dfrac{6s}{s^2 + s - 2}$

30. $\dfrac{4}{x^2 - 9} - \dfrac{3}{x^2 - 4x + 3}$

31. $\dfrac{x^2 - 14x - 8}{x^2 - 2x - 8} + \dfrac{2x}{x - 4} - \dfrac{3}{x + 2}$

32. $\dfrac{w^2 + 2wz + z^2}{w^2 - wz - 2z^2} \cdot \left(\dfrac{3}{w + z} - \dfrac{1}{w - z} \right)$

Simplify each of the following complex fractions.

33. $\dfrac{\dfrac{x^2}{12}}{\dfrac{x^3}{8}}$

34. $\dfrac{\dfrac{y-1}{y^2-4}}{\dfrac{y^2-1}{y^2-y-2}}$

35. $\dfrac{1+\dfrac{a}{b}}{1-\dfrac{a}{b}}$

36. $\dfrac{2-\dfrac{x}{y}}{4-\dfrac{x^2}{y^2}}$

37. $\dfrac{\dfrac{1}{r}-\dfrac{1}{s}}{\dfrac{1}{r^2}-\dfrac{1}{s^2}}$

38. $\dfrac{1-\dfrac{1}{x+2}}{1+\dfrac{1}{x+2}}$

39. $\dfrac{1-\dfrac{2}{x-1}}{x+\dfrac{3}{x-4}}$

40. $\dfrac{\dfrac{w}{w+1}-\dfrac{1}{w-1}}{\dfrac{w}{w-1}+\dfrac{1}{w+1}}$

41. $\dfrac{1}{1-\dfrac{1}{1-\dfrac{1}{y-1}}}$

42. $1-\dfrac{1}{1+\dfrac{1}{1-\dfrac{1}{x}}}$

43. $\dfrac{1-\dfrac{1}{x-1}}{x-\dfrac{8}{x+2}}$

44. $\dfrac{1}{1+\dfrac{1}{1+\dfrac{1}{y+1}}}$

The purpose of this self-test is to help you check your progress and to review for a chapter test in class. Allow yourself about an hour to take the test. When you are done, check your answers in the back of the book. If you missed any problems, be sure to go back and review the appropriate sections in the chapter and the exercises that are provided.

Simplify each of the following rational expressions.

1. $\dfrac{-21x^5y^3}{28xy^5}$

2. $\dfrac{3w^2 + w - 2}{3w^2 - 8w + 4}$

3. $\dfrac{x^3 - 2x^2 - 3x}{x^3 + 3x^2 + 2x}$

4. $\dfrac{x^4 - xy^3}{x^3 - xy^2}$

Multiply or divide as indicated.

5. $\dfrac{3ab^2}{5ab^3} \cdot \dfrac{20a^2b}{21b}$

6. $\dfrac{m^2 - 3m}{m^2 - 9} \div \dfrac{4m}{m^2 - m - 12}$

7. $\dfrac{x^2 - 3x}{5x^2} \cdot \dfrac{10x}{x^2 - 4x + 3}$

8. $\dfrac{x^2 + 3xy}{2x^3 - x^2y} \div \dfrac{x^2 + 6xy + 9y^2}{4x^2 - y^2}$

9. $\dfrac{9x^2 + 9x - 4}{6x^2 - 11x + 3} \cdot \dfrac{15 - 10x}{3x + 4}$

10. $\dfrac{x^2 - 7x - 18}{2x^2 + 9x + 10} \div (2x + 5)$

Add or subtract as indicated.

11. $\dfrac{5}{x - 2} - \dfrac{1}{x}$

12. $\dfrac{2}{x + 3} + \dfrac{12}{x^2 - 9}$

ANSWERS

1 _____

2 _____

3 _____

4 _____

5 _____

6 _____

7 _____

8 _____

9 _____

10 _____

11 _____

12 _____

13. $\dfrac{6x}{x^2 - x - 2} - \dfrac{2}{x + 1}$

14. $\dfrac{3}{x^2 - 3x - 4} + \dfrac{5}{x^2 - 16}$

15. $\dfrac{1}{x + 2} + \dfrac{1}{x + 1} + \dfrac{1}{x - 3}$

16. $\dfrac{4}{x^2 - 9} - \dfrac{5}{x^2 - 4x + 3}$

Simplify each of the following complex fractions.

17. $\dfrac{3 - \dfrac{x}{y}}{9 - \dfrac{x^2}{y^2}}$

18. $\dfrac{1 - \dfrac{10}{z + 3}}{2 - \dfrac{12}{z - 1}}$

19. $\dfrac{\dfrac{1}{x} + \dfrac{1}{y}}{x^2 - y^2}$

20. $\dfrac{\dfrac{1}{x + y} - \dfrac{1}{x - y}}{\dfrac{2y}{x^2 - y^2}}$

Solving Quadratic Equations by Factoring

OBJECTIVE
To solve quadratic equations by factoring

The factoring techniques we considered in our coverage of polynomial expressions provide us with tools for solving equations that can be written in the form

This is a quadratic equation in one variable, here x. You can recognize such a *quadratic* equation by the fact that the highest power of the variable x is the second power.

$$ax^2 + bx + c = 0 \qquad a \neq 0$$

where a, b, and c are constants. This is called a *quadratic equation in standard form*. Using factoring to solve quadratic equations requires the *zero-product principle*. It says that if the product of two factors is 0, then one or both of the factors must be equal to 0. In symbols:

ZERO-PRODUCT PRINCIPLE

If $a \cdot b = 0$, then $a = 0$ or $b = 0$ or both.

Let's see how the principle is applied to solving quadratic equations.

Example 1

Solve

To use the zero-product principle, 0 must be on one side of the equation.

$$x^2 - 2x - 15 = 0$$

Factoring on the left, we have

$$(x - 5)(x + 3) = 0$$

By the zero-product principle, we know that one or both of the factors must be zero. We can then write

$$x - 5 = 0 \qquad \text{or} \qquad x + 3 = 0$$

Solving each equation gives

$$x = 5 \qquad \text{or} \qquad x = -3$$

The two solutions are 5 and -3. These are sometimes called the zeros, or roots, of the equation.

Quadratic equations can be checked another way. For instance, if $x = 5$, we have

$$5^2 - 2 \cdot 5 - 15 \stackrel{?}{=} 0$$
$$25 - 10 - 15 \stackrel{?}{=} 0$$
$$0 = 0$$

which is a true statement. We leave it to you to check the solution of -3.

CHECK YOURSELF 1

Solve $x^2 - 9x + 20 = 0$.

Other factoring techniques are also used in solving quadratic equations. The following examples illustrate.

Example 2

(a) Solve $x^2 - 5x = 0$.

Again, factor the left side of the equation and apply the zero-product principle:

$$x(x - 5) = 0$$

Now

<CAUTION>

Note: A *common mistake* is to forget the statement $x = 0$ in solving equations of this type. Be sure to include the *two* solutions.

$$x = 0 \qquad \text{or} \qquad x - 5 = 0$$
$$x = 5$$

The two solutions are 0 and 5.

(b) Solve $x^2 - 9 = 0$.

Factoring yields

$$(x + 3)(x - 3) = 0$$
$$x + 3 = 0 \qquad \text{or} \qquad x - 3 = 0$$
$$x = -3 \qquad\qquad x = 3$$

The two solutions are -3 and 3.

CHECK YOURSELF 2

Solve by factoring.

1. $x^2 + 8x = 0$ $\qquad\qquad$ **2.** $x^2 - 16 = 0$

307

Example 3 illustrates a crucial point. Our solution technique depends on the zero-product principle. This means that the product of factors *must be set equal to 0*. The importance of this is shown now.

Example 3

Solve $2x^2 = x + 3$.

The first step in the solution is to write the equation in standard form (that is, set it equal to 0). So start by adding $-x$ and -3 to both sides of the equation. Then

Make sure all terms are on one side of the equation. The other side will be 0.

$$2x^2 - x - 3 = 0$$

You can now factor and solve as before.

$$(2x - 3)(x + 1) = 0$$

$$
\begin{array}{lll}
2x - 3 = 0 & \text{or} & x + 1 = 0 \\
\quad 2x = 3 & & \quad x = -1 \\
\quad\ x = \dfrac{3}{2} & &
\end{array}
$$

The two solutions are $\dfrac{3}{2}$ and -1.

‹CAUTION›

Be Careful! Consider the equation

$x(x - 2) = 3$

Students are sometimes tempted to now write

$x = 3$ or $x - 2 = 3$

That is *not correct*. The fact that the product of factors is 3 does *not* ensure that one or both of the factors is equal to 3.
  Subtract 3 from both sides of the equation *as the first step,* to write

$x^2 - 2x - 3 = 0$

in standard form. Only *now* can you factor and proceed as before.

CHECK YOURSELF 3

Solve $3x^2 = 5x + 2$.

In all the examples above, the quadratic equations have had two distinct real number solutions. That may or may not always be the case, as we shall see.

Example 4

Solve $x^2 - 4x + 4 = 0$.

Factoring, we have

$$(x - 2)(x - 2) = 0$$

and

$$
\begin{array}{lll}
x - 2 = 0 & \text{or} & x - 2 = 0 \\
\quad x = 2 & & \quad x = 2
\end{array}
$$

Even though a quadratic equation will always have two solutions, they may not always be real numbers. More about this in our coverage of solving quadratic equations by completing the square.

The solution is 2. A quadratic (or second-degree) equation always has *two* solutions. When an equation such as this one has two solutions which are the same number, we call 2 the *repeated* (or *double*) *solution* of the equation.

CHECK YOURSELF 4

Solve $x^2 + 6x + 9 = 0$.

Always examine the quadratic member of an equation for common factors. It will make your work much easier, as the next example illustrates.

Example 5

Solve $3x^2 - 3x - 60 = 0$.

First, note the common factor 3 in the quadratic member of the equation. Removing that factor, we have

$$3(x^2 - x - 20) = 0$$

Now divide both sides of the equation by 3:

Note the advantage of dividing both members by 3. The coefficients in the quadratic member become smaller, and so that member is much easier to factor.

$$\frac{3}{3}(x^2 - x - 20) = \frac{0}{3}$$

or

$$x^2 - x - 20 = 0$$

We can now factor and solve as before:

$$(x - 5)(x + 4) = 0$$
$$x - 5 = 0 \quad \text{or} \quad x + 4 = 0$$
$$x = 5 \qquad\qquad x = -4$$

The two solutions are 5 and -4.

CHECK YOURSELF 5

Solve $2x^2 - 10x - 48 = 0$.

CHECK YOURSELF ANSWERS

1. $4, 5$.
2. $(1)\ 0, -8;\ (2)\ 4, -4$.
3. $-\dfrac{1}{3}, 2$.
4. -3.
5. $-3, 8$.

Name _____

Exercises

Date _____

Build Your Skills

1. _____

Solve each of the following quadratic equations by factoring.

2. _____

  1. $x^2 + 4x + 3 = 0$ **2.** $x^2 - 5x + 4 = 0$

3. _____

4. _____

  3. $x^2 - 2x - 15 = 0$ **4.** $x^2 + 4x - 32 = 0$

5. _____

  5. $x^2 - 11x + 30 = 0$ **6.** $x^2 + 14x + 48 = 0$

6. _____

7. _____

  7. $x^2 - 4x - 21 = 0$ **8.** $x^2 + 5x - 36 = 0$

8. _____

9. _____

  9. $x^2 - 5x = 50$ **10.** $x^2 + 14x = -33$

10. _____

11. _____

  11. $x^2 = 2x + 35$ **12.** $x^2 = 6x + 27$

12. _____

13. _____

  13. $x^2 - 8x = 0$ **14.** $x^2 + 7x = 0$

14. _____

  15. $x^2 + 10x = 0$ **16.** $x^2 - 9x = 0$

15. _____

16. _____

  17. $x^2 = 5x$ **18.** $4x = x^2$

17. _____

18. _____

  19. $x^2 - 25 = 0$ **20.** $x^2 - 49 = 0$

19. _____

20. _____

  21. $x^2 = 64$ **22.** $x^2 = 36$

21. _____

  23. $4x^2 + 12x + 9 = 0$ **24.** $9x^2 - 30x + 25 = 0$

22. _____

23. _____

  25. $2x^2 - 17x + 36 = 0$ **26.** $5x^2 + 17x - 12 = 0$

24. _____

25. _____

26. _____

ANSWERS

27. _____

28. _____

29. _____

30. _____

31. _____

32. _____

33. _____

34. _____

35. _____

36. _____

37. _____

38. _____

39. _____

40. _____

41. _____

42. _____

43. _____

44. _____

45. _____

46. _____

47. _____

48. _____

49. _____

50. _____

51. _____

52. _____

27. $3x^2 - x = 4$

28. $6x^2 = 13x - 6$

29. $6x^2 = 7x - 2$

30. $4x^2 - 3 = x$

31. $3x^2 - 24x + 36 = 0$

32. $2x^2 - 6x - 56 = 0$

33. $4x^2 + 16x - 20 = 0$

34. $3x^2 - 33x + 54 = 0$

35. $2m^2 = 12m + 54$

36. $5x^2 - 55x = 60$

37. $4x^2 - 24x = 0$

38. $6x^2 - 9x = 0$

39. $5x^2 = 15x$

40. $7x^2 = -49x$

41. $x(x - 2) = 15$

42. $x(x + 3) = 28$

43. $x(2x - 3) = 9$

44. $x(3x + 1) = 52$

45. $2x(3x + 1) = 28$

46. $3x(2x - 1) = 30$

47. $(x - 3)(x - 1) = 15$

48. $(x + 4)(x + 1) = 18$

49. $(2x + 1)(x - 4) = 11$

50. $(3x - 5)(x + 2) = 14$

51. $(x + 2)(x - 1) = (3x + 1)(x + 2)$

52. $(x - 3)(x + 7) = (4x - 5)(x - 3)$

ANSWERS

Skillscan (Simplifying of Radical Expressions)

Simplify each of the following expressions.

a. _____

a. $\sqrt{25}$

b. $\sqrt{121}$

b. _____

c. $\sqrt{32}$

d. $\sqrt{50}$

c. _____

d. _____

e. $\dfrac{4 + \sqrt{48}}{4}$

f. $\dfrac{3 + \sqrt{45}}{3}$

e. _____

f. _____

ANSWERS

1. $-1, -3$ **3.** $-3, 5$ **5.** $5, 6$ **7.** $-3, 7$ **9.** $-5, 10$ **11.** $-5, 7$ **13.** $0, 8$

15. $0, -10$ **17.** $0, 5$ **19.** $-5, 5$ **21.** $-8, 8$ **23.** $-\dfrac{3}{2}$ **25.** $4, \dfrac{9}{2}$ **27.** $-1, \dfrac{4}{3}$

29. $\dfrac{1}{2}, \dfrac{2}{3}$ **31.** $2, 6$ **33.** $-5, 1$ **35.** $-3, 9$ **37.** $0, 6$ **39.** $0, 3$ **41.** $-3, 5$

43. $-\dfrac{3}{2}, 3$ **45.** $-\dfrac{7}{3}, 2$ **47.** $-2, 6$ **49.** $-\dfrac{3}{2}, 5$ **51.** $-1, -2$ **a.** 5 **b.** 11

c. $4\sqrt{2}$ **d.** $5\sqrt{2}$ **e.** $1 + \sqrt{3}$ **f.** $1 + \sqrt{5}$

Solving Quadratic Equations by Using the Quadratic Formula

OBJECTIVES

1. To solve quadratic equations by using the quadratic formula
2. To determine the nature of the solutions of a quadratic equation using the discriminant

The factoring and square root methods are limited to certain types of quadratic equations. We know that *any* quadratic equation can be solved by the method of completing the square. However, that method can become involved and time-consuming. Therefore, we now want to derive a general formula that will provide solutions for any quadratic equation. That formula is found by using the algorithm for completing the square on the standard form of the quadratic equation

$$ax^2 + bx + c = 0 \qquad a \neq 0$$

DERIVING THE QUADRATIC FORMULA

STEP 1   Isolate the constant on the right side of the equation.

$$ax^2 + bx = -c$$

STEP 2   Divide both sides by the coefficient of the x^2 term.

$$x^2 + \frac{b}{a}x = -\frac{c}{a}$$

STEP 3   Add the square of one-half the x coefficient to both sides.

$$x^2 + \frac{b}{a}x + \frac{b^2}{4a^2} = -\frac{c}{a} + \frac{b^2}{4a^2}$$

STEP 4   Factor the left side as a perfect-square binomial. Then apply the square root property.

$$\left(x + \frac{b}{2a}\right)^2 = \frac{-4ac + b^2}{4a^2}$$

$$x + \frac{b}{2a} = \pm\sqrt{\frac{b^2 - 4ac}{4a^2}}$$

STEP 5   Solve the resulting linear equations.

$$x = -\frac{b}{2a} \pm \frac{\sqrt{b^2 - 4ac}}{2a}$$

STEP 6   Simplify.

$$= \frac{-b \pm \sqrt{b^2 - 4ac}}{2a}$$

We now use the result derived above to state the *quadratic formula,* a formula that allows us to find the solutions for any quadratic equation.

THE QUADRATIC FORMULA

Given any quadratic equation in the form

$$ax^2 + bx + c = 0 \qquad \text{where } a \neq 0$$

the two solutions to the equation are

$$x = \frac{-b \pm \sqrt{b^2 - 4ac}}{2a}$$

Example 1

Solve, using the quadratic formula:

$$6x^2 - 7x - 3 = 0$$

First, we determine the values for a, b, and c. Here

$$a = 6 \qquad b = -7 \qquad c = -3$$

Substituting those values into the quadratic formula, we have

$$x = \frac{-(-7) \pm \sqrt{(-7)^2 - 4(6)(-3)}}{2(6)}$$

Now simplifying inside the radical gives

Since $b^2 - 4ac = 121$, a perfect square, the two solutions in this case are rational numbers.

$$x = \frac{7 \pm \sqrt{121}}{12}$$

$$= \frac{7 \pm 11}{12}$$

This gives us the solutions

$$x = \frac{3}{2} \qquad \text{or} \qquad x = -\frac{1}{3}$$

Note that since the solutions for the equation of this example were rational, the original equation could have been solved by our earlier method of factoring.

CHECK YOURSELF 1

Solve, using the quadratic formula:

$$3x^2 + 2x - 8 = 0$$

To use the quadratic formula, first the equation must be written in standard form.

Example 2

Solve by using the quadratic formula:

The equation *must be in standard form* to determine *a*, *b*, and *c*.

$$9x^2 = 12x - 4$$

First, we must write the equation in standard form:

Subtract 12*x*, and add 4 to both sides. The resulting left member will be *set equal to 0.*

$$9x^2 - 12x + 4 = 0$$

Second, we find the values of a, b, and c. Here

$$a = 9 \qquad b = -12 \qquad c = 4$$

Substituting these values into the quadratic formula, we find

$$x = \frac{-(-12) \pm \sqrt{(-12)^2 - 4(9)(4)}}{2(9)}$$

$$= \frac{12 + \sqrt{0}}{18}$$

and simplifying yields

The quadratic equation has but one real solution. This is sometimes called a *repeated solution.*

$$x = \frac{2}{3}$$

CHECK YOURSELF 2

Using the quadratic formula, solve

$$4x^2 - 4x = -1$$

Thus far our examples and exercises have led to rational solutions. That is not always the case, as the next example illustrates.

Example 3

Using the quadratic formula, solve

$$x^2 - 3x = 5$$

Once again, we write the equation in standard form:

$$x^2 - 3x - 5 = 0$$

We now determine values for a, b, and c and substitute.

$$x = \frac{-(-3) \pm \sqrt{(-3)^2 - 4(1)(-5)}}{2(1)}$$

Simplifying as before, we have

$$x = \frac{3 \pm \sqrt{29}}{2}$$

CHECK YOURSELF 3

Using the quadratic equation, solve $2x^2 = x + 7$.

The following example will require some special care in simplifying the solution.

Example 4*

Using the quadratic formula, solve

$$3x^2 - 6x + 2 = 0$$

Here we have $a = 3$, $b = -6$, and $c = 2$. Substituting gives

$$x = \frac{-(-6) \pm \sqrt{(-6)^2 - 4(3)(2)}}{2(3)}$$

$$= \frac{6 \pm \sqrt{12}}{6}$$

We look for the largest perfect-square factor of 12, the radicand.

Simplifying, we note that $\sqrt{12}$ is equal to $\sqrt{4 \cdot 3}$, or $2\sqrt{3}$. We can then write our solutions as

$$x = \frac{6 \pm 2\sqrt{3}}{6} = \frac{2(3 \pm \sqrt{3})}{6} = \frac{3 \pm \sqrt{3}}{3}$$

⟨CAUTION⟩

Be Careful! Students are sometimes tempted to reduce this result to

$$\frac{\cancel{6} \pm 2\sqrt{3}}{\cancel{6}} = 1 \pm 2\sqrt{3}$$

This is *not a valid step*. We must divide *each of the terms* in the numerator by 2 in simplifying the expression.

*A screen is used to indicate an expression that is being simplified.

316

CHECK YOURSELF 4

Solve by using the quadratic formula.

$x^2 - 4x = 6$

Let's examine a case in which the solutions are non-real complex numbers.

Example 5

Solve by using the quadratic formula:

$x^2 - 2x = -2$

Rewriting in standard form, we have

$x^2 - 2x + 2 = 0$

Labeling the coefficients, we find that

$a = 1 \qquad b = -2 \qquad c = 2$

Applying the quadratic formula, we have

The solutions will be complex any time $b^2 - 4ac$ is negative.

$$x = \frac{2 \pm \sqrt{-4}}{2}$$

and noting that $\sqrt{-4}$ becomes $2i$, we can simplify our result to

$x = 1 \pm i$

CHECK YOURSELF 5

Solve by using the quadratic formula:

$x^2 - 4x + 6 = 0$

To summarize our discussion thus far, in attempting to solve a quadratic equation, you should first try the factoring method or the square root method. If these methods don't work, you can apply the quadratic formula to find the solution. The following algorithm outlines the steps.

SOLVING A QUADRATIC EQUATION BY USING THE QUADRATIC FORMULA

STEP 1 Write the equation in standard form (set equal to 0).

STEP 2 Determine the values for *a*, *b*, and *c*.

STEP 3 Substitute those values into the quadratic formula.

STEP 4 Simplify.

You may have noticed that the radicand, $b^2 - 4ac$, determines the number of real solutions for a quadratic equation. Because of this, we call the result of substituting *a*, *b*, and *c* into that part of the quadratic formula the *discriminant*.

Because the discriminant is a real number, there are three possibilities (the *trichotomy property*):

> *Although not necessarily distinct or real, every second-degree equation has two solutions.*

If $b^2 - 4ac$ is $\begin{cases} < 0 \text{ then there are } \textit{no real solutions, } \text{but two complex} \\ \quad \text{solutions} \\ = 0 \text{ then there is } \textit{one real solution} \text{ (a double solution)} \\ > 0 \text{ then there are } \textit{two distinct real solutions} \end{cases}$

Example 6

How many real solutions are there for each of the following quadratic equations?

(*a*) $x^2 + 7x - 15 = 0$

The discriminant $[49 - 4(1)(-15)]$ is 109. This indicates there are two real solutions.

> *We could find two complex solutions by using the quadratic formula.*

(*b*) $3x^2 - 5x + 7 = 0$

The discriminant is negative. There are no real solutions.

(*c*) $9x^2 - 12x + 4 = 0$

The discriminant is 0. There is exactly one real solution (a double solution).

CHECK YOURSELF 6

How many real solutions are there for each of the following quadratic equations?

1. $2x^2 - 3x + 2 = 0$ 2. $3x^2 + x - 11 = 0$
3. $4x^2 - 4x + 1 = 0$ 4. $x^2 = -5x - 7$

Frequently (see Examples 3 and 4, for instance) the solutions of a quadratic equation involve square roots. When we are solving algebraic equations, it is generally best to leave solutions in this form. However, if an equation resulting from an application has been solved by the use of the quadratic formula, we will often estimate the root and sometimes accept only positive solutions. Consider the following application that leads to the use of the quadratic formula.

Example 7

If a ball is thrown upward from the ground, the equation to find the height h of such a ball thrown with an initial velocity of 80 ft/s is

h measures the height above the ground, in feet, t seconds after the ball is thrown upward.

$$h = 80t - 16t^2$$

Find the time it takes the ball to reach a height of 48 ft.

First we substitute 48 for h, and then we rewrite the equation in standard form.

$$16t^2 - 80t + 48 = 0$$

To simplify the computation, we divide both sides of the equation by the common factor 16. This yields

Note that dividing by 16 leaves

$$\frac{0}{16} = 0$$

on the right.

$$t^2 - 5t + 3 = 0$$

We solve for t as before, using the quadratic equation, with the result

$$t = \frac{5 \pm \sqrt{13}}{2}$$

There are two solutions because the ball reaches the height *twice*, once on the way up and once on the way down.

This gives us two solutions, $\frac{5 + \sqrt{13}}{2}$ and $\frac{5 - \sqrt{13}}{2}$. But because we have specified units of time, we would generally estimate our answer to the nearest tenth or hundredth of a second.

In this case, estimating to the nearest tenth of a second gives solutions 0.7 and 4.3 s.

CHECK YOURSELF 7

The equation to find the height h of a ball thrown with an initial velocity of 64 ft/s is

$$h = 64t - 16t^2$$

Find the time it takes the ball to reach a height of 32 ft.

Example 8

The height of a ball thrown downward from the top of a 240-ft. tall building with an initial velocity of 64 ft/sec is given by

$$h = 240 - 64t - 16t^2 .$$

At what time will the ball reach a height of 176 feet?

Letting $h = 176$,

$$176 = 240 - 64t - 16t^2$$

By shifting all terms to the left-hand-side, we arrive at standard form

Again we divide both sides of the equation by 16 to simplify the computation.

$$16t^2 + 64t - 64 = 0 \quad \text{or} \quad t^2 + 4t - 4 = 0 .$$

The quadratic formula (using a = 1, b = 4, c = -4) yields

$$t = -2 \pm 2\sqrt{2} .$$

The ball has a height of 176 ft. at approximately 0.8 sec.

Estimating these solutions, we have $t = -4.8$ and $t = 0.8$ seconds, but only the *positive value* makes any sense. (To accept the negative solution would be to say that the ball reached the specified height before it was thrown.)

CHECK YOURSELF 8

The height h of a ball thrown upward from the top of a 96-ft building with an initial velocity of 16 ft/s is given by

$$h = 96 + 16t - 16t^2$$

When will the ball have a height of 32 ft? (Estimate your answer to the nearest tenth of a second.)

CHECK YOURSELF ANSWERS

1. $-2, \dfrac{4}{3}$ 2. $\dfrac{1}{2}$ 3. $\dfrac{1 \pm \sqrt{57}}{4}$

4. $2 \pm \sqrt{10}$ 5. $2 \pm i\sqrt{2}$ or "no real number solution"

6. (1)   none   (2)   two   (3)   one

     (4)   none   7.   3.4142 and .5858 seconds

8. 2.6 sec.

Name _____

Date _____

Exercises

ANSWERS

Build Your Skills

1. _____

2. _____

3. _____

Solve each of the following quadratic equations by first factoring and then using the quadratic formula.

1. $x^2 - 5x - 14 = 0$

2. $x^2 + 7x - 18 = 0$

4. _____

3. $t^2 + 8t - 65 = 0$

4. $q^2 + 3q - 130 = 0$

5. _____

6. _____

5. $5x^2 + 4x - 1 = 0$

6. $3x^2 + 2x - 1 = 0$

7. _____

8. _____

7. $16t^2 - 24t + 9 = 0$

8. $6m^2 - 23m + 10 = 0$

9. _____

Solve each of the following quadratic equations by (a) completing the square and (b) using the quadratic formula.

10. _____

9. $x^2 - 2x - 5 = 0$

10. $x^2 + 6x - 1 = 0$

11. _____

12. _____

11. $x^2 + 3x - 27 = 0$

12. $t^2 + 4t - 7 = 0$

13. _____

14. _____

13. $2x^2 - 6x - 3 = 0$

14. $2x^2 - 6x + 1 = 0$

15. _____

16. _____

15. $2q^2 - 4q + 1 = 0$

16. $4r^2 - 2r + 1 = 0$

17. _____

17. $3x^2 - x - 2 = 0$

18. $2x^2 - 8x + 3 = 0$

18. _____

19. _____

19. $2y^2 - y - 5 = 0$

20. $3m^2 + 2m - 1 = 0$

20. _____

Solve each of the following equations by using the quadratic formula.

21. _____

21. $x^2 - 4x + 3 = 0$

22. $x^2 - 7x + 3 = 0$

22. _____

23. _____

23. $p^2 - 8p + 16 = 0$

24. $u^2 + 7u - 30 = 0$

24. _____

ANSWERS

25. _____

26. _____

27. _____

28. _____

29. _____

30. _____

31. _____

32. _____

33. _____

34. _____

35. _____

36. _____

37. _____

38. _____

39. _____

40. _____

41. _____

42. _____

43. _____

44. _____

45. _____

46. _____

47. _____

48. _____

49. _____

50. _____

25. $2x^2 - 2x - 3 = 0$

26. $2x^2 - 3x - 7 = 0$

27. $-3s^2 + 2s - 1 = 0$

28. $5t^2 - 2t - 2 = 0$

Hint: Clear each of following equations of fractions or grouping symbols first.

29. $2x^2 - \dfrac{1}{2}x - 5 = 0$

30. $3x^2 + \dfrac{1}{3}x - 3 = 0$

31. $5t^2 - 2t - \dfrac{2}{3} = 0$

32. $3y^2 + 2y + \dfrac{3}{4} = 0$

33. $(x - 2)(x + 3) = 4$

34. $(x + 1)(x - 8) = 3$

35. $(t + 1)(2t - 4) - 7 = 0$

36. $(2w + 1)(3w - 2) = 1$

37. $3x - 5 = \dfrac{1}{x}$

38. $x + 3 = \dfrac{1}{x}$

39. $2t - \dfrac{3}{t} = 3$

40. $4p - \dfrac{1}{p} = 6$

41. $\dfrac{5}{y^2} + \dfrac{2}{y} - 1 = 0$

42. $\dfrac{6}{x^2} - \dfrac{2}{x} = 1$

For each quadratic equation, find the value of the discriminant and give the number of real solutions that exist.

43. $2x^2 - 5x = 0$

44. $3x^2 + 8x = 0$

45. $m^2 - 8m + 16 = 0$

46. $4p^2 + 12p + 9 = 0$

47. $3x^2 - 7x + 1 = 0$

48. $2x^2 - x + 5 = 0$

49. $2w^2 - 5w + 11 = 0$

50. $7q^2 - 3q + 1 = 0$

Find all the solutions of each of the following quadratic equations. Use any applicable method.

51. $x^2 - 8x + 16 = 0$

52. $4x^2 + 12x + 9 = 0$

53. $3t^2 - 7t + 1 = 0$

54. $2z^2 - z + 5 = 0$

55. $2x^2 - 5x + 11 = 0$

56. $7x^2 + 8x + 1 = 0$

57. $5y^2 - 2y = 0$

58. $7z^2 - 6z - 2 = 0$

59. $(x - 1)(2x + 7) = -6$

60. $4x^2 - 3 = 0$

61. $x^2 + 9 = 0$

62. $(4x - 5)(x + 2) = 1$

63. $x - 3 - \dfrac{10}{x} = 0$

64. $1 + \dfrac{2}{x} + \dfrac{2}{x^2} = 0$

$h = 112t - 16t^2$

is the equation for the height of an arrow, shot upward from the ground with an initial velocity of 112 ft/s, where t is the time, in seconds, after the arrow leaves the ground. Your answer to problems 65 and 66 should be to the nearest tenth of a second.

65. Find the time it takes for the arrow to reach a height of 112 ft.

66. Find the time it takes for the arrow to have a height of 144 ft.

$h = 320 - 32t - 16t^2$

is the equation for the height of a ball, thrown downward from the top of a 320-ft building with an initial velocity of 32 ft/s, where t is the time, to the nearest tenth of a second, after the ball is thrown down from the top of the building.

67. Find the time it takes for the ball to reach a height of 240 ft.

68. Find the time it takes for the ball to reach a height of 96 ft.

ANSWERS

Skillscan (Solving Linear Inequalities)

Graph each of the following inequalities.

a. _____

b. _____

c. _____

d. _____

e. _____

f. _____

g. _____

h. _____

a. $x \geq 2$

b. $x > 3$

c. $x < -4$

d. $x \leq -5$

e. $1 < x < 5$

f. $-2 \leq x \leq 3$

g. $x < -3$ or $x > 2$

h. $x \leq -4$ or $x \geq 5$

ANSWERS

1. $-2, 7$ **3.** $-13, 5$ **5.** $-1, \dfrac{1}{5}$ **7.** $\dfrac{3}{4}$ **9.** $1 \pm \sqrt{6}$ **11.** $\dfrac{-3 \pm 3\sqrt{13}}{2}$

13. $\dfrac{3 \pm \sqrt{15}}{2}$ **15.** $\dfrac{2 \pm \sqrt{2}}{2}$ **17.** $-\dfrac{2}{3}, 1$ **19.** $\dfrac{1 \pm \sqrt{41}}{4}$ **21.** $1, 3$ **23.** 4

25. $\dfrac{1 \pm \sqrt{7}}{2}$ **27.** $\dfrac{1 \pm i\sqrt{2}}{3}$ **29.** $\dfrac{1 \pm \sqrt{161}}{8}$ **31.** $\dfrac{3 \pm \sqrt{39}}{15}$ **33.** $\dfrac{-1 \pm \sqrt{41}}{2}$

35. $\dfrac{1 \pm \sqrt{23}}{2}$ **37.** $\dfrac{5 \pm \sqrt{37}}{6}$ **39.** $\dfrac{3 \pm \sqrt{33}}{4}$ **41.** $1 \pm \sqrt{6}$ **43.** $25,$ two

45. $0,$ one   **47.** $37,$ two   **49.** $-63,$ none   **51.** 4 **53.** $\dfrac{7 \pm \sqrt{37}}{6}$ **55.** $\dfrac{5 \pm 3i\sqrt{7}}{4}$

57. $0, \dfrac{2}{5}$ **59.** $\dfrac{-5 \pm \sqrt{33}}{4}$ **61.** $\pm 3i$ **63.** $-2, 5$ **65.** $\dfrac{7 \pm \sqrt{21}}{2}, \approx 1.2$ or 5.8 s

67. $-1 + \sqrt{6}, \approx 1.4$ s

a. $x > 2$ **b.** $x > 3$

c. $x < -4$ **d.** $x \leq -5$

e. $1 < x < 5$ **f.** $-2 \leq x \leq 3$

g. $x < -3$ or $x > 2$

h. $x \leq -4$ or $x \geq 5$

Graphing Equations of the Form $y = a(x - h)^2 + k$

OBJECTIVES
Given equations of the form $y = (x - h)^2 + k,$
1. To find the axis of symmetry
2. To find the vertex
3. To graph the parabola by the method of translation

We dealt with the graphs of linear equations in two variables of the form

$$ax + by = c \qquad \text{where } a \text{ and } b \text{ cannot both be } 0$$

The graphs of all the linear equations were straight lines. Suppose that we now allow the terms in x and/or y to be quadratic; that is, we will allow squares in one or both of those terms. The graphs of such equations will form a family of curves called the *conic sections*. Conic sections are curves formed when a plane cuts through, or forms a section of, a cone. The conic sections comprise four curves—the *parabola, circle, ellipse,* and *hyperbola*. Examples of how these curves are formed are shown below.

The inclination of the plane determines which of the sections is formed.

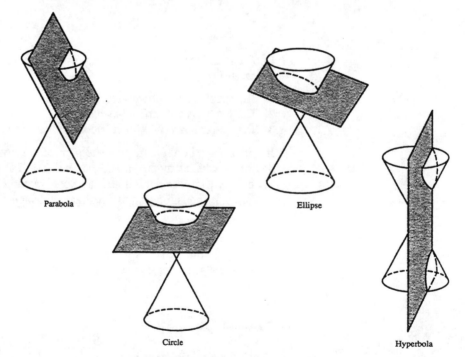

Parabola

Ellipse

Circle

Hyperbola

The names "ellipse," "parabola," and "hyperbola" are attributed to Apollonius, a third-century B.C. Greek mathematician and astronomer.

Our attention in this section is focused on the first of these sections, the parabola. Consider the equation $y = x^2$. This equation is quadratic in x and linear in y. Its graph is a parabola. Let's look at that graph.

Note that the parabola is rounded, and not pointed at the bottom.

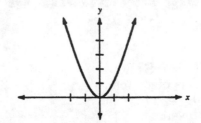

We could plot points, then connect them.

x	y
-2	4
-1	1
0	0
1	1
2	4

There are three elements of the graph that should be noted.

1. The graph opens upward.
2. The y axis cuts the graph into two equal parts. A line that does this is called an *axis of symmetry*.
3. The graph has a minimum point, called the *vertex*.

Let's compare that graph to the graph of the equation $y = -x^2$.

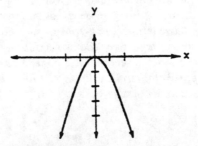

Looking at the three elements we examined earlier, we make three observations:

1. The graph opens downward.
2. The y axis is the *axis of symmetry*.
3. The graph has a maximum point, called the *vertex*.

It will always be the case that the sign of the coefficient of the x^2 term will determine which way the parabola opens. It will also be the case that a parabola opening upward has a minimum, and one opening downward has a maximum.

For every equation that is quadratic in x and linear in y, we will look for three things:

1. Does the graph open upward or downward?
2. Where is the axis of symmetry?
3. What are the coordinates of the vertex?

Example 1

Graph the equation $y = x^2 - 3$.

The difference between this graph and that of equation $y = x^2$ is that each y value has been decreased by 3. This results in a *translation* of 3 units in the negative direction on the y axis.

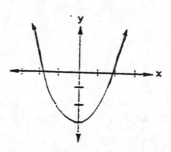

Note that the curve opens upward, the axis of symmetry is $x = 0$ (the y axis), and the vertex is $(0, -3)$.

CHECK YOURSELF 1

Graph the equation $y = -x^2 + 2$.

An equation of the form $y = (x - h)^2$ will be translated along the x axis with the axis of symmetry at $x = h$.

Example 2

Graph the equation $y = -(x - 3)^2$.

Since the coefficient to the x^2 term is negative, the parabola opens downward and has a maximum point. Notice that when $x = 3$, y is 0. If x is more than 3, y will be negative. Try substituting values for x in the equation, then evaluate y. When x is less than 3, y is also negative. Thus, the vertex is at $(3, 0)$, and the axis of symmetry is at $x = 3$.

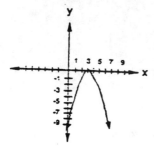

CHECK YOURSELF 2

Graph the equation $y = (x + 2)^2$.

Combining the lessons of the last two examples, we see that the graph of an equation of the form $y = (x - h)^2 + k$ is simply the parabola $y = x^2$ translated horizontally h units and vertically k units.

Example 3

Graph the equation $y = (x + 3)^2 + 1$.

The parabola will be translated to the left 3 units and up 1 unit. The parabola opens upward, with an axis of symmetry at $x = -3$ and a vertex at $(-3, 1)$.

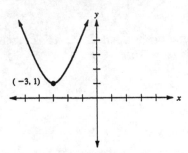

CHECK YOURSELF 3

Graph the equation $y = -(x - 2)^2 - 3$.

The rate at which the sides of a parabola rise (or fall) is determined by the coefficient of the x term.

Example 4

Graph the parabolas $y = 2x^2$, $y = x^2$, and $y = \dfrac{1}{2}x^2$ on the same axes.

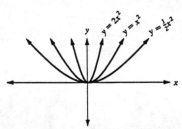

Notice that the larger the coefficient of x^2, the faster the parabola rises, thus the thinner the parabola appears.

CHECK YOURSELF 4

Graph the parabolas $y = -2x^2$, $y = -x^2$, and $y = -\dfrac{1}{2}x^2$ on the same axes.

We can now graph any equation of the form $y = a(x - h)^2 + k$.

Example 5

Graph the equation $y = -2(x - 3)^2 - 4$.

This parabola will open downward, the axis of symmetry is at $x = 3$, the vertex is at $(3, -4)$, and it has the shape of $y = 2x^2$.

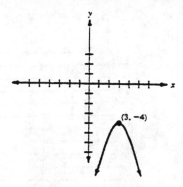

CHECK YOURSELF 5

Graph the equation $y = \dfrac{1}{4}(x + 3)^2 - 1$.

CHECK YOURSELF ANSWERS

1.

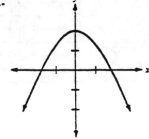

2.

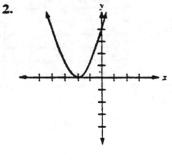

3.

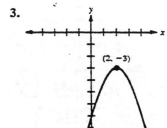

4.

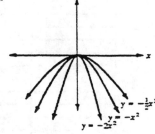

5.

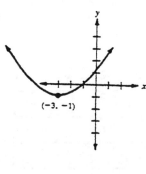

329

EXERCISES

Build Your Skills

Graph each of the following equations of parabolas and give the coordinates of the vertex, the equation of its axis of symmetry, and its weight (coefficient of x^2).

1. $y = x^2 + 3$

2. $y = -x^2 + 2$

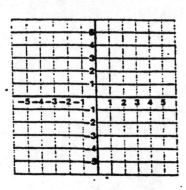

3. $y = -x^2 - 1$

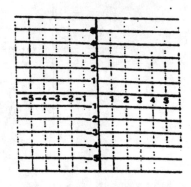

4. $y = 2x^2 - 1$

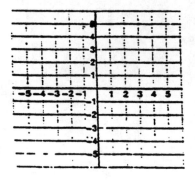

5. $y = (x - 2)^2$

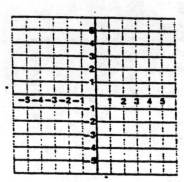

6. $y = 3(x - 1)^2 + 2$

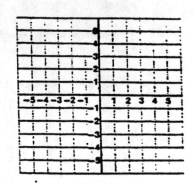

7. $y = (x + 3)^2 - 1$

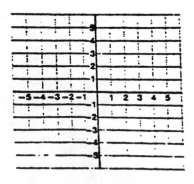

8. $y = \frac{1}{2}(x - 2)^2 + 1$

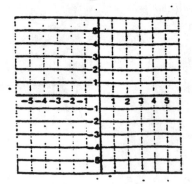

9. $y - x^2 = 4$

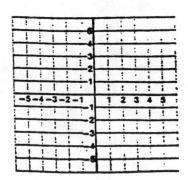

Find the x-intercepts (if any) for each of the following parabolas.

10. $y = (x - 3)^2$

11. $y = (x - 2)^2 - 1$

12. $y = (x + 4)^2$

13. $y = (x - 3)^2 + 1$

14. $y = \frac{1}{2}(x - 3)^2 + 2$

15. $y = x^2$

16. $y = -x^2$

17. $y = -3x^2 + 1$

18. $y = -2x^2 + 4$

19. $y = -2x^2 - 4$

Determine which of the following must be performed on the graph of the equation $y = x^2$ to produce the graph of the following equations:
- a) Translation up
- b) Translation down
- c) Translation left
- d) Translation right
- e) Weight change
- f) Inverted

20. $y = x^2 + 7$

21. $y - x^2 = 2$

22. $y + x^2 = 5$

23. $y = x^2 - 6$

24. $y = (x + 5)^2$

25. $y = (x - 4)^2 + 2$

26. $y = -2(x - 1)^2$

27. $y = -2x^2 + 1$

28. $y = -\frac{1}{2}(x - 2)^2 - 1$

29. $y = \frac{1}{3}(x + 1)^2 - 4$

30. $y = 2x^2 - 1$

31. $y = -\frac{1}{4}(x - 2)^2 + 3$

Construct a parabola satisfying the following conditions (there are many possible answers for these problems.)

32. Write the equation of a parabola which opens upward with vertex on the y-axis, but not at the origin. Are there any x-intercepts?

33. Write the equation of a parabola which opens downward with vertex on the y-axis but not at the origin. Are there any x-intercepts?

34. Write the equation of a parabola with vertex in the first quadrant and having two x-intercepts.

35. Write the equation of a parabola with vertex in the first quadrant and having no x-intercepts.

36. Write the equation of a parabola with vertex in the second quadrant and having two x-intercepts.

37. Write the equation of a parabola with vertex in the second quadrant and having no x-intercepts.

38. Write the equation of a parabola with vertex in the third quadrant and having two x-intercepts.

39. Write the equation of a parabola with vertex in the third quadrant and having no x-intercepts.

40. Write the equation of a parabola with vertex in the fourth quadrant and having two x-intercepts.

41. Write the equation of a parabola with vertex in the fourth quadrant and having no x-intercepts.

For problems 42 through 47, match the graph with the equation.

a) $y = x^2 - 1$ b) $y = x^2 + 1$ c) $y = (x + 2)^2$

d) $y = (x - 2)^2 + 1$ e) $y = (x - 2)^2 - 1$ f) $y - x^2 = 0$

42.
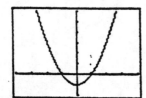

43.
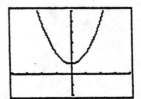

44.
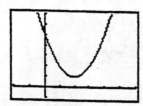

45.
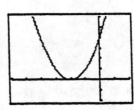

46.
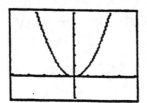

47.
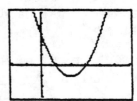

48. Graph $y = x^2$, $y = 3x^2$, and $y = \frac{1}{3}x^2$ on the same coordinate system. Discuss how changing the weight of the parabola (coefficient of x^2) affects the graph.

49. Graph $y = x^2$, $y = x^2 + 2$, and $y = x^2 - 2$ on the same coordinate system. What is the effect on the graph of $y = x^2$ caused by adding a constant to x^2?

ANSWERS

1. $y = x^2 + 3$

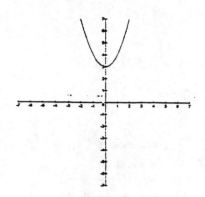

Vertex: (0,3)
Axis of symmetry: x = 0
Weight: 1

2. $y = -x^2 + 2$

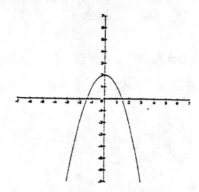

Vertex: (0,2)
Axis of symmetry: x = 0
Weight: -1

3. $y = -x^2 - 1$

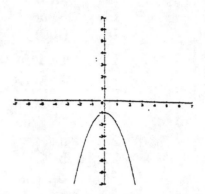

Vertex: (0,-1)
Axis: x = 0
Weight: -1

4. $y = 2x^2 - 1$

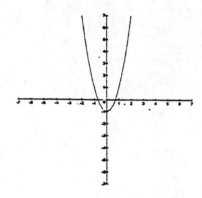

Vertex: (0,-1)
Axis of symmetry: x = 0
Weight: 2

5. $y = (x - 2)^2$

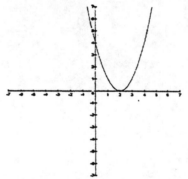

Vertex: (2,0)
Axis: x = 2
Weight: 1

6. $y = 3(x - 1)^2 + 2$

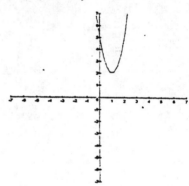

Vertex: (1,2)
Axis: x = 1
Weight: 3

7. $y = (x + 3)^2 - 1$

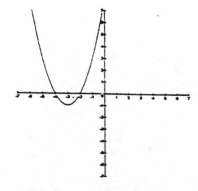

Vertex: (-3,-1)
Axis of symmetry: x = -3
Weight: 1

8. $y = \frac{1}{2}(x - 2)^2 + 1$

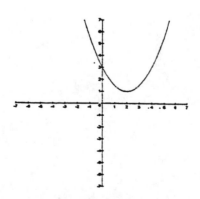

Vertex: (2,1)
Axis of symmetry: x = 2
Weight: ½

9. $y - x^2 = 4$

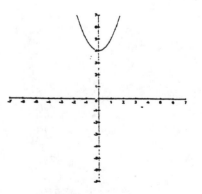

Vertex: (0,4)
Axis: x = 0
Weight: 1

10.	(3,0)	11.	(3,0) and (1,0)	12.	(-4,0)
13.	None	14.	None	15.	(0,0)
16.	(0,0)				

17. $(\sqrt{1/3},0) \approx (0.577,0)$ *AND* $(-\sqrt{1/3},0) \approx (-0.577,0)$

18. $(\sqrt{2},0) \approx (1.414,0)$ *AND* $(-\sqrt{2},0) \approx (-1.414,0)$

19. None

20.	a	21.	a	22.	a , e & f
23.	b	24.	c	25.	a & d
26.	d , e & f	27.	a , e & f	28.	b , d , e & f
29.	b , c & e	30.	b & e	31.	a , d , e & f

42.	a	43.	b	44.	d
45.	c	46.	f	47.	e

48.

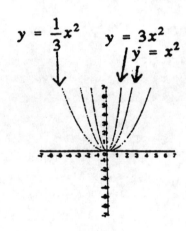

49.

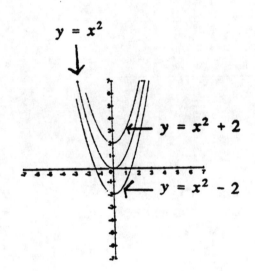

334

Graphing Equations of the Form $y = ax^2 + bx + c$

OBJECTIVES
1. To graph parabolas
2. To solve applications that result in quadratic equations

In the last section we graphed equations of the form $y = a(x - h)^2 + k$. The standard form for a quadratic equation in two variables is $y = ax^2 + bx + c$. Any quadratic equation can be written in either of these forms.

Consider an equation of the form

$$y = ax^2 + bx + c \qquad a \neq 0$$

This equation is quadratic in x and linear in y. Its graph will always be the curve called the parabola.

In an equation of the form

$$y = ax^2 + bx + c \qquad a \neq 0$$

the parabola opens upward or downward, as follows:

1. If $a > 0$, the parabola opens *upward*.
2. If $a < 0$, the parabola opens *downward*.

$$y = ax^2 + bx + c$$

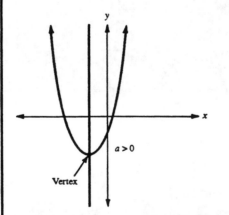

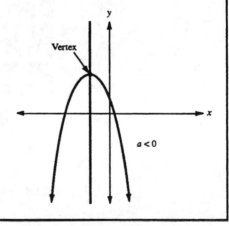

Two points regarding the parabola can be made by observation. Consider the above illustrations.

1. There is always a **minimum** (or lowest) point on the parabola if it opens upward. There is always a **maximum** (or highest) point on the parabola if it opens downward. In either case, that maximum or minimum value occurs at the **vertex** of the parabola.

2. Every parabola has an **axis of symmetry**. In the case of parabolas that open upward or downward, that axis of symmetry is a vertical line midway between any pair of symmetric points on the parabola. Also, the point where this axis of symmetry intersects the parabola is the vertex of the parabola.

The following figure summarizes these observations.

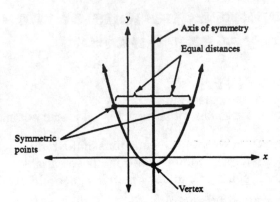

Our objective is to be able to quickly sketch a parabola. This can be done with *as few as three points* if those points are carefully chosen. For this purpose you will want to find the vertex and two symmetric points.

First, let's see how the coordinates of the vertex can be determined from the standard equation

$$y = ax^2 + bx + c \tag{1}$$

In equation (1), if $x = 0$, then $y = c$, and so $(0, c)$ gives the point where the parabola intersects the y axis (the y intercept).

Look at the sketch. To determine the coordinates of the symmetric point (x_1, c), note that it lies along the horizontal line $y = c$.

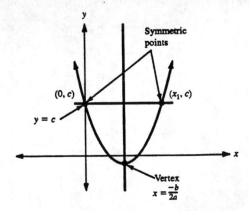

Therefore, let $y = c$ in equation (1):

$$c = ax^2 + bx + c$$
$$0 = ax^2 + bx$$
$$0 = x(ax + b)$$

and

$$x = 0 \qquad \text{or} \qquad x = -\frac{b}{a}$$

We now know that

$$(0, c) \quad \text{and} \quad \left(-\frac{b}{a}, c\right)$$

are the coordinates of the symmetric points shown. Since the axis of symmetry must be midway between these points, the x value along that axis is given by

$$x = \frac{0 + (-b/a)}{2} = -\frac{b}{2a} \tag{2}$$

Since the vertex for any parabola lies on the axis of symmetry, we can now state the following general result.

Vertex of a Parabola

If

$$y = ax^2 + bx + c \qquad a \neq 0$$

then the x coordinate of the vertex of the corresponding parabola is

$$x = -\frac{b}{2a}$$

Note: The y coordinate of the vertex can be found most easily by substituting the value found for x into the original equation.

In fact, we will always have *two* symmetric x intercepts unless the quadratic member is a perfect square, and that case can be handled by techniques presented later.

We now know how to find the vertex of a parabola, and if two symmetric points can be determined, we are well on our way to the desired graph. Perhaps the simplest case is when the quadratic member of the given equation is factorable. In most cases, the two x intercepts will then give two symmetric points that are very easily found. Example 1 illustrates such a case.

• Example 1

Graphing a Parabola

Sketch the information to help you solve the problem. Begin by drawing—as a dashed line—the axis of symmetry.

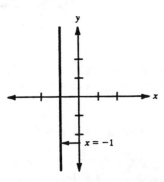

At this point you can plot the vertex along the axis of symmetry.

Graph the equation

$$y = x^2 + 2x - 8$$

First, find the axis of symmetry. In this equation, $a = 1$, $b = 2$, and $c = -8$. We then have

$$x = -\frac{b}{2a} = \frac{-2}{2 \cdot 1} = \frac{-2}{2} = -1$$

Thus, $x = -1$ is the axis of symmetry.

Second, find the vertex. Since the vertex of the parabola lies on the axis of symmetry, let $x = -1$ in the original equation. If $x = -1$,

$$y = (-1)^2 + 2(-1) - 8 = -9$$

and $(-1, -9)$ is the vertex of the parabola.

337

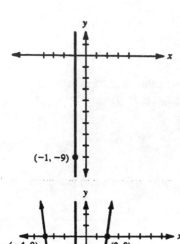

(−1, −9)

(−4, 0)   (2, 0)

(−1, −9)

Third, find two symmetric points. Note that the quadratic member in this case is factorable, and so setting $y = 0$ in the original equation will quickly give two symmetric points (the x intercepts):

$$0 = x^2 + 2x - 8$$
$$= (x + 4)(x - 2)$$

So when $y = 0$,

$$x + 4 = 0 \qquad \text{or} \qquad x - 2 = 0$$
$$x = -4 \qquad\qquad\qquad x = 2$$

and our x intercepts are $(-4, 0)$ and $(2, 0)$.

Fourth, draw a smooth curve connecting the points found above, to form the parabola.

Note: You can choose to find additional pairs of symmetric points at this time if necessary. For instance, the symmetric points $(0, -8)$ and $(-2, -8)$ are easily located.

CHECK YOURSELF 1

Graph the equation

$$y = -x^2 - 2x + 3$$

Hint: Since the coefficient of x^2 is negative, the parabola opens downward.

A similar process will work if the quadratic member of the given equation is *not* factorable. In that case, one of two things happens:

1. The x intercepts are irrational and therefore not particularly helpful in the graphing process.
2. The x intercepts do not exist.

Consider Example 2.

●Example 2

Graphing a Parabola

Graph the equation

$$y = x^2 - 6x + 3$$

First, find the axis of symmetry. Here $a = 1$, $b = -6$, and $c = 3$. So

$$x = -\frac{b}{2a} = \frac{-(-6)}{2 \cdot 1} = \frac{6}{2} = 3$$

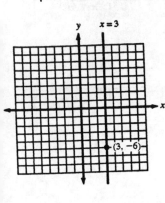

Thus, $x = 3$ is the axis of symmetry.

Second, find the vertex. If $x = 3$,

$$y = 3^2 - 6 \cdot 3 + 3 = -6$$

and $(3, -6)$ is the vertex of the desired parabola.

Third, find two symmetric points. Here the quadratic member is not factorable, and the x intercepts are irrational, so we would prefer to find another pair of symmetric points.

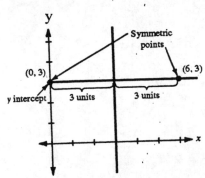

Note that $(0, 3)$ is the y intercept of the parabola. We found the axis of symmetry at $x = 3$ in step 1. Note that the symmetric point to $(0, 3)$ lies along the horizontal line through the y intercept at the same distance (3 units) from the axis of symmetry. Hence, $(6, 3)$ is our symmetric point.

Fourth, draw a smooth curve connecting the points found above to form the parabola.

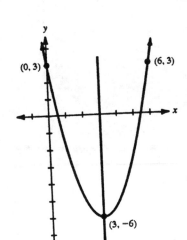

Note: An alternate method is available in step 3. Observing that 3 is the y intercept and that the symmetric point lies along the line $y = 3$, set $y = 3$ in the original equation:

$$3 = x^2 - 6x + 3$$
$$0 = x^2 - 6x$$
$$0 = x(x - 6)$$

so

$$x = 0 \quad \text{or} \quad x - 6 = 0$$
$$x = 6$$

and $(0, 3)$ and $(6, 3)$ are the desired symmetric points.

⚬ ⚬ ⚬ **CHECK YOURSELF 2**

Graph the equation

$$y = x^2 + 4x + 5$$

Thus far the coefficient of x^2 has been 1 or -1. The following example shows the effect of different coefficients on the term in x^2.

• Example 3

Graphing a Parabola

Graph the equation

$$y = 3x^2 - 6x + 5$$

First, find the axis of symmetry.

$$x = -\frac{b}{2a} = \frac{-(-6)}{2 \cdot 3} = \frac{6}{6} = 1$$

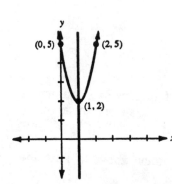

Second, find the vertex. If $x = 1$,

$$y = 3(1)^2 - 6 \cdot 1 + 5 = 2$$

So (1, 2) is the vertex.

  Third, find symmetric points. Again the quadratic member is not factorable, and we use the y intercept (0, 5) and its symmetric point (2, 5).

  Fourth, connect the points with a smooth curve to form the parabola. Compare this curve to those in previous examples. Note that the parabola is "tighter" about the axis of symmetry. That is the effect of the larger x^2 coefficient.

⬤ ⬤ ⬤   CHECK YOURSELF 3

Graph the equation

$$y = \frac{1}{2}x^2 - 3x - 1$$

The following algorithm summarizes our work thus far.

To Graph a Parabola

STEP 1 Find the axis of symmetry.
STEP 2 Find the vertex.
STEP 3 Determine two symmetric points.
   Note: You can use the x intercepts if the quadratic member of the given equation is factorable. Otherwise use the y intercept and its symmetric point.
STEP 4 Draw a smooth curve connecting the points found above to form the parabola. You may choose to find additional pairs of symmetric points at this time.

We will now look at the second method of graphing a quadratic equation of the form $y = ax^2 + bx + c$. We will first complete the square to change our equation from the form $y = ax^2 + bx + c$ to $y = a(x - h)^2 + k$.

Example 4

Graph the equation

$$y = x^2 - 2x - 3$$

We will first complete the square to graph this equation.

One-half the middle term squared will complete the square.

$$y = x^2 - 2x - 3$$
$$= x^2 - 2x + 1 - 3 - 1$$
$$= (x - 1)^2 - 4$$

From our work in our coverage of graphing equations of the form $y = a(x - h)^2 + k$, we know the parabola opens upward, the axis of symmetry is $x = 1$, and the vertex is at $(1, -4)$.

To improve the sketch, we can find the x intercepts. These are the x values for which $y = 0$, so

$$0 = (x - 1)^2 - 4$$
$$4 = (x - 1)^2$$
$$\pm 2 = x - 1$$
$$x = 1 + 2 \quad \text{or} \quad x = 1 - 2$$
$$= 3 \qquad\qquad = -1$$

The x intercepts are $(3, 0)$ and $(-1, 0)$.

Now draw a smooth curve connecting the vertex and the x intercepts.

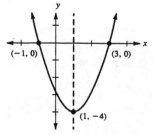

*A screen is used to indicate an expression that is being simplified.

CHECK YOURSELF 4

Graph the equation

$$y = -x^2 + 6x - 5$$

Hint: Since the coefficient of x^2 is negative, the parabola opens downward.

A similar process will work if the quadratic member of the given equation is *not* factorable. In that case, one of two things happens:

1. The x intercepts are irrational. In this case, a calculator can be used to estimate the intercepts.
2. The x intercepts do not exist.

Consider the following example.

Example 5

Graph the equation

$$\begin{aligned} y &= x^2 - 4x + 2 \\ &= x^2 - 4x + 2 \\ &= x^2 - 4x + 4 + 2 - 4 \\ &= (x - 2)^2 - 2 \end{aligned}$$

To keep the equation balanced, we both add and subtract 4.

The parabola opens upward, the axis of symmetry is $x = 2$, and the vertex is $(2, -2)$.

Again, we can improve the sketch if we find two symmetric points. Here the quadratic member is not factorable, and the x intercepts are irrational, so we would prefer to find another pair of symmetric points.

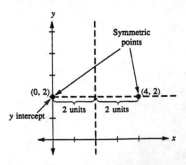

Note that $(0, 2)$ is the y intercept of the parabola. We found the axis of symmetry at $x = 2$ earlier. Note that the symmetric point to $(0, 2)$ lies along the horizontal line through the y intercept at the same distance (2 units) from the axis of symmetry, or at $x = 4$. Hence, $(4, 2)$ is our symmetric point.

Draw a smooth curve connecting the points found above to form the parabola.

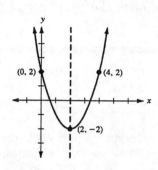

CHECK YOURSELF 5

Graph the equation $y = x^2 + 2x + 3$.

The coefficient of x^2 was 1 or -1 in our previous example and exercises. The following example shows the effect of different coefficients of the x^2 term.

Example 6

Graph the equation

$$y = 2x^2 - 4x + 3$$

Step 1 Complete the square.

We have added 2 times 1, so we must also subtract 2.

$$y = 2(x^2 - 2x) + 3$$
$$= 2(x^2 - 2x + 1) + 3 - 2$$
$$= 2(x - 1)^2 + 1$$

Step 2 The axis of symmetry is $x = 1$, the vertex is at $(1, 1)$.

Step 3 Find symmetric points. Again the quadratic member is not factorable, and we use the y intercept $(0, 3)$ and its symmetric point $(2, 3)$.

Step 4 Connect the points with a smooth curve to form the parabola.

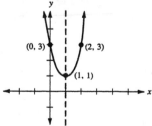

Compare this curve to those in previous examples. Note that the parabola is "tighter" about the axis of symmetry. That is the effect of the larger x^2 coefficient.

CHECK YOURSELF 6

Graph the equation $y = \dfrac{1}{2}x^2 - 2x - 2$.

The following algorithm summarizes the second method of graphing a quadratic equation.

GRAPHING A QUADRATIC EQUATION

1. Complete the square for the quadratic variable.
2. Find the axis of symmetry and the vertex.
3. Determine two symmetric points.

Note You can use the x intercepts if the quadratic member of the given equation is factorable. Otherwise, use the y intercept and its symmetric point.

4. Draw a smooth curve connecting the points found above, to form the parabola. You may choose to find additional pairs of symmetric points at this time.

If we use the algorithm to find the vertex of the equation $y = ax^2 + bx + c$, we get a useful result. The axis of symmetry will always occur at $x = -b/(2a)$.

From graphs of equations of the form $y = ax^2 + bx + c$, we know that if $a > 0$, then the vertex is the lowest point on the graph (the minimum value). Also, if $a < 0$, then the vertex is the highest point on the graph (the maximum value). We can use this result to solve a variety of problems in which we want to find the maximum or minimum value of a variable.

Example 7

A software company sells a word processing program for personal computers. They have found that their monthly profit in dollars P from selling x copies of the program is approximated by

$$P = -0.2x^2 + 80x - 1,200$$

Find the number of copies of the program that should be sold in order to maximize the profit.

Solution Since the relating equation is quadratic, the graph must be a parabola. Also since the coefficient of x^2 is negative, the parabola must open downward and thus the vertex will give the maximum value for the profit P. To find the vertex,

$$x = -\frac{b}{2a} = \frac{-80}{2(-0.2)} = \frac{-80}{-0.4} = 200$$

The maximum profit must then occur when $x = 200$, and we substitute that value into the original equation:

$$P = -0.2(200)^2 + 80(200) - 1,200$$
$$= \$6,800$$

The maximum profit will occur when 200 copies are sold per month, and that profit will be $6800.

CHECK YOURSELF 7

A company which sells portable radios finds that its weekly profit in dollars P and the number of radios sold x are related by

$$P = -0.1x^2 + 20x - 200$$

Find the number of radios that should be sold to have the largest weekly profit and the amount of that profit.

Example 8

A farmer has 1000 ft of fence and wishes to enclose the largest possible rectangular area with that fencing. Find the length and width of the largest possible area that can be enclosed.

As usual, when dealing with geometric figures, we start by drawing a sketch of the problem.

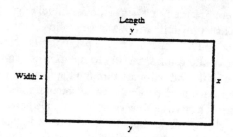

First, we can write the area A as

Area = length × width

$$A = xy \qquad (1)$$

Also since 1000 ft of fence is to be used, we know that

The perimeter of the region is

$2x + 2y$

$$2x + 2y = 1000$$
$$2y = 1000 - 2x$$
$$y = 500 - x \qquad (2)$$

Substituting for y in Equation (1), we have

$$A = x(500 - x) = 500x - x^2$$
$$= -x^2 + 500x \qquad (3)$$

Again, the graph for A is a parabola opening downward, and the largest possible area will occur at the vertex. As before,

The width x is 250 ft. From (2)

$y = 500 - 250$

$= 250$ ft

$$x = \frac{-500}{2(-1)} = \frac{-500}{-2} = 250$$

and the largest possible area is

The length is also 250 ft. The desired region is a square.

$$A = -(250)^2 + 500(250) = 62,500 \text{ ft}^2$$

CHECK YOURSELF 8

For any point (x, y) on the parabola,

$$d_1 = d_2$$

The Parabola

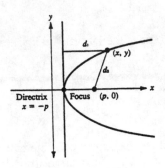

We want to enclose the largest possible rectangular area by using 400 ft of fence. The fence will be connected to the house, so only three sides of fence will be needed. What should be the dimensions of the area?

We conclude with a formal geometric description of the parabola. As is true of all the conic sections, this geometric definition can be combined with the distance formula to write the corresponding algebraic equation for the parabola.

> A *parabola* is the set of all points in the plane equidistant from a fixed point, called the *focus* of the parabola, and a fixed line, called the *directrix* of the parabola.

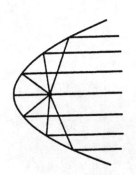

There are many physical models involving a parabolic path or design. The fact that a projectile follows a parabolic path was known in the time of Galileo. The reflective properties of the parabola also are important. If light rays enter a parabola along lines parallel to the axis of symmetry, the rays will reflect off the parabola and will pass through the focus of the parabola. That fact accounts for the design of parabolic radar antennas and solar collectors.

The reflective surface of an automobile headlight is also a parabolic surface. The light source in the headlight is placed approximately at the focus, so that the light rays will reflect off the surface as nearly parallel rays.

● ● ● CHECK YOURSELF ANSWERS

1. $y = -x^2 - 2x + 3$

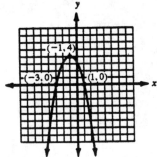

2. $y = x^2 + 4x + 5$

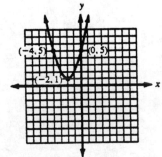

3. $y = \dfrac{1}{2}x^2 - 3x - 1$

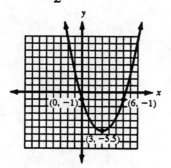

4 $y = -x^2 + 6x - 5$

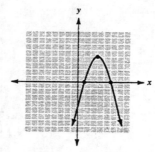

5 $y = x^2 + 2x + 3$

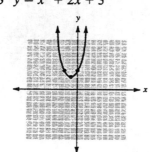

6 $y = \dfrac{1}{2}x^2 - 2x - 2$

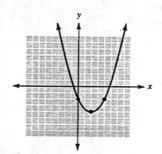

7 100 radios, $800

8 Width 100 ft, length 200 ft

Name _____

Date _____

Exercises

ANSWERS

Build Your Skills

1. _____ Match each graph with one of the equations below.

2. _____

1. 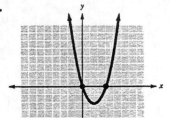 **2.**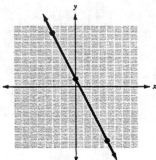

3. _____

4. _____

5. _____ **3.** 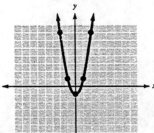 **4.**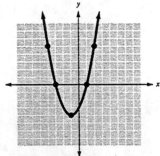

6. _____

7. _____

8. _____ **5.** 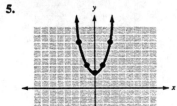 **6.**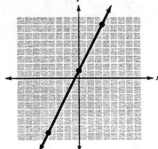

Equations
(a) $y = x^2 + 2$
(b) $y = 2x^2 - 1$
(c) $y = 2x + 1$
(d) $y = x^2 - 3x$
(e) $y = -x^2 - 4x$
(f) $y = -2x + 1$
(g) $y = x^2 + 2x - 3$
(h) $y = -x^2 + 6x - 8$

7. 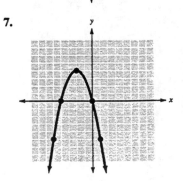 **8.**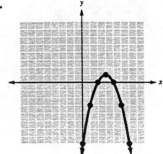

ANSWERS

Which of the given conditions apply to the graphs of each of the following equations? Note that more than one condition will apply.

9. _____

(a) The parabola opens upward.
(b) The parabola opens downward.
(c) The parabola has two x intercepts.
(d) The parabola has one x intercept.
(e) The parabola has no x intercept.

10. _____

9. $y = x^2 - 2$ **10.** $y = -x^2 + 2x$

11. _____

11. $y = x^2 - 2x - 3$ **12.** $y = x^2 - 4x + 5$

13. $y = -x^2 - 4x + 12$ **14.** $y = x^2 - 6x + 9$

12. _____

Find the equation of the axis of symmetry, the coordinates of the vertex, and the x intercepts. Sketch the graph of each equation.

15. $y = x^2 - 2x$ **16.** $y = x^2 - 4$

13. _____

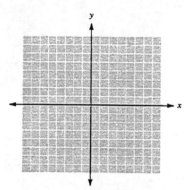

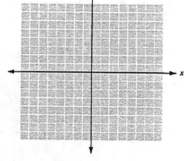

14. _____

15. _____

17. $y = -x^2 + 1$ **18.** $y = x^2 + 4x$

16. _____

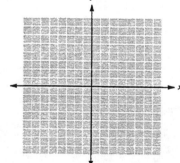

17. _____

18. _____

ANSWERS

19. _____

20. _____

21. _____

22. _____

23. _____

24. _____

25. _____

26. _____

19. $y = -x^2 - 4x$

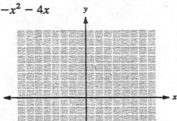

20. $y = -x^2 + 3x$

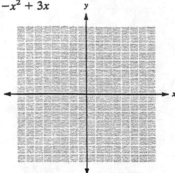

21. $y = x^2 - 2x - 3$

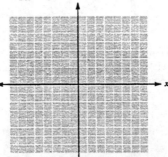

22. $y = x^2 - x - 6$

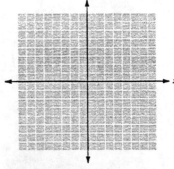

23. $y = x^2 - 5x + 4$

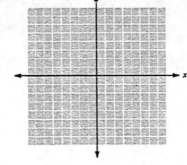

24. $y = x^2 + 3x + 2$

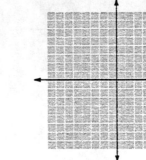

25. $y = -x^2 + 3x + 4$

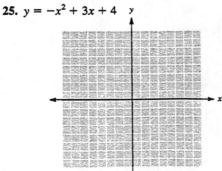

26. $y = x^2 - 6x + 8$

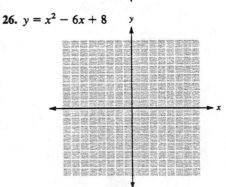

ANSWERS

27. _____

28. _____

27. $y = -x^2 + 6x - 5$

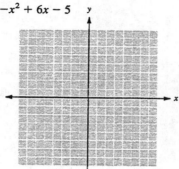

28. $y = -x^2 + 4x - 3$

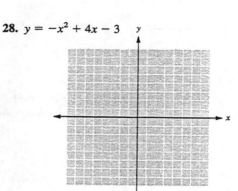

Find the equation of the axis of symmetry, the coordinates of the vertex, and at least two symmetric points. Sketch the graph of each equation.

29. _____

30. _____

29. $y = x^2 - 2x - 2$

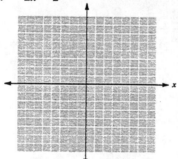

30. $y = x^2 - 4x - 3$

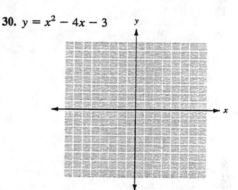

31. _____

32. _____

31. $y = x^2 + 4x + 5$

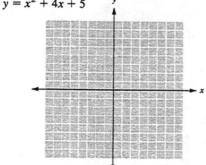

32. $y = -x^2 + 3x - 3$

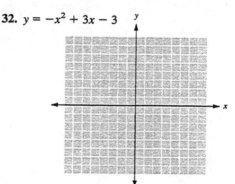

ANSWERS

33. _____

34. _____

35. _____

36. _____

37. _____

38. _____

33. $y = -x^2 + 6x - 2$

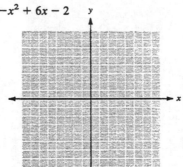

34. $y = x^2 + 5x + 2$

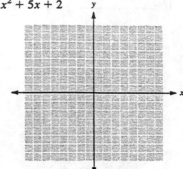

35. $y = 2x^2 - 4x + 1$

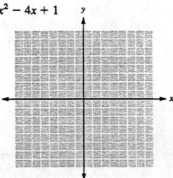

36. $y = \frac{1}{2}x^2 + x - 2$

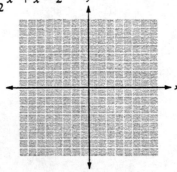

37. $y = -\frac{1}{3}x^2 + x - 2$

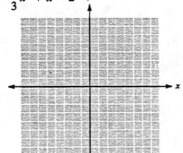

38. $y = -2x^2 + 4x - 3$

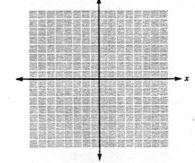

39. $y = 3x^2 + 6x - 1$

40. $y = -3x^2 \div 12x - 5$

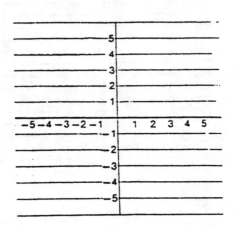

For each of the following equations, do the following:
   1)   Find the vertex
   2)   Find the axis of symmetry
   3)   List the maximum or minimum (and tell whether or not it is a maximum or minimum.)
   4)   Find the y-intercept
   5)   Find the x-intercept(s), if there are any
   6)   Draw the graph of the parabola.

41. $y = 2x^2 - 6x - 36$ **42.** $y = x^2 - 9x + 20$ **43.** $y = 4x^2 - 1$

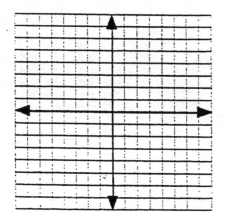   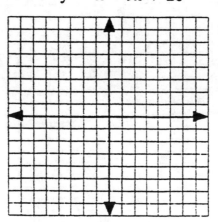   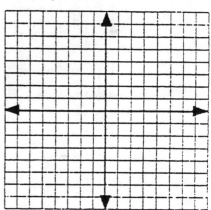

Vertex: _____   Vertex: _____   Vertex: _____

Axis: _____   Axis: _____   Axis: _____

Max/Min: _____   Max/Min: _____   Max/Min: _____

y-intercept: _____   y-intercept: _____   y-intercept: _____

x-intercept(s): _____   x-intercept(s): _____   x-intercept(s): _____

44. $y = x^2 - 2x - 6$

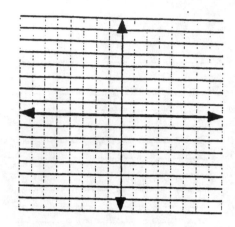

Vertex: _____

Axis: _____

Max/Min: _____

y-intercept: _____

x-intercept(s): _____

45. $y = x^2 - 5x - 6$

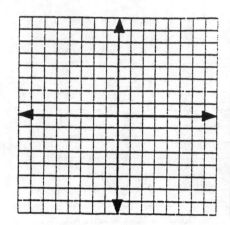

Vertex: _____

Axis: _____

Max/Min: _____

y-intercept: _____

x-intercept(s): _____

46. $y = x^2 - 5x + 6$

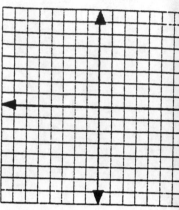

Vertex: _____

Axis: _____

Max/Min: _____

y-intercept: _____

x-intercept(s): ____

47. $y = x^2 - 25$

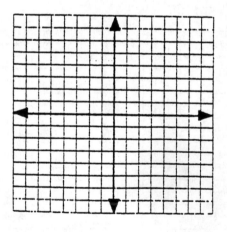

Vertex: _____

Axis: _____

Max/Min: _____

y-intercept: _____

x-intercept(s): _____

48. $y = 10x^2 - 13x - 3$

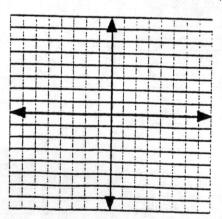

Vertex: _____

Axis: _____

Max/Min: _____

y-intercept: _____

x-intercept(s): _____

49. $y = 2x^2 + 3x - 4$

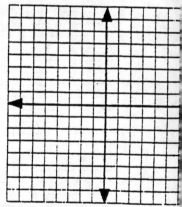

Vertex: _____

Axis: _____

Max/Min: _____

y-intercept: _____

x-intercept(s): _____

50. A company's weekly profit P is related to the number of items sold by the equation
$$P = -0.2x^2 + 40x - 500 .$$
Find the number of items that should be sold each week in order to maximize the profit. Then find the amount of that weekly profit.

51. A company's monthly profit P is related to the number of items sold by the equation
$$P = -0.1x^2 + 30x - 1000 .$$
How many items should be sold each month to obtain the largest possible profit? What is that profit?

52. A builder wants to enclose the largest possible rectangular area with 1600 feet of fencing. What should be the dimensions of the rectangle, and what will its area be?

53. A farmer wants to enclose a field along a river on three sides. If 1200 feet of fencing is to be used, what dimensions will give the maximum enclosed area? Find that maximum area.

54. A ball is thrown upward into the air with an initial velocity of 64 feet per second (ft/sec). If h gives the height of the ball at time t, then the equation relating h to t is
$$h = -16t^2 + 64t .$$
Find the maximum height that the ball will attain.

55. A ball is thrown upward into the air with an initial velocity of 32 (ft/sec). If h gives the height of the ball at time t, then the equation relating h to t is
$$h = -16t^2 + 32t .$$
Find the maximum height that the ball will attain.

ANSWERS

1. (d)　3. (b)　5. (a)　7. (e)　9. (a), (c)　11. (a), (c)　13. (b), (c)
15. $y = x^2 - 2x$; $x = 1$　17. $y = -x^2 + 1$; $x = 0$　19. $y = -x^2 - 4x$; $x = -2$

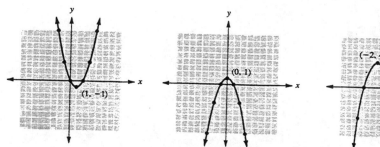

355

21. $y = x^2 - 2x - 3$; $x = 1$

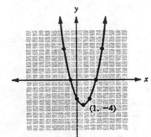

$(1, -4)$

23. $y = x^2 - 5x + 4$; $x = \dfrac{5}{2}$

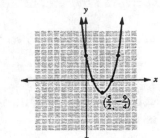

$\left(\dfrac{5}{2}, -\dfrac{9}{4}\right)$

25. $y = -x^2 + 3x + 4$; $x = \dfrac{3}{2}$

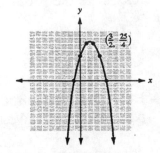

$\left(\dfrac{3}{2}, \dfrac{25}{4}\right)$

27. $y = -x^2 + 6x - 5$; $x = 3$

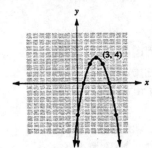

$(3, 4)$

29. $y = x^2 - 2x - 2$; $x = 1$

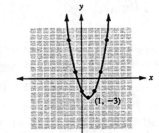

$(1, -3)$

31. $y = x^2 + 4x + 5$; $x = -2$

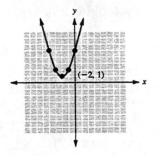

$(-2, 1)$

33. $y = -x^2 + 6x - 2$; $x = 3$

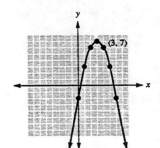

$(3, 7)$

35. $y = 2x^2 - 4x + 1$; $x = 1$

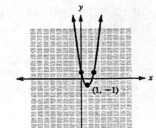

$(1, -1)$

37. $y = -\dfrac{1}{3}x^2 + x - 2$; $x = \dfrac{3}{2}$

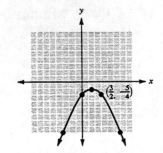

$\left(\dfrac{3}{2}, -\dfrac{5}{4}\right)$

39. $y = 3x^2 + 6x - 1$; $x = -1$

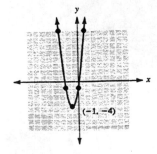

$(-1, -4)$

41.

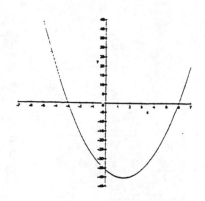

Vertex: (1.5,-40.5)

Axis: x = 1.5

Max/Min: min is -40.5

y-intercept: (0,-36)

x-int.: (-3,0),(6,0)

42.

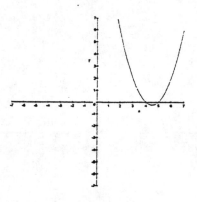

Vertex: (4.5,-0.25)

Axis: x = 4.5

Max/Min: min is -0.25

y-intercept: (0,20)

x-int.: (4,0),(5,0)

43.

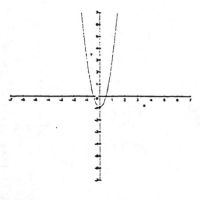

Vertex: (0,-1)

Axis: x = 0

Max/Min: min is -1

y-intercept: (0,-1)

x-int.: $\left(\dfrac{-1}{2},0\right) , \left(\dfrac{1}{2},0\right)$

44.

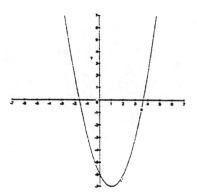

Vertex: (1,-7)

Axis: x = 1

Max/Min: min is -7

y-intercept: (0,-6)

x-int.: $\left(1 \pm \sqrt{7},0\right)$

45.

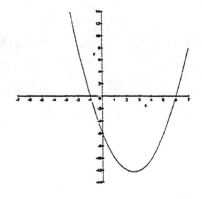

Vertex: (2.5,-12.25)

Axis: x = 2.5

Max/Min: min is -12.25

y-intercept: (0,-6)

x-int.: (6,0),(-1,0)

46.

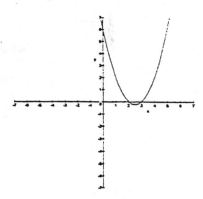

Vertex: (2.5,-0.25)

Axis: x = 2.5

Max/Min: min -.25

y-intercept: (0,6)

x-int.: (2,0),(3,0)

47.

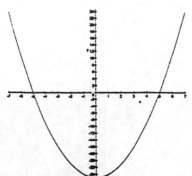

Vertex: __(0,-25)__

Axis: __x = 0__

Max/Min: __min is -25__

y-intercept: __(0,-25)__

x-int.: __(-5,0),(5,0)__

48.

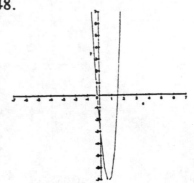

Vertex: $\left(\dfrac{13}{20}, -7\dfrac{9}{40}\right)$

Axis: __x = 13/20__

Max/Min: __-289/40 min__

y-intercept: __(0,-3)__

x-int.: $\left(\dfrac{13 \pm \sqrt{181}}{20}, 0\right)$

49.

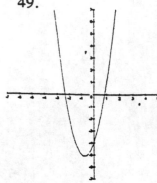

Vertex: $\left(-\dfrac{3}{4}, -\dfrac{41}{8}\right)$

Axis: __x = -.75__

Max/Min: __min -5.125__

y-intercept: __(0,-4)__

x-int.: $\left(\dfrac{-3 \pm \sqrt{41}}{4}, 0\right)$

50.   100 items, $1,500   **52.**   400 ft. by 400 ft., 160,000 square feet   **54.**   64 feet

358

Applications and Problem Solving

OBJECTIVE
To use quadratic equations in the solution of applications

With the techniques for solving quadratic equations by factoring, we can now approach a new group of applications that lead to quadratic equations. Whether or not a problem leads to a quadratic equation, the key to problem solving lies in a step-by-step, organized approach to the process. You might want to take time now to review the five-step process introduced in our coverage of applications and problem solving since all the examples of this section are built on that same model.

Of course, we can expect more than one solution to check where models lead to quadratic equations. Remember that quadratic equations may have two real number solutions.

Step 5, the process of verifying or checking your solution, is of particular importance when an application leads to a quadratic equation. By verifying solutions you may find that both, only one, or none of the derived solutions satisfy the physical conditions stated in the original problem.

As an example, consider the following: The product of a whole number and 1 more than twice that number is 55. What is the number?

As you will see, this problem leads to the equation

This is a result of the equation $x(2x + 1) = 55$.

$$2x^2 + x - 55 = 0 \qquad \text{or} \qquad (2x + 11)(x - 5) = 0$$

The equation has solutions of $-\dfrac{11}{2}$ and 5.

However, since the problem asks for a *whole* number, we must reject the solution $-\dfrac{11}{2}$ because it does not meet the original conditions of the problem.

Similarly, we reject other values that are not meaningful, such as a negative solution in a problem asking for a length or other dimension.

Example 1

One integer is 3 less than twice another. If their product is 35, find the two integers.

Step 1 The unknowns are the two integers.

Step 2 Let x represent the first integer. Then

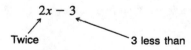
$$2x - 3$$
Twice   3 less than

represents the second.

Step 3 Form an equation:

$$\underbrace{x(2x - 3)}_{\substack{\text{Product of} \\ \text{the two integers}}} = 35$$

Step 4 Remove the parentheses and solve as before.

$$2x^2 - 3x = 35$$
$$2x^2 - 3x - 35 = 0$$

Factor on the left:

$$(2x + 7)(x - 5) = 0$$

$$2x + 7 = 0 \qquad \text{or} \qquad x - 5 = 0$$
$$2x = -7 \qquad\qquad x = 5$$
$$x = -\frac{7}{2}$$

This represents the solutions to the equation but not the answer to the original problem.

Step 5 Solving in step 4, we have the two solutions $-\frac{7}{2}$ and 5. Since the original problem asks for *integers,* we must consider only 5 as a solution.

The desired integers, (x) and $(2x - 3)$, are then 5 and 7.

To verify, their product is 35.

CHECK YOURSELF 1

One integer is 2 more than 3 times another. If their product is 56, what are the two integers?

Problems involving consecutive integers may also lead to quadratic equations. Recall that consecutive integers can be represented by x, $x + 1$, $x + 2$, and so on. Consecutive even (or odd) integers are represented by x, $x + 2$, $x + 4$, and so on.

Example 2

The sum of the squares of two consecutive integers is 85. What are the two integers?

Step 1 The unknowns are the two consecutive integers.

Step 2 Let x be the first integer and $x + 1$ the second.

Step 3 Form the equation.

$$\underbrace{x^2 + (x + 1)^2}_{\text{Sum of squares}} = 85$$

Step 4 Solve.

$$
\begin{aligned}
x^2 + (x + 1)^2 &= 85 \\
x^2 + x^2 + 2x + 1 &= 85 \qquad &\text{Remove parentheses.} \\
2x^2 + 2x - 84 &= 0 \qquad &\text{Note common factor of 2.} \\
x^2 + x - 42 &= 0 \qquad &\text{Divide both members of equation by 2.} \\
(x + 7)(x - 6) &= 0 \\
\end{aligned}
$$

$$x + 7 = 0 \qquad \text{or} \qquad x - 6 = 0$$
$$x = -7 \qquad\qquad x = 6$$

Step 5 The solution in step 4 leads to two possibilities, -7 or 6. Since *both numbers are integers*, both meet the conditions of the original problem. The consecutive integers are

The two consecutive integers we are looking for are

$\quad -7 \quad$ and $\quad -6$

or $\quad 6 \quad$ and $\quad 7$

| -7 (x) | or | 6 (x) |
| -6 $(x + 1)$ | | 7 $(x + 1)$ |

You should verify that in both cases the sum of the squares is 85.

CHECK YOURSELF 2

The sum of the squares of two consecutive even numbers is 100. Find the two integers.

Let's proceed now to applications involving geometry.

Example 3

The length of a rectangle is 3 cm greater than its width. If the area of the rectangle is 108 cm², what are the dimensions of the rectangle?

Step 1 You are asked to find the dimensions (the length and the width) of the rectangle.

Step 2 Whenever geometric figures are involved in an application, start by drawing, and *then labeling*, a sketch of the problem. Letting x represent the width and $x + 3$ the length, we have

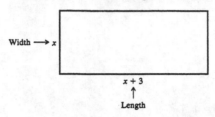

Step 3 Once the drawing is correctly labeled, this step should be easy. The area of a rectangle is the product of its length and width, so

$$x(x + 3) = 108$$

Multiply and write in standard form.

Factor and solve as before.

Step 4
$$x(x + 3) = 108$$
$$x^2 + 3x - 108 = 0$$
$$(x + 12)(x - 9) = 0$$
$$x + 12 = 0 \qquad \text{or} \qquad x - 9 = 0$$
$$x = -12 \qquad\qquad x = 9$$

Step 5 We reject -12 (cm) as a solution. A length cannot be negative, and so we must consider only 9 (cm) in finding the required dimensions.

The width x is 9 cm, and the length $x + 3$ is 12 cm. Since this gives a rectangle of area 108 cm^2, the solution is verified.

CHECK YOURSELF 3

In a triangle, the base is 4 in less than its height. If its area is 30 in^2, find the length of the base and the height of the triangle.

Example 4

An open box is formed from a rectangular piece of cardboard, whose length is 2 in more than its width, by cutting 2-in squares from each corner and folding up the sides. If the volume of the box is to be 96 in^3, what must be the size of the original piece of cardboard?

Step 1 We are asked for the dimensions of the sheet of cardboard.

Step 2 Again sketch the problem.

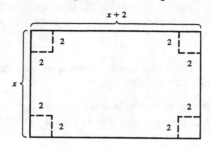

Step 3 To form an equation for volume, we sketch the completed box.

Note: The original width of the cardboard was x. Removing two 2-in squares leaves $x - 4$ for the width of the box. Similarly, the length of the box is $x - 2$. Do you see why?

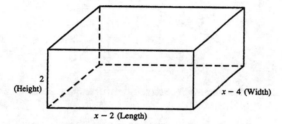

Since volume is the product of height, length, and width,

$$2(x - 2)(x - 4) = 96$$

Step 4

$$
\begin{aligned}
2(x - 2)(x - 4) &= 96 \\
(x - 2)(x - 4) &= 48 \\
x^2 - 6x + 8 &= 48 \\
x^2 - 6x - 40 &= 0 \\
(x - 10)(x + 4) &= 0 \\
x = 10 \text{ in} \quad &\text{or} \quad x = -4 \text{ in}
\end{aligned}
$$

Divide both sides by 2, multiply on the left, and write in standard form. Then solve as before.

Step 5 Again, we need consider only the positive solution. The width x of the original piece of cardboard is 10 in, and its length $x + 2$ is 12 in. The dimensions of the completed box will be 6 by 8 by 2 in, which gives the required volume of 96 in^3.

CHECK YOURSELF 4

A similar box is to be made by cutting 3-in squares from a piece of cardboard that is 4 in longer than it is wide. If the required volume is 180 in^3, find the dimensions of the original square of cardboard.

Another geometric result that generates quadratic equations in applications is the *Pythagorean theorem*. Recall that the theorem gives an important relationship between the lengths of the sides of a right triangle (a triangle with a 90° angle).

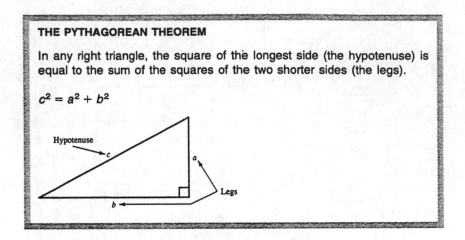

THE PYTHAGOREAN THEOREM

In any right triangle, the square of the longest side (the hypotenuse) is equal to the sum of the squares of the two shorter sides (the legs).

$$c^2 = a^2 + b^2$$

Let's look at an application of the theorem.

Example 5

One leg of a right triangle is 2 in longer than the other. If the hypotenuse is 4 in longer than the shortest side, find the lengths of the three sides of the triangle.

Step 1 You must find the lengths of the three sides of the triangle.

Step 2 Since the legs can be represented by x and $x + 2$ and the hypotenuse by $x + 4$, a sketch of the problem should look like this:

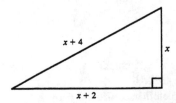

Step 3 Now apply the Pythagorean theorem to write an equation:

$$\underbrace{x^2 + (x + 2)^2}_{\text{Sum of squares of legs}} = \underbrace{(x + 4)^2}_{\text{Square of hypotenuse}}$$

Step 4 Clearing the parentheses, we have

$$x^2 + x^2 + 4x + 4 = x^2 + 8x + 16$$

or

364

Write in standard form.

$$x^2 - 4x - 12 = 0$$
$$(x - 6)(x + 2) = 0$$
$$x = 6 \quad \text{or} \quad x = -2$$

Step 5 Again, since a length cannot be negative, we reject the solution of -2. The legs then are 6 and 8 in long, and the hypotenuse has length 10 in.

CHECK YOURSELF 5

One leg of a right triangle is 7 cm greater than the other. The hypotenuse is 8 cm greater than the length of the shorter leg. Find the lengths of the three sides of the triangle.

In the next example, the solution of the quadratic equation contains radicals. Substituting a pair of solutions such as $\dfrac{3 \pm \sqrt{5}}{2}$ is a very difficult process. The emphasis is on checking the "reasonableness" of the answer.

Example 6

One leg of a right triangle is 4 cm longer than the other leg. The length of the hypotenuse of the triangle is 12 cm. Find the length of the two legs.

Step 1 We wish to find the length of the two legs of the right triangle.

Step 2 We assign variable x to the shorter leg and $x + 4$ to the other leg.

As in any geometric problem, a sketch of the information will help us visualize.

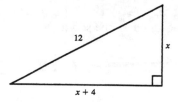

Step 3 Now we apply the Pythagorean theorem to write an equation for the solution.

The sum of the squares of the legs of the triangle is equal to the square of the hypotenuse.

$$x^2 + (x + 4)^2 = (12)^2$$

Step 4 From step 3 we have the equation

$$x^2 + x^2 + 8x + 16 = 144$$

or

$$2x^2 + 8x - 128 = 0$$

Dividing both sides by 2, we have the equivalent equation

$$x^2 + 4x - 64 = 0$$

Dividing both sides of a quadratic equation by a common factor is always a prudent step. It simplifies your work with the quadratic formula.

Using the quadratic formula, we get

$$x = -2 + 2\sqrt{17} \qquad \text{or} \qquad x = -2 - 2\sqrt{17}$$

Step 5 We can reject $-2 - 2\sqrt{17}$ (do you see why?), but we should still check the reasonableness of the value $-2 + 2\sqrt{17}$.

We could substitute $-2 + 2\sqrt{17}$ into the original equation, but it seems more prudent to simply check that it "makes sense" as a solution.

$\sqrt{17}$ is just slightly *more* than $\sqrt{16}$, or 4.

Remembering that $\sqrt{16} = 4$, we will estimate $-2 + 2\sqrt{17}$ as

$$-2 + 2(4) = 6$$

Our equation of step 3,

$$x^2 + (x + 4)^2 = (12)^2$$

where x equals 6, becomes

$$36 + 100 \approx 144$$

This indicates that our answer is reasonable at least.

CHECK YOURSELF 6

One leg of a right triangle is 2 cm longer than the other. The hypotenuse is 1 cm less than twice the length of the shorter leg. Find the length of each side of the triangle.

As we continue looking at examples that demonstrate applications of quadratic equations, we will use the five-step problem-solving process, but we will not always label the steps. However, be sure to think about those steps as you read through the examples.

Example 7

Bill has a swimming pool that is 15 ft wide and 25 ft long. He is going to pour a concrete patio of uniform width around the pool.

If he has enough concrete to cover 400 ft², how wide will the patio be?

We will first draw a picture of the problem, letting the patio width be represented by x.

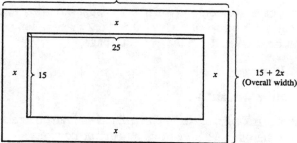

One approach to the problem is to think of the area of the patio as the total area (patio and pool) minus the area of the pool.

From our sketch, we see the total region has width $15 + 2x$ and length $25 + 2x$. Its area is then given by

$$(25 + 2x)(15 + 2x)$$

while the area of the pool is $25 \cdot 15$, or 375 ft^2.

Let's translate those last two paragraphs to an algebraic sentence:

$$(25 + 2x)(15 + 2x) - 375 = 400$$

Now we want to solve the above equation. We remove the parentheses, and after simplifying on the left, we have

$$4x^2 + 80x = 400$$

or, in standard form,

$$4x^2 + 80x - 400 = 0$$

We divide both sides of the equation by 4, so

$$x^2 + 20x - 100 = 0$$

and applying the quadratic formula, we have

$$x = -10 \pm 10\sqrt{2}$$

Because the width must be positive, we need only verify the value $-10 + 10\sqrt{2}$.

Not only would this make for a difficult substitution, but also it is not the kind of answer that Bill is looking for. (Can you imagine calling Bill to tell him that the patio should be exactly $-10 + 10\sqrt{2}$ ft wide?) This leads us to a second reason for estimating our solutions in these application problems—it gives us answers that fit our real-world experience.

$x \approx -10 - 10(1.4)$
$= -10 - 14$
$= 4$

In this case, we could say that $\sqrt{2}$ is approximately equal to 1.4. That makes the patio 4 ft wide, an answer that works well when we substitute it into the equation derived from the previous page.

CHECK YOURSELF 7

Assume (from Example 7) that Bill has enough concrete for 800 ft². How wide would the patio be given this amount of concrete?

Note: It would *not* be twice as wide.

Let's turn to another field for an application that leads to solving a quadratic equation. Many equations of motion in physics involve quadratic equations.

Example 8

If a ball is thrown vertically upward from the ground, with an initial velocity of 48 ft/s, its height h, in feet, above the ground after t seconds is given by

This equation does not take into account any air resistance.

$$h = 48t - 16t^2$$

(*a*) How long does it take the ball to return to the ground?

Since $h = 0$ represents a height of 0 (the ground), we simply substitute 0 for h and solve for t:

$$0 = 48t - 16t^2$$
$$= 16t(3 - t)$$

So

$16t = 0$ or $3 - t = 0$
$t = 0$ $t = 3$

The solution $t = 0$ represents the starting point (on the ground), so it takes the ball 3 s to return to the ground.

(*b*) How long will it take the ball to reach a height of 32 ft on the way up?

In this case we want the time t to reach a height of 32 ft, so we substitute 32 for h and again solve for t. Letting h be 32, we have

$$32 = 48t - 16t^2$$

Writing the equation in standard form yields

Note that we have chosen to write the quadratic member *on the left* so that the coefficient of t^2 (16) is positive. That will simplify the later factoring step. We then divide both sides by 16 and factor as before.

$$16t^2 - 48t + 32 = 0$$
$$t^2 - 3t + 2 = 0$$
$$(t - 1)(t - 2) = 0$$
$$t = 1 \text{ s} \qquad \text{or} \qquad t = 2 \text{ s}$$

Which solution do we want? The following figure will help.

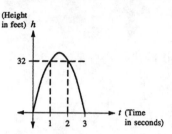

It takes 2 s to reach 32 ft on the way down.

Since we want the time t to reach the height of 32 ft on the way *up*, the desired solution is 1 s.

CHECK YOURSELF 8

The height of a ball thrown upward from the ground with a velocity 80 ft/s is given by

$$h = 80t - 16t^2$$

where h represents the height above the ground, in feet.

1. How long will it take the ball to return to the ground?
2. How long will it take the ball to pass through a height of 96 ft on the way back *down* to the ground?

Example 9

If a ball is thrown vertically upward from the roof of a building 70 m tall with an initial velocity of 15 m/s, its approximate height h, after t seconds, is given by

$$h = 70 + 15t - 16t^2$$

Note that when $t = 0$, the height is 70 m.

(*a*) How long does it take the ball to reach the ground?

Substituting 0 for h, we have a quadratic equation in t:

$$0 = 70 + 15t - 5t^2$$

Dividing both sides of the equation by 5 and writing the quadratic member on the left, we have

$$t^2 - 3t - 14 = 0$$

Using the quadratic formula yields

$$t = \frac{3 \pm \sqrt{65}}{2}$$

Since $\sqrt{65}$ is only slightly more than 8, we can estimate the two solutions for t as

Our values for t are approximately

$$\frac{3 + 8}{2} \quad \text{or} \quad \frac{3 - 8}{2}$$

$$t = -\frac{5}{2}\,\text{s} \quad \text{or} \quad t = \frac{11}{2}\,\text{s}$$

The solution must be positive (why?), so the ball falls to the ground after approximately $\frac{11}{2}$, or $5\frac{1}{2}$ s.

A "picture" of the tossed ball will help you see what is happening. Try to use this picture in solving part b.

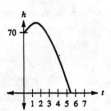

(b) At what two times will the ball reach a height of 75 m?

We substitute 75 for h in our original equation.

$$75 = 70 + 15t - 5t^2$$

or

$$5t^2 - 15t + 5 = 0$$

Dividing by 5, we have the equivalent equation

$$t^2 - 3t + 1 = 0$$

Using the quadratic formula yields

$$t = \frac{3 \pm \sqrt{5}}{2}$$

If we use 2.2 as an estimate for $\sqrt{5}$, we find that

$$t = 0.4\,\text{s} \quad \text{or} \quad t = 2.6\,\text{s}$$

Another look at the sketch of the problem above will help us to interpret these results.

CHECK YOURSELF 9

A ball is thrown vertically upward from the top of a building 100 m high with an initial velocity of 25 m/s. After t seconds, the height h is given by

$$h = 100 + 25t - 5t^2$$

1. How long does it take the ball to reach the ground?
2. How long does it take the ball to reach a height of 80 m?

An important economic application involves supply and demand. Our next example illustrates that application.

Example 10

The number of intermediate algebra workbooks that a publisher is willing to produce is determined by the supply curve

$$S = -p^2 + 30p - 180 \qquad \text{where } p \text{ is the unit price in dollars}$$

The demand for these workbooks is determined by the equation

$$D = -10p + 130$$

Find the equilibrium price (the price at which supply and demand are equal).

Because supply equals demand ($S = D$), we can write

$$-p^2 + 30p - 180 = -10p + 130$$

Rewriting this statement as a quadratic equation in standard form yields

$$p^2 - 40p + 310 = 0$$

When we apply the quadratic formula, we find the solutions

$$p = 20 \pm 3\sqrt{10}$$

If we approximate $\sqrt{10}$ as 3.2, we have

$$p \approx 10.40 \qquad \text{or} \qquad p \approx 29.60$$

Although you might assume that the publisher will choose the higher price, it will, in fact, choose $10.40. If you want to discover why, try substituting the two solutions into the original demand equation.

CHECK YOURSELF 10

The demand equation for floppy disks that accompany a text is predicted to be

$D = -6p + 30$ where p is the unit price in dollars

The supply equation is predicted to be

$S = -p^2 + 12p - 20$

Find the equilibrium price.

CHECK YOURSELF ANSWERS

1. 4, 14.
2. −8 and −6   or   6 and 8
3. Base 6 in, height 10 in.
4. 12 in by 16 in.
5. 5 cm, 12 cm, 13 cm.
6. Approximately 4.3, 6.3, and 7.6
7. $-10 \pm 10\sqrt{3}$, approximately 7.3 ft.
8. (1) 5 s; (2) 3 s.
9. (1) $\dfrac{5 + \sqrt{105}}{2} \approx 7.6$ s; (2) $\dfrac{5 + \sqrt{41}}{2} \approx 5.7$ s.
10. Approximately $3.43.

Name _____

Date _____

Exercises

Build Your Skills

1. _____

2. _____

3. _____

4. _____

5. _____

6. _____

7. _____

8. _____

9. _____

10. _____

1. One integer is 3 more than twice another. If the product of those integers is 65, find the two integers.

2. One positive integer is 5 less than 3 times another, and their product is 78. What are the two integers?

3. The sum of two integers is 10, and their product is 24. Find the two integers.

4. The sum of two integers is 12. If the product of the two integers is 27, what are the two integers?

5. The product of two consecutive integers is 72. What are the two integers?

6. If the product of two consecutive odd integers is 63, find the two integers.

7. The sum of the squares of two consecutive whole numbers is 61. Find the two whole numbers.

8. If the sum of the squares of two consecutive even integers is 100, what are the two integers?

9. The sum of two integers is 9, and the sum of the squares of those two integers is 41. Find the two integers.

10. The sum of two natural numbers is 12. If the sum of the squares of those numbers is 74, what are the two numbers?

ANSWERS

11. _____

11. The sum of the squares of three consecutive integers is 50. Find the three integers.

12. If the sum of the squares of three consecutive odd positive integers is 83, what are the three integers?

12. _____

13. Twice the square of a positive integer is 12 more than 5 times that integer. What is the integer?

13. _____

14. Find an integer such that if 10 is added to the integer's square, the result is 40 more than that integer.

14. _____

15. The width of a rectangle is 3 ft less than its length. If the area of the rectangle is 70 ft^2, what are the dimensions of the rectangle?

16. The length of a rectangle is 5 cm more than its width. If the area of the rectangle is 84 cm^2, find the dimensions of the rectangle.

15. _____

17. The length of a rectangle is 2 cm more than 3 times its width. If the area of the rectangle is 85 cm^2, find the dimensions of the rectangle.

16. _____

18. If the length of a rectangle is 3 ft less than twice its width and the area of the rectangle is 54 ft^2, what are the dimensions of the rectangle?

17. _____

19. The length of a rectangle is 1 cm more than its width. If the length of the rectangle is doubled, the area of the rectangle is increased by 30 cm^2. What were the dimensions of the original rectangle?

18. _____

19. _____

ANSWERS

20. _____

20. The height of a triangle is 2 in more than the length of the base. If the base is tripled in length, the area of the new triangle is 48 in^2 more than the original. Find the height and base of the original triangle.

21. One leg of a right triangle is twice the length of the other. The hypotenuse is 6 m long. Find the length of each leg.

21. _____

22. One leg of a right triangle is 2 ft longer than the shorter side. If the length of the hypotenuse is 14 ft, how long is each leg?

22. _____

23. One leg of a right triangle is 1 in shorter than the other leg. The hypotenuse is 3 in longer than the shorter side. Find the length of each side.

24. The hypotenuse of a given right triangle is 5 cm longer than the shorter leg. The length of the shorter leg is 2 cm less than that of the longer leg. Find the length of each side.

23. _____

25. The sum of the lengths of the two legs of a right triangle is 25 m. The hypotenuse is 22 m long. Find the length of the two legs.

26. The sum of the lengths of one side of a right triangle and the hypotenuse is 15 cm. The other leg is 5 cm shorter than the hypotenuse. Find the length of each side.

24. _____

25. _____

26. _____

ANSWERS

27. _____

27. A box is to be made from a rectangular piece of tin that is twice as long as it is wide. To accomplish this, a 10-cm square is cut from each corner, and the sides are folded up. The volume of the finished box is to be 5000 cm³. Find the dimensions of the original piece of tin.

Hint 1: To solve this equation, you will want to use the following sketch of the piece of tin. Note that the original dimensions are represented by x and $2x$. Do you see why? Also, recall that the volume of the resulting box will be the product of the length, width, and height.

28. _____

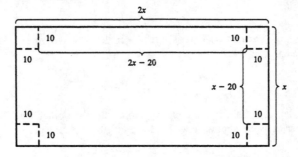

Hint 2: From this sketch, you can see that the equation that results from $V = LWH$ will be

$$(2x - 20)(x - 20)10 = 5000$$

29. _____

28. An open box is formed from a square piece of material by cutting 2-in squares from each corner of the material and folding up the sides. If the volume of the box that is formed is to be 72 in³, what was the size of the original piece of material?

29. An open carton is formed from a rectangular piece of cardboard that is 4 ft longer than it is wide, by removing 1-ft squares from each corner and folding up the sides. If the volume of the carton is then 12 ft³, what were the dimensions of the original piece of cardboard?

30. _____

30. A box that has a volume of 2000 in³ was made from a square piece of tin. The square piece cut from each corner had sides of length 4 in. What were the original dimensions of the square?

31. A square piece of cardboard is to be formed into a box. After 5-cm squares are cut from each corner and the sides are folded up, the resulting box will have a volume of 400 cm³. Find the length of a side of the original piece of cardboard.

31. _____

ANSWERS

32. _____

32. A rectangular piece of cardboard has a length that is 2 cm longer than twice its width. If 2-cm squares are cut from each of its corners, it can be folded into a box that has a volume of 250 cm³. What were the original dimensions of the piece of cardboard?

33. _____

33. Shirley has a swimming pool that is 20 ft wide and 30 ft long. She wishes to pour a concrete patio of uniform width around the pool. If she has enough concrete to cover 400 ft², find the maximum width of the patio. (*Hint:* See Example 7 in this section.)

34. Repeat Exercise 33 to find the width of the patio if Shirley has enough concrete to cover 500 ft².

34. _____

35. Jason has a greenhouse that is 20 ft long and 12 ft wide. He wishes to pour a concrete sidewalk all the way around the greenhouse. If he has enough concrete to cover 160 ft², what will the width of the sidewalk be?

35. _____

36. In Exercise 35, if Jason doubles the amount of concrete available, what will the maximum sidewalk width become?

36. _____

37. A rectangular lawn measures 30 by 35 m. It is surrounded by a sidewalk of uniform width. The total area of the property, including both lawn and sidewalk, is 1200 m². Find the width of the sidewalk.

38. Christine owns a rectangular lot that has a total area of 2000 ft². The lot consists of a garden surrounded by a path of uniform width. If the garden is 60 by 30 ft, find the width of the path.

37. _____

39. A rectangular mirror measures 40 by 60 cm. It is surrounded by a wooden frame of uniform width. The total area of the frame and mirror is 3000 cm². Find the width of the frame.

38. _____

39. _____

ANSWERS

40. _____

40. A rectangular mirror is 25 by 40 in. The total area of the mirror and its frame is 1500 in^2. Find the width of the frame.

41. Jacob wishes to create a cross path through his garden, as indicated by the sketch below. The dimensions of the garden are 4 by 5 m. Find the width of the path that would take up one-fourth of the garden area.

41. _____

(*Hint:* The area of the path must be $5x + 4x - x^2$. Do you see why?)

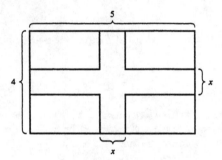

42. _____

42. In Exercise 41, find the width of the path that would take up one-fifth of the area of Jacob's garden.

43. _____

43. Having seen the path in Jacob's garden, Gretchen would like to do the same in her garden. If her garden is 7 m long and 5 m wide, what is the width of the path that would take up one-fifth of the garden area?

44. _____

44. What is the maximum width of the path that would take up no more than one-seventh of the area of Gretchen's garden?

45. One leg of a right triangle is 3 cm longer than the other. The hypotenuse of the triangle is 6 cm longer than the shorter leg. Find the lengths of the three sides of the triangle.

45. _____

46. The lengths of the shorter leg, the longer leg, and the hypotenuse of a right triangle can be represented by consecutive even integers. Find the lengths of the three sides of the triangle.

46. _____

ANSWERS

47. _____

47. The length of a rectangle is 7 in more than its width. If the diagonal of the rectangle is 8 in longer than the width, find the dimensions of the rectangle.

48. The length of a rectangle is 7 ft longer than its width, and the diagonal is 9 ft longer than its width. Find the length of the diagonal of the rectangle.

48. _____

49. The diagonal of a square is 5 cm long. Find the length of one side of the square.

49. _____

50. Find the length of one side of a square that has a diagonal $7\sqrt{5}$ in long.

51. The diagonal of a square is 3 in longer than one of the sides. Find the length of the sides.

50. _____

52. The length of the diagonal of a square is 2 cm less than the sum of the lengths of the four sides. Find the length of the sides.

51. _____

53. If a ball is thrown vertically upward from the ground, its height h after t seconds is given by

$$h = 64t - 16t^2$$

(a) How long does it take the ball to return to the ground? (*Hint:* Let $h(t) = 0$)

(b) How long does it take the ball to reach a height of 48 ft on the way up?

52. _____

54. If a ball is thrown vertically upward from the ground, its height h after t seconds is given by

$$h = 96t - 16t^2$$

53. _____

(a) How long does it take the ball to return to the ground?

(b) How long does it take the ball to pass through a height of 128 ft on the way back down to the ground?

54. _____

ANSWERS

55. _____

55. Suppose that the cost $C(x)$, in dollars, of producing x chairs is given by

$$C = 2400 - 40x + 2x^2$$

How many chairs can be produced for $5400?

56. Suppose that the profit $T(x)$, in dollars, of producing and selling x appliances is given by

56. _____

$$T = -3x^2 + 240x - 1,800$$

How many appliances must be produced and sold to achieve a profit of $3000?

If a ball is thrown vertically upward from the roof of a building 32 ft high with an initial velocity of 64 ft/s, its approximate height h after t seconds is given by

$$h = 32 + 64t - 16t^2$$

57. _____

Note: The difference between this equation and the one we used in Example 9 has to do with the units used. When we used meters, the t^2 coefficient was -5 (from the fact that the acceleration due to gravity is approximately 10 m/s^2). When we use feet as our unit for height, the t^2 coefficient is -16 (that same acceleration becomes 32 ft/s^2).

57. How long does it take the ball to fall back to the ground?

58. _____

58. When will the ball reach a height of 64 ft?

Changing the initial velocity to 96 ft/s will change only the t coefficient (although this is a velocity that would require an arm like Dwight Gooden's). Our new equation becomes

$$h = 32 + 96t - 16t^2$$

59. How long will it take the ball to return to the thrower?

59. _____

60. When will the ball reach a height of 144 ft?

60. _____

ANSWERS

61. _____

The only part of the height equation that we have not discussed is the constant. You have probably noticed that the constant is always equal to the initial height of the ball (50 ft in our previous problems). Now, let's have *you* develop an equation.

A ball is thrown upward from the roof of a 100-m building with an initial velocity of 20 m/s.

61. Find the equation for the height of the ball h after t seconds.

62. _____

62. How long will it take the ball to fall back to the ground?

63. _____

63. When will the ball reach a height of 75 m?

64. Will the ball ever reach a height of 125 m? (*Hint:* Check the discriminant.)

64. _____

A ball is thrown upward from the roof of a 100-ft building with an initial velocity of 20 ft/s.

65. Find the height of the ball h after t seconds.

65. _____

66. How long will it take the ball to fall back to the ground?

66. _____

67. When will the ball have a height of 80 ft?

67. _____

68. Will the ball ever reach a height of 120 ft? Explain.

69. A small manufacturer's weekly profit in dollars is given by

68. _____

$$P = -3x + 270x$$

Find the number of items x that must be produced to realize a profit of $5100.

69. _____

70. Suppose the profit in dollars is given by

$$P = -2x^2 + 240x$$

Now how many items must be sold to realize a profit of $5100?

70. _____

ANSWERS

71. _____

72. _____

71. The demand equation for a certain computer chip is given by

$$D = -2p + 14$$

The supply equation is predicted to be

$$S = -p^2 + 16p - 2$$

Find the equilibrium price.

72. The demand equation for a certain type of printer is predicted to be

$$D = -200p + 36,000$$

The supply equation is predicted to be

$$S = -p^2 + 400p - 24,000$$

Find the equilibrium price.

ANSWERS

1. 5, 13　　**3.** 4, 6　　**5.** −9, −8 or 8, 9　　**7.** 5, 6　　**9.** 4, 5　　**11.** −5, −4, −3 or 3, 4, 5

13. 4　　**15.** 7 ft by 10 ft　　**17.** 5 cm by 17 cm　　**19.** 5 cm by 6 cm　　**21.** $\dfrac{6\sqrt{5}}{5}$,

$\dfrac{12\sqrt{5}}{5}$, or 2.7, 5.4 m　　**23.** $2 + 2\sqrt{3}, 3 + 2\sqrt{3}, 5 + 2\sqrt{3}$, or 5.5, 6.5, 8.5 in　　**25.** $\dfrac{25 \pm 7\sqrt{7}}{2}$

or 3.2, 21.8 m　　**27.** $15 + 5\sqrt{11}, 30 + 10\sqrt{11}$, or 31.6 by 63.2 cm　　**29.** 4 by 8 ft

31. $10 + 4\sqrt{5}$ or 18.9 cm　　**33.** $\dfrac{-25 + 5\sqrt{41}}{2}$ or 3.5 ft　　**35.** $-8 + \sqrt{104}$ or 2.2 ft

37. $\dfrac{-65 + 5\sqrt{193}}{4}$ or 1.1 m　　**39.** $-25 + 5\sqrt{31}$ or 2.8 cm　　**41.** $\dfrac{9 - \sqrt{61}}{2}$ or 0.6 m

43. $6 - \sqrt{29}$ or 0.6 m　　**45.** 9, 12, 15 cm　　**47.** 5 in by 12 in　　**49.** $\dfrac{5\sqrt{2}}{2}$ or 3.5 cm

51. $3 + 3\sqrt{2}$ or 7.2 in　　**53.** (a) 4 s, (b) 1 s　　**55.** 50　　**57.** $2 + \sqrt{6}$ or 4.4 s　　**59.** 6 seconds
or 6.3 s　　**61.** $h(t) = 100 + 20t - 5t^2$　　**63.** 5 s　　**65.** $h(t) = 100 + 20t - 16t^2$

67. $\dfrac{5 + \sqrt{105}}{8}$ or 1.9 s　　**69.** $45 \pm 5\sqrt{13}$ or 63, 27　　**71.** $9 - \sqrt{65}$ or $0.94

Distance and Midpoints

OBJECTIVES

1. To find the distance between two points on a plane
2. To find the midpoint of two points on a plane
3. To determine if three points are collinear

In general, given (x_1, y_1) and (x_2, y_1), two points with the same y coordinate,

$$d = |x_2 - x_1|$$

The absolute value ensures a nonnegative distance.

Another geometric concept that can be approached through the use of the Cartesian coordinate system is distance. For instance, we may want to find the length of a line segment in the plane—or the distance between two points in a plane.

Let's start with two particular cases.

Example 1

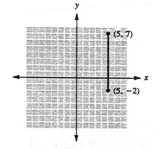

Find the distance between points $(-3, 4)$ and $(2, 4)$.

From a sketch of the problem we know that the segment between the points is horizontal, and the distance between the points is given by

$$d = |2 - (-3)| = |5| = 5$$

CHECK YOURSELF 1

Find the distance between points $(-3, 2)$ and $(5, 2)$.

Example 2

Find the distance between points $(5, -2)$ and $(5, 7)$.

Now the segment between the points is vertical, and the distance is given by

$$d = |7 - (-2)| = |9| = 9$$

Here the distance is given by $|y_2 - y_1|$.

CHECK YOURSELF 2

Find the distance between points $(4, -3)$ and $(4, 7)$.

Now, to approach the more general problem of the distance between any two points in the plane, we need the Pythagorean theorem. Let's restate that theorem.

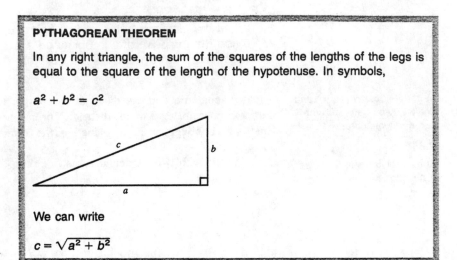

PYTHAGOREAN THEOREM

In any right triangle, the sum of the squares of the lengths of the legs is equal to the square of the length of the hypotenuse. In symbols,

$$a^2 + b^2 = c^2$$

We can write

$$c = \sqrt{a^2 + b^2}$$

Recall that the square root symbol, $\sqrt{}$, represents the positive square root.

Example 3

Find the distance between points $P(2, -3)$ and $Q(5, 4)$.

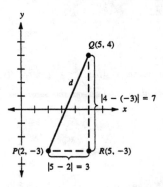

Draw a horizontal line through P and a vertical line through Q. These lines must intersect at the point $R(5, -3)$. From our sketch and the Pythagorean theorem, the distance, labeled d, is given by

$$d = \sqrt{7^2 + 3^2}$$
$$= \sqrt{49 + 9} = \sqrt{58}$$

CHECK YOURSELF 3

Use the Pythagorean theorem to find the distance between the two points $(-1, 4)$ and $(3, 1)$.

We can now apply the same strategy to derive a general formula for the distance between two points in the plane.

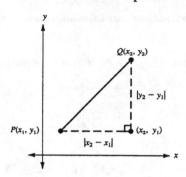

If $P(x_1, y_1)$ and $Q(x_2, y_2)$ are any two points in the plane, the distance between those points is the length of the hypotenuse of the right triangle, as shown. By the Pythagorean theorem,

Note the use of the fact that $|a|^2 = a^2$ in this derivation.

$$d^2 = |x_2 - x_1|^2 + |y_2 - y_1|^2$$

Also d is positive since the indicated root is the principal root which is positive.

or

There is further discussion of principal roots in our coverage of radical expressions.

$$d = \sqrt{(x_2 - x_1)^2 + (y_2 - y_1)^2}$$

This result is known as the *distance formula*.

DISTANCE BETWEEN TWO POINTS

The distance between two points $P(x_1, y_1)$ and $Q(x_2, y_2)$ is given by

$$d = \sqrt{(x_2 - x_1)^2 + (y_2 - y_1)^2} \qquad (2)$$

Example 4

Find the distance between $(-2, 3)$ and $(5, 5)$.

Again in finding distance, as with slope, it makes no difference which point is chosen as (x_1, y_1) or (x_2, y_2). Applying Equation (2), we have

$$
\begin{aligned}
d &= \sqrt{[5 - (-2)]^2 + (5 - 3)^2} \\
&= \sqrt{7^2 + 2^2} \\
&= \sqrt{53}
\end{aligned}
$$

CHECK YOURSELF 4

Find the distance between points $(-3, -4)$ and $(2, 3)$.

Let's work through one further example which applies the distance formula.

Example 5

Show that points $P(-1, 3)$, $Q(3, 6)$, and $R(6, 2)$ form an isosceles triangle (a triangle with two sides of equal length).

From the sketch of the problem, we can make the following calculations:

You may also have observed that

$$d_1{}^2 + d_2{}^2 = d_3{}^2$$

which, by the Pythagorean theorem, means that the triangle is also a right triangle. Considering the slopes of PQ and QR shows another means of verifying that triangle PQR is a right triangle. Try that for yourself.

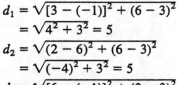
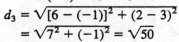

$$d_1 = \sqrt{[3 - (-1)]^2 + (6 - 3)^2}$$
$$= \sqrt{4^2 + 3^2} = 5$$
$$d_2 = \sqrt{(2 - 6)^2 + (6 - 3)^2}$$
$$= \sqrt{(-4)^2 + 3^2} = 5$$
$$d_3 = \sqrt{[6 - (-1)]^2 + (2 - 3)^2}$$
$$= \sqrt{7^2 + (-1)^2} = \sqrt{50}$$

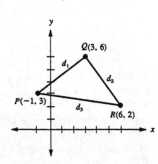

Since $d_1 = d_2 = 5$, the triangle is isosceles.

CHECK YOURSELF 5

Show that points $A(-2, 1)$, $B(3, 4)$, and $C(1, -4)$ are the vertices of an isosceles triangle.

When we connect two points, we have a line segment. The two points are called *endpoints*. The point on the line segment that is an equal distance from the two endpoints is called the *midpoint*.

Example 6

Find the midpoint on the line segment connecting the points $A(2, -1)$ and $B(2, 7)$.

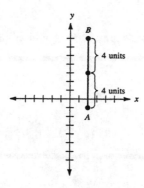

From the sketch, we can see that $(2, 3)$ is on the segment and an equal distance from the endpoints.

CHECK YOURSELF 6

Find the midpoint on the line segment connecting $A(3, 5)$ and $B(-5, 5)$.

To find the midpoint for any line segment, we find the point that has as its coordinates the average x and average y of the endpoints. The following formula is used.

MIDPOINT FORMULA

The midpoint between (x_1, y_1) and (x_2, y_2) is

$$\left(\frac{x_1 + x_2}{2}, \frac{y_1 + y_2}{2}\right)$$

Example 7

Find the midpoint of the segment with endpoints $(-1, 9)$ and $(5, 5)$.

Substituting into our formula, we get

$$\left(\frac{-1 + 5}{2}, \frac{9 + 5}{2}\right)$$

or $(2, 7)$.

CHECK YOURSELF 7

Find the midpoint of the segment with endpoints $(3, -6)$ and $(7, 4)$.

CHECK YOURSELF ANSWERS

1. 8. **2.** 10. **3.** 5. **4.** $\sqrt{74}$.
5. $AB = AC = \sqrt{34}$. **6.** $(-1, 5)$. **7.** $(5, -1)$.

Name _____

Date _____

Exercises

ANSWERS

Build Your Skills

1. _____

Find the distance between each of the following pairs of points.

2. _____

1. $(5, 2)$ and $(5, 4)$ **2.** $(1, 4)$ and $(5, 4)$

3. _____

3. $(-1, 3)$ and $(9, 3)$ **4.** $(4, -2)$ and $(4, -3)$

4. _____

5. $(2, 2)$ and $(5, -4)$ **6.** $(4, 7)$ and $(-2, -3)$

5. _____

6. _____

7. $(-2, 1)$ and $(-1, 6)$ **8.** $(-2, 3)$ and $(3, -4)$

7. _____

9. $(-3, -4)$ and $(-2, 5)$ **10.** $(3, -4)$ and $(-4, 0)$

8. _____

11. Using the distance formula, show that points $A(-2, 1)$, $B(2, 4)$, and $C(5, 0)$ are the vertices of a right triangle.

9. _____

10. _____

12. Using the distance formula, show that points $P(-1, 3)$, $Q(2, 1)$, and $R(4, 4)$ are the vertices of a right triangle.

11. _____

12. _____

Find the midpoint for the segment with the given endpoints.

13. _____

13. $(0, 4)$ and $(-8, 4)$ **14.** $(2, -5)$ and $(2, 7)$

14. _____

15. $(3, 6)$ and $(7, 18)$ **16.** $(1, 0)$ and $(13, -24)$

15. _____

16. _____

17. $(-2, 5)$ and $(-5, -8)$ **18.** $(-8, 12)$ and $(9, -3)$

17. _____

19. $(2, -5)$ and $\left(\dfrac{1}{2}, -\dfrac{3}{2}\right)$ **20.** $\left(-\dfrac{1}{4}, -\dfrac{3}{4}\right)$ and $(3, 1)$

18. _____

19. _____

20. _____

ANSWERS

Skillscan (Formulas and Literal Equations)

a. _____

Solve each equation for y.

a. $x + y = 3$ **b.** $2x - y = 5$

c. $x + 3y = 9$ **d.** $2x + 3y = 6$

b. _____

e. $3x - y = 0$ **f.** $x + 2y = 0$

g. $2x - 5y = 10$ **h.** $3x - 4y = 12$

c. _____

d. _____

e. _____

f. _____

g. _____

ANSWERS

1. 2   **3.** 10   **5.** $\sqrt{45}$ **7.** $\sqrt{26}$ **9.** $\sqrt{82}$ **11.** Show that $(AB)^2 + (BC)^2 = (AC)^2$

13. $(-4, 4)$ **15.** $(5, 12)$ **17.** $\left(-\frac{7}{2}, -\frac{3}{2}\right)$ **19.** $\left(\frac{5}{4}, -\frac{13}{4}\right)$ **a.** $y = -x + 3$

b. $y = 2x - 5$ **c.** $y = -\frac{1}{3}x + 3$ **d.** $y = -\frac{2}{3}x + 2$ **e.** $y = 3x$ **f.** $y = -\frac{1}{2}x$

g. $y = \frac{2}{5}x - 2$ **h.** $y = \frac{3}{4}x - 3$

h. _____

Streeter-Hutchison-Hoelzle:
Intermediate Algebra
Form A

Section
The Circle

Text

From Section 10.3 of the
traditional text

© McGraw-Hill, Inc., 1993

The Circle

OBJECTIVES

1. To identify the graph of an equation as a line, parabola, or circle
2. To write the equation of a circle in standard form and graph the circle

In our coverage of graphing equations of the forms $y = a(x - h)^2 + k$ and $y = ax^2 + bx + c$, we examined the parabola. We now turn our attention to another conic section, the circle.

The distance formula is central to any discussion of conic sections, and we restate it here for reference.

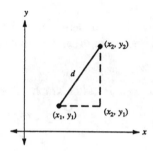

THE DISTANCE FORMULA

The distance d between two points (x_1, y_1) and (x_2, y_2) is given by

$$d = \sqrt{(x_2 - x_1)^2 + (y_2 - y_1)^2}$$

Let's consider the circle. We offer the following definition.

A *circle* is the set of all points in the plane equidistant from a fixed point, called the *center* of the circle. The distance between the center of the circle and any point on the circle is called the *radius* of the circle.

From this definition we can use the distance formula to derive the algebraic equation of a circle, given its center and its radius.

Suppose a circle has its center at a point with coordinates (h, k) and radius r. If (x, y) represents any point on the circle, then by the definition the distance from (h, k) to (x, y) is r. Applying the distance formula, we have

$$r = \sqrt{(x - h)^2 + (y - k)^2}$$

Squaring both sides of the equation gives the equation of the circle

$$r^2 = (x - h)^2 + (y - k)^2$$

In general, we can write the following:

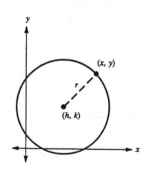

A special case is the circle centered at the origin with radius r. Then $(h, k) = (0, 0)$, and its equation is

$$x^2 + y^2 = r^2$$

EQUATION OF A CIRCLE

The equation of a circle with center (h, k) and radius r is

$$(x - h)^2 + (y - k)^2 = r^2 \tag{1}$$

Equation (1) can be used in two ways. Given the center and radius of the circle, we can write its equation; or given its equation, we can find the center and radius.

Example 1

Find the equation of a circle with center at $(2, -1)$ and radius 3. Sketch the circle.

Solution Let $(h, k) = (2, -1)$ and $r = 3$. Applying Equation (1) yields

$$(x - 2)^2 + [y - (-1)]^2 = 3^2$$
$$(x - 2)^2 + (y + 1)^2 = 9$$

To sketch the circle, we locate the center of the circle. Then we determine four points which are 3 units, to the right and left and up and down, from the center of the circle.

Drawing a smooth curve through those four points completes the graph.

CHECK YOURSELF 1

Find the equation of the circle with center at $(-2, 1)$ and radius 5. Sketch the circle.

Now, given an equation for a circle, we can also find the radius and center and then sketch the circle. We start with an equation in the special form of Equation (1).

Example 2

Find the center and radius of the circle with equation

$$(x - 1)^2 + (y + 2)^2 = 9$$

Remember, our general form is

$$(x - h)^2 + (y - k)^2 = r^2$$

Our equation "fits" this form when it is written as

Note: $y + 2 = y - (-2)$

$$(x - 1)^2 + [y - (-2)]^2 = 3^2$$

So the center is at $(1, -2)$, and the radius is 3. The graph is shown.

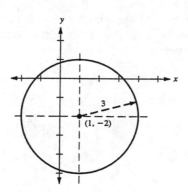

CHECK YOURSELF 2

Find the center and radius of the circle with equation

$$(x + 3)^2 + (y - 2)^2 = 16$$

Sketch the circle.

To graph the equation of a circle that is not in standard form, we *complete the square*.

Let's see how completing the square can be used in graphing the equation of a circle.

Example 3*

Find the center and radius of the circle with equation

To recognize the equation as having the form of a circle, note that the coefficients of x^2 and y^2 are equal.

The linear terms in x and y show a translation of the center away from the origin.

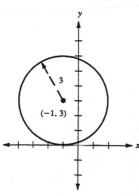

$$x^2 + 2x + y^2 - 6y = -1$$

Then sketch the circle.

Solution We could, of course, simply substitute values of x and try to find the corresponding values for y. A much better approach is to rewrite the original equation so that it matches our standard form.

First, add 1 to both sides to complete the square in x:

$$x^2 + 2x + 1 + y^2 - 6y = -1 + 1$$

Then add 9 to both sides to complete the square in y:

$$x^2 + 2x + 1 + y^2 - 6y + 9 = -1 + 1 + 9$$

We can factor the two trinomials on the left (they are both perfect squares) and simplify on the right:

$$(x + 1)^2 + (y - 3)^2 = 9$$

*A screen is used to indicate an expression that is being simplified.

The equation is now in standard form, and we can see that the center is at $(-1, 3)$ and the radius is 3. The sketch of the circle is shown. Note the "translation" of the center to $(-1, 3)$.

CHECK YOURSELF 3

Find the center and radius of the circle with equation

$$x^2 - 4x + y^2 + 2y = -1$$

Sketch the circle.

CHECK YOURSELF ANSWERS

1. $(x + 2)^2 + (y - 1)^2 = 25$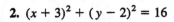

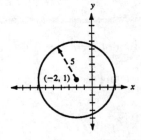

2. $(x + 3)^2 + (y - 2)^2 = 16$

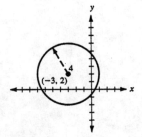

3. $(x - 2)^2 + (y + 1)^2 = 4$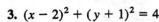

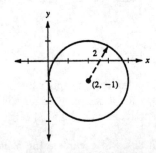

Name _____

Date _____

Exercises

Build Your Skills

1. _____

Decide whether each of the following equations has as its graph a line, a parabola, a circle, or none of these.

2. _____

1. $y = x^2 - 2x + 5$ **2.** $y^2 + x^2 = 64$

3. _____

3. $y = 3x - 2$ **4.** $2y - 3x = 12$

4. _____

5. _____

5. $(x - 3)^2 + (y + 2)^2 = 10$ **6.** $y + 2(x - 3)^2 = 5$

6. _____

7. $x^2 + 4x + y^2 - 6y = 3$ **8.** $4x = 3$

7. _____

9. $y^2 - 4x^2 = 36$ **10.** $x^2 + (y - 3)^2 = 9$

8. _____

9. _____

11. $y = -2x^2 + 8x - 3$ **12.** $2x^2 - 3y^2 + 6y = 13$

10. _____

Find the center and the radius for each circle.

11. _____

13. $x^2 + y^2 = 25$ **14.** $x^2 + y^2 = 72$

12. _____

15. $(x - 3)^2 + (y + 1)^2 = 16$ **16.** $(x + 3)^2 + y^2 = 81$

13. _____

17. $x^2 + 2x + y^2 = 15$ **18.** $x^2 + y^2 - 6y = 72$

14. _____

15. _____

19. $x^2 - 6x + y^2 + 8y = 16$ **20.** $x^2 - 5x + y^2 - 3y = 8$

16. _____

17. _____

18. _____

19. _____

20. _____

ANSWERS

Graph each of the following circles by finding the center and the radius.

21. _____

21. $x^2 + y^2 = 4$

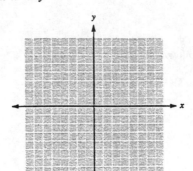

22. $x^2 + y^2 = 25$

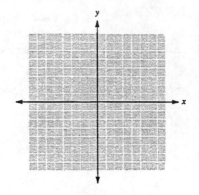

22. _____

23. $4x^2 + 4y^2 = 36$

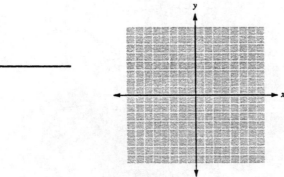
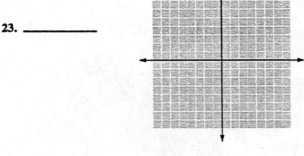

24. $9x^2 + 9y^2 = 144$

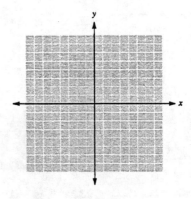

23. _____

24. _____

25. $(x - 1)^2 + y^2 = 9$

26. $x^2 + (y + 2)^2 = 16$

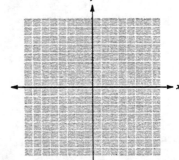

25. _____

26. _____

ANSWERS

27. _____

28. _____

29. _____

30. _____

31. _____

32. _____

27. $(x - 4)^2 + (y + 1)^2 = 16$

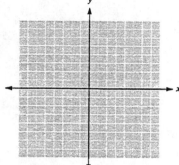

28. $(x + 3)^2 + (y + 2)^2 = 25$

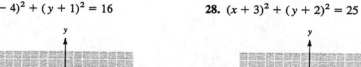

29. $x^2 + y^2 - 4y = 12$

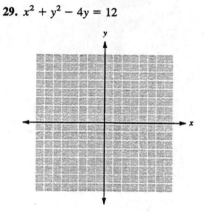

30. $x^2 - 6x + y^2 = 0$

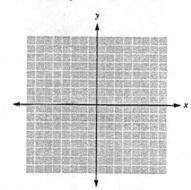

31. $x^2 - 4x + y^2 + 2y = -1$

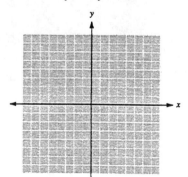

32. $x^2 - 2x + y^2 - 6y = 6$

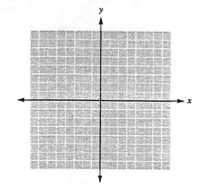

ANSWERS

33. _____

34. _____

33. $x^2 + 6x + y^2 - 4y = -4$

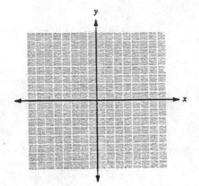

34. $x^2 + 8x + y^2 + 4y = -4$

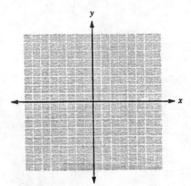

Additional Exercises

ANSWERS

Build Your Skills

1 _____

2 _____

3 _____

4 _____

5 _____

6 _____

7 _____

8 _____

9 _____

10 _____

11 _____

12 _____

Use the given information to find the equation for each circle.

1. End points of a diameter are A(3,6) and B(7,2).

2. End points of a diameter are A(0,4) and B(-8,4).

3. End points of a diameter are A(-2,5) and B(-6,-3).

4. End points of a diameter are A(2,5) and B(-4,-3).

5. The center of the circle is (5,3) and the circle passes through the poir

6. The center of the circle is (-6,1) and the circle passes through the poir

7. The center of the circle is (1,-1) and the circle passes through the poir

8. The center of the circle is (4,1) and the circle passes through the point

9. The center of the circle is (0,0) and a y-intercept of the circle is -4.

10. The center of the circle is (-3,0) and the circle passes through the ori

11. The center of the circle is (5,0) and a y-intercept is 3.

12. The center of the circle is (0,-2) and an x-intercept is 5.

1. Parabola   3. Line   5. Circle   7. Circle   9. None   11. Parabola   13. $(0, 0)$, $r = 5$ 15. $(3, -1)$, $r = 4$ 17. $(-1, 0)$, $r = 4$ 19. $(3, -4)$, $r = \sqrt{41}$ 21. $x^2 + y^2 = 4$ 23. $4x^2 + 4y^2 = 36$

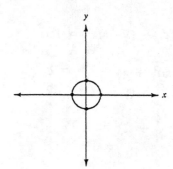

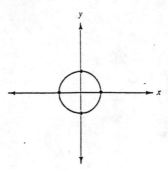

25. $(x - 1)^2 + y^2 = 9$

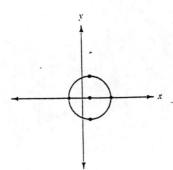

27. $(x - 4)^2 + (y + 1)^2 = 16$

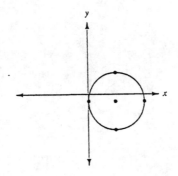

29. $x^2 + y^2 - 4y = 12$

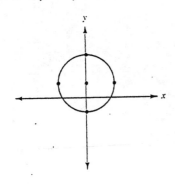

31. $x^2 - 4x + y^2 + 2y = -1$

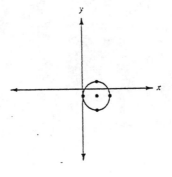

33. $x^2 + 6x + y^2 - 4y = -4$

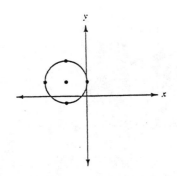

Answers - Additional Exercises

1. $(x - 5)^2 + (y - 4)^2 = 8$
3. $(x + 4)^2 + (y - 1)^2 = 20$
5. $(x - 5)^2 + (y - 3)^2 = 5$
7. $(x - 1)^2 + (y + 1)^2 = 25$
9. $x^2 + y^2 = 16$
11. $(x - 5)^2 + y^2 = 34$

2. $(x + 4)^2 + (y - 4)^2 = 16$
4. $(x + 1)^2 + (y - 1)^2 = 25$
6. $(x + 6)^2 + (y - 1)^2 = 8$
8. $(x - 4)^2 + (y - 1)^2 = 25$
10. $(x + 3)^2 + y^2 = 9$
12. $x^2 + (y + 2)^2 = 29$

ISBN 0-390-98007-2

How to Interview, Hire, & Retain High-Quality New Teachers

JOHN C. DARESH

BRIDGET N. DARESH

A Joint Publication

Essentials for Principals is a registered trademark of the National Association of Elementary School Principals.

555 North Morton Street
Bloomington, IN 47404
800.733.6786 (toll free) / 812.336.7700
FAX: 812.336.7790

email: info@solution-tree.com
solution-tree.com

Visit **go.solution-tree.com/leadership** to download the reproducibles in this book.

Printed in the United States of America

16 15 14 13 12   1 2 3 4 5

Library of Congress Cataloging-in-Publication Data

Daresh, John C.
  How to interview, hire, and retain high-quality new teachers / John C. Daresh, Bridget N. Daresh. -- 3rd ed.
    p. cm.
  Includes bibliographical references and index.
  ISBN 978-1-935542-72-8 (perfect bound) 1. Teachers--Recruiting. 2. Teachers--Selection and appointment. 3. Teachers--Rating of. 4. Teacher turnover--Prevention. I. Daresh, Bridget N. II. Title.
  LB2835.D37 2013
  371.1--dc23
                    2012035562

Solution Tree

Jeffrey C. Jones, CEO
Edmund M. Ackerman, President

Solution Tree Press

President: Douglas M. Rife
Publisher: Robert D. Clouse
Editorial Director: Lesley Bolton
Managing Production Editor: Caroline Wise
Special Projects Editor: Tara Perkins
Copy Editor: Rachel Rosolina
Proofreader: Elisabeth Abrams
Text Designer: Jenn Taylor
Text Compositor: Amy Shock
Cover Designers: Orlando Angel and Rian Anderson

ACKNOWLEDGMENTS

The authors wish to thank many colleagues—past and present—who have contributed to this work by providing support and motivation to us. Included are colleagues and friends at Spring Valley Elementary School in Dallas, Texas. Among the many who have helped are Keith Forte (whose caring approach to the selection of a young college graduate to teach in his school serves as an example of good practice described in this book) and Kelly Colburn—a principal of extraordinary sensitivity and patience who will always serve as a role model and mentor for an entire career. Also, staff members in the main office who contributed so much to the formation of a new teacher were Mollye Taylor, Pat Quinn, Betsy Davis, and nurse Sherry Freedman. They made every day a good one filled with humor, understanding, caring, and insights, even when challenges truly felt insurmountable. Thanks also go to special colleagues like Irma Carranza and Vicky Farias who have become lifelong friends. In addition, "sisters" Stephanie Godfrey, Elizabeth Palmer, and Nikki Zanikas have remained central to life way beyond the marching band at Texas Tech. Now, as a teacher at Wildwood School in the Chicago Public Schools, new friends and colleagues like principal Mary Beth Cunat continue to inspire and provide direction to all teachers, community, and staff.

From the perspective of higher education, many colleagues from the past and present have been continuous supporters. Among those meriting special attention are Rick Sorenson, Zulma Mendez, Arturo Pacheco, Teresa Cortez, Don Schulte, Rudy Rincones, and so many students at the University of Texas at El Paso.

Both authors are also thankful for the opportunity to work with Douglas Rife, Robb Clouse, and all of the team in Bloomington! It has been a most rewarding and pleasant professional experience, and we look forward to future projects. We also wish to acknowledge those who reviewed this work as it was developed. We know that this is a far better resource with the input from colleagues across the United States.

While we appreciate the assistance from so many colleagues and friends, we cannot conclude this list of important people without a special word of thanks to "Mammy" who has been with us throughout this project. Without her support, understanding, and patience, this book would not be possible.

Solution Tree Press would like to thank the following reviewers:

Kevin Brennan
Principal
Carrington Elementary School
Waterbury, Connecticut

Debra Connaughton
Kindergarten Teacher
Enterprise Elementary
Cocoa, Florida

Vicky Gabriel
Principal
Southport Elementary School
Kenosha, Wisconsin

Betsy Kinkade
Principal
Joe Mathias Elementary
Rogers, Arkansas

Celestina Martinez
Principal
Crespo Elementary School
Houston, Texas

Kenneth D. Peterson
Professor, Department of Curriculum and
    Instruction
Portland State University
Portland, Oregon

Jack Pitzer
Principal
Bush Hill Elementary School
Alexandria, Virginia

Patricia Simmons
Principal
Independence Elementary School
Aliquippa, Pennsylvania

Larry Smith
Principal
Indian Springs Elementary School
Broken Arrow, Oklahoma

Peggy Yelverton
Resource Teacher
Brevard County Induction Program
Alternative Certification Program
Viera, Florida

Solution Tree Press wishes to acknowledge the contributions of the author of previous editions of this book, Mary C. Clement.

TABLE OF CONTENTS

Reproducible pages are in italics.

Visit **go.solution-tree.com/leadership** to download the reproducibles in this book.

9

ABOUT THE AUTHORS

John C. Daresh began his career as a high school teacher in Iowa and Chicago. After completing his doctorate at the University of Wisconsin–Madison, he has spent his career as a faculty member and administrator at the University of Cincinnati, The Ohio State University, the University of Northern Colorado, and now at the University of Texas at El Paso. As a professor of educational leadership, he has carried out research and written extensively about a variety of topics related to the preservice, induction, and inservice activities for aspiring and beginning school leaders, and also high school reform issues. In total, he has authored more than one hundred articles and papers presented at local, national, and international conferences, and he has written more than twenty books related to his areas of interest and expertise. But more than any other experience, being the father of his coauthor is by far the greatest source of pride in his years of professional activity.

Bridget N. Daresh is a primary school teacher at Wildwood School in the Chicago Public Schools. Prior to that, she worked at Spring Valley Elementary School in the Richardson Independent Schools, a suburban district adjacent to Dallas, Texas. Bridget completed her undergraduate teaching preparation at Texas Tech University and received her master of education degree in educational leadership at the University of Texas at El Paso.

She has rapidly gained a reputation as an innovative and enthusiastic educator who has served as a role model and mentor for a number of aspiring teachers enrolled at universities in Texas and now in Illinois. She loves to travel and has worked to share her learning experiences and appreciation of cultures gained from visiting more than thirty countries around the world.

To book John Daresh or Bridget Daresh for professional development, contact pd@solution -tree.com.

INTRODUCTION

The purpose of this book is to provide insights into a variety of issues schools face when recruiting, hiring, and, hopefully, keeping excellent new teachers. We expect our readers will be teacher leaders and aspiring principals who will soon face the challenges associated with selection of staff, those who are new to the role of the principal, or in some cases, those who have considerable experience. This latter group may not have assumed or been assigned activities such as site-based recruiting, screening, interviewing, hiring, and ultimately retaining teachers. In many cases, principals who read this book may have been successful in many areas of their professional responsibilities, but recent reforms in schools have added these new duties to their plates. Another possible audience for this book is school administrators who simply want to stay abreast of current practices, as the importance of selecting teachers is a critical ingredient in the site-based leadership of effective schools.

We want to share a number of insights that have led to suggested practices in the important area of hiring new teachers. The most immediate need for this information is based on the fact that due to a decline in economic conditions, the job market has increasingly turned to favor the "buyers," or employing organizations, in many fields, including education. In public and private schools, this means there are more people applying for jobs compared to when the situation was quite the reverse and schools had to engage in very proactive recruitment practices just to find enough qualified teachers.

This situation may create the impression that schools can now be more selective in their choices of new teachers, making active recruitment no longer necessary. But the issue remains the same in terms of teacher selection. Despite all the proposed remedies for problems in schools (charter schools, schools of choice, accountability mandates, and many similar measures), the key ingredient to successfully promoting student learning remains the work of the classroom teacher in the United States, Canada, and most other countries around the world. And even though principals' work as instructional leaders is very important, school leaders will not be able to improve student learning without having talented and dedicated educators in classrooms.

We propose that taking an active role in finding, hiring, and supporting new teachers as they enter the profession of education is a critical responsibility for school principals. Current teachers should also be involved in the interview process and mentor newly hired teachers. Schools are enjoying a buyers' market when it comes to selecting teachers, but even this kind of situation demands attention by the buyers in order to make the best investment. There are, after all, many certified, licensed teachers seeking jobs, and some with past experience, but not everyone suited to the challenges facing an individual school may be right for the open positions. Despite the pool of talent out there, the process still involves careful searching to find excellent teachers, interviewing applicants, carrying out successful hiring activities, and ultimately protecting the hard work of finding new teachers by providing those who are brought on board with support to ensure their success.

Not every suggested activity, question, or practice in this book is necessarily right in every school seeking new teachers, as there are thousands of school districts in the United States and Canada with a variety of employment policies and procedures, but we invite readers—whether they are principals, assistant principals, or teacher leaders—to consider the issues we share in these pages. As noted in a 2003 report by the National Commission on Teaching and America's Future (NCTAF), finding and supporting good people to work in classrooms will do much more to strengthen education than anything else we do. Having good teachers will make a greater impact than requiring school uniforms, lengthening the school year, or testing students once each year with standardized assessment activities. It takes dedicated and well-prepared people to find similar dedicated and well-prepared colleagues to work in today's schools.

In preparation for writing this book, we talked to many principals and participated in discussions with administrators, teachers, and other educators in Texas, Illinois, New Hampshire, and other states and nations to determine others' insights. We describe and refer to the responses we received regarding their experiences, and the things we heard and saw in their schools, as support for the needs we identify and the processes we explain and advocate in the following chapters. The accounts we describe in this book are composites, and we have used pseudonyms. In no case are the real names of educators, schools, communities, or districts used.

In the first chapter, we illustrate the need for teacher support and the consequences schools face when adequate support is not available. In the following chapters, we discuss the recruiting and hiring process, make suggestions for interview methods, and provide examples of productive interview questions. We then explore some of the issues that principals need to consider with beginning teachers as the typical school year progresses. The last chapters take a deeper look at how principals and school districts can support new teachers, and we explore some special issues that principals need to consider as they craft a strategy that will enable them to successfully address the needs and interests of those who will be stepping into teaching positions for the first time.

Why It Is So Important to Help Rookie Teachers

Jane Crewe is like most school principals today. She never seems to have half the time needed to do what people expect her to do in her school. In her five years on the job, she has learned that people expect principals to be miracle workers and do more with fewer resources each day. That is why she is frustrated when she reviews her teacher roster for the next year and suddenly realizes that she will be leading a school with four first-year teachers without prior experience outside student teaching. Two members of this new group went through alternative teacher certification programs at a local university, one left a career as an investment banker when that line of business began to lose its appeal, and the other is entering the classroom after twenty years in the U.S. Air Force. This means that Jane's school, Kingsley Elementary, will now have eighteen teachers (out of forty-six) with three or fewer years of experience on staff.

Jane is not frustrated simply by the fact that she will be working with several new teachers. There were a few years when she had even more rookies. This anxiety is unfortunately common among the principals in the Gulf Streams Local Schools, a school system currently facing not only growth in student enrollment but also numerous departures by many experienced teachers who are either retiring or seeking positions in neighboring school districts that pay more for experience. What adds to Jane's frustration is that, at the most recent principals' meeting with the superintendent, they were told each principal would be expected to submit a plan for helping newly appointed teachers in their schools. Susan Shamonsky, the superintendent, made it clear that she looked at the new teachers entering the school district as a key ingredient to creating one of the most highly respected systems in the entire state.

The superintendent was aware that school improvement begins by recruiting and retaining dedicated and talented teachers. In fact, she was keenly aware that there is no more powerful determinant of school effectiveness than strong teaching, as research on school effectiveness clearly shows that good teachers are undeniably the single most critical ingredient for any good school (Darling-Hammond, 2000). She also frequently pointed to the fact that it was increasingly important to save taxpayer money in whatever ways possible. Superintendent Shamonsky looked over the district's costs for recruitment of new teachers for each of the past five years, and she realized that quite a bit of money was going toward finding replacements for teachers who were leaving the district only a year or two after they began their teaching careers. In three schools, she found cases where new teachers had to replace new teachers who were hired to replace new teachers from the year before. There was an economic need to keep people in the district once they were recruited and hired.

Jane is becoming weary of the annual need to break in new staff. But she also knows that helping beginning teachers is an investment in her own job security in a way. She realizes that her performance as a school leader will be judged in large measure by her students' successes in achieving their academic goals on the statewide achievement test. She also knows that her teaching staff's efforts will be the most critical predictor of school success. She is convinced that effective teachers equal successful students, and successful students are a big part of her personal vision of being the leader of a great school.

The superintendent's stated expectation that district principals will now work more directly to guide and assist beginning teachers means more work, but Jane knows that ensuring stability in the teaching ranks is truly an important foundation for continuing school improvement.

Jane Crewe knows she will be the first boss of the newly hired educators in their new careers. The ways in which Jane works with these beginners and makes them comfortable in their new jobs will have a significant impact on these individuals. Jane is also aware that her ability to be perceived as an effective principal is dependent to some degree on how successful new teachers are in working with children.

In addition to serving the needs of new teachers, Jane is going to play an important role for the school district and the field of education in general. A most distressing fact is that, from 1995 to 2006, more than 50 percent of newly hired teachers dropped out of the profession after five or fewer years in classrooms (National Education Association [NEA], 2007). This means that, even in the smallest school systems, the need to recruit, hire, and train new teachers is likely to be an annual event. And there are significant costs (in terms of both time and money) associated with this activity. It takes time to hire new teachers, and time is a very limited resource in school districts where principals, assistant principals, and central office administrators are expected to invest the bulk of their time in working to improve student achievement and ensure that every child in every school will be able to learn in a safe, secure environment. Finances are an issue as well. In difficult economic times, schools can ill afford to take on additional costs associated with maintaining recruiters to keep searching for teachers to replace those who leave the system after brief periods of time. Hours of salary time are spent conducting additional background checks and conversing with references. By providing support to new teachers in an effort to retain them, principals can hopefully avoid these costs and ensure that students receive a high-quality education.

We believe that the active involvement of the leader of a school is the single most powerful force in assisting newly hired individuals in getting off to a good start in their professional careers. This is not to suggest that other aspects of the preparation and development of beginning teachers are not also critical, however. Sound academic programs containing information related to the theory of educational practice are certainly important, and so is the student teaching experience that enables people to blend theory with the realities of work in the field.

While it is clear that school principals are constantly being asked to take on more duties, it is critical for them to recognize that they have an even more significant responsibility to assume. That responsibility is finding, hiring, and providing ongoing support for teachers in their schools. There are many reasons why supporting beginning teachers is important enough to warrant the attention of busy principals, regardless of competing time demands, as we discuss in the following sections.

Questions to Consider

- If you were Jane Crewe, what would be your reaction to the superintendent's call for principals to become more engaged in providing support to new teachers in the district?

- As a school principal or assistant principal, have you received a similar directive from your central office? How was that expectation met by the principals of your district? Do you agree or disagree with that reaction?

Beginning Teachers Need Help

Researchers and others have considered the issues facing new teachers for many years. For example, in his classic analysis of the world of classroom teachers, Dan Lortie (1975) noted that the profession of teaching is one that does not provide newcomers with *mediated entry*. What this means is that from the moment a beginning teacher signs his or her first teaching contract with a school district, he or she is a full-fledged teacher—nothing more nor less. From the first day that the new teacher takes over a particular classroom and students walk in the door, he or she is expected to do the same quality job as every other teacher in the school, from relative beginner to experienced veteran.

By contrast, consider the process used in other professions to enable new practitioners to ease into a new job and new duties not covered in preservice preparation programs at universities. Beginning attorneys do not walk into positions in law firms as partners. They typically spend a few years working as associates, with regular guidance and monitoring provided by senior colleagues who have achieved status as partners in larger firms. Even young lawyers who choose the path of small or even independent private practice do not ordinarily walk into the pressures associated with experienced law practice. A beginning attorney who opens an office as a sole practitioner goes through a slow and deliberate process of building a client base, and with that, gradual experience and expertise may be gained in a variety of cases. It is rare that an individual fresh from law school or the state bar exam will engage in much courtroom activity—at least activity in higher-level state or federal courts.

The same is true in other fields. Beginning physicians work as residents in large hospitals in most cases, and that experience is generally supervised quite carefully by senior staff. A first-year surgeon, regardless of ranking upon graduation from a first-rate medical school, will not be the lead surgeon in complicated cases. And young journalists rarely step in as front-page byline reporters in newspapers like the *New York Times*, *Chicago Tribune*, or the *Washington Post*. Spending time as a beat reporter in a smaller-city newspaper (coupled with developing writing ability) is a normal path to high-visibility assignments in major national or international newspapers. Workers in most settings start at the bottom and work their way up, and during that period of mediated entry to a profession, they acquire skills, knowledge, and perhaps most important of all, increasing confidence to apply in the future.

By contrast, beginning teachers are expected to immediately fit in a school simply because they have a teaching certificate that makes them "right" for a job. All expectations for performance are assumed to be met from the first day they walk into a classroom. Consider, for example, a young teacher who graduated from a university with a degree in early childhood education and state certification to teach all subjects in preK through grade 4 in any elementary school in the state. The teacher graduated midyear and took a job in a school district that needed a replacement for an experienced third-grade teacher. Midyear teaching jobs are not easily found even in days of teacher shortages, so the recent graduate felt fortunate to be employed. All of this said, she suddenly discovered that she was stepping in to replace a teacher who was terminated for cause that included incompetent performance in the classroom. Furthermore, the rookie arrived on the job less than three months before her third graders were expected to complete and pass the statewide achievement tests in reading and mathematics. The students had not been receiving effective and adequate instruction, and that fact led to the dismissal of their teacher in December. The challenge for the new teacher was not simply to fit into a whole new social system and community but also to provide expert guidance to a group of children who were, in essence, a year behind other third graders in the school, district, and state.

The new teacher in this case had been well prepared at her university, which was recognized both statewide and nationally as having a strong teacher preparation program in early childhood education. She also had an extremely positive student teaching experience under the direction of an outstanding mentor. In short, she was as well prepared for a successful career in teaching as anyone could be. But upon arrival at her new school, she was expected to do the job as if she had years of experience and could immediately make a difference for children who had faced significant challenges in their learning over the past several months. In essence, she was like a young surgeon stepping in to treat another doctor's critical patient and perform complicated surgery on her own, even though she had never been the primary physician in any procedure in the past. The expectation was that there would be a seamless continuation of education and support provided to students as responsibility was shifted from an experienced, albeit incompetent, predecessor to a grass-green rookie with the possibility of an extremely negative outcome when the state achievement tests were given soon after the new teacher arrived and met her class for the first time.

Fortunately for all parties concerned, this young teacher successfully met the challenges in her path. Certainly, excellent university preparation and outstanding and caring support from a cooperating student teacher mentor helped prepare the newcomer throughout her schooling. The personality and commitment of the rookie instructor were also instrumental in helping her succeed. Her students were able to achieve remarkable success on the tests despite all the odds against them.

People in this new teacher's school also played a very important role in helping her achieve success on the job. Other teachers who worked at her grade level provided not only specific technical information that they believed their new colleague needed but also a great deal of positive reinforcement and encouragement. No one single teacher took on the role of being the new teacher's mentor, but everyone assisted her, understanding she had inherited a very difficult situation.

Another person who was extremely helpful to the rookie teacher was the principal of the school. It was he who interviewed her for the opening and recruited her to come to his school. Once she was on board at the school, the principal continued his support by providing information in an honest and forthright manner, being available, providing advice when asked, and giving candid feedback. These are all critical ways in which principals can support new teachers. Above all, however, he honored all commitments made to the young teacher during her recruitment, and he continued to give the single most important resource that all teachers need at different points of each school year: he gave his time to the newcomer.

School principals face many challenges. One pressure that leads to stress is the expectation that the administrator can take specific action to ensure that students are learning, and that means scores on standardized achievement tests are expected to rise consistently. School staffs are responsible for increasing student achievement, particularly in fundamental skill areas. This expectation results in stress as student test performance is highly visible to the public because of presentation of test scores in local newspapers or other public demonstrations of student performance on one measure. The principal is the most visible representative of a school's apparent success or failure. Principals are well aware of the fact that they cannot personally do everything that will increase test scores for students. After all, with only great rarity do principals actually teach courses on a regular basis. It follows, then, that the key to any effective school may be the ability to attract and retain good teachers who will have a great impact on student learning. An important responsibility of a principal is to ensure that the new teachers succeed. Not only do the students in the school benefit from good teaching, but so do the teachers and principal.

Questions to Consider

- Think back to your first year as a teacher. What are some issues or areas you felt particularly unprepared to address as a beginner?
- When you were a rookie, what role did the principal of your school play in addressing your concerns and the concerns of other beginning teachers in the school?
- In what ways did other teachers make you and other beginners feel welcome as you stepped into your first teaching assignment?
- In what ways do you believe you could have been assisted by experienced colleagues when you stepped into your first classroom?
- Now, as a principal, how do you assist beginning teachers at your school?

Consequences of Not Supporting New Teachers

The field of teaching is increasingly one that attracts individuals for only a short period of time before they begin to look for jobs outside of education. As previously mentioned, more than 50 percent of all first-year teachers leave the teaching profession within their first five years on the job

(NEA, 2007). Perhaps even more distressing, though, is the fact that nearly 30 percent of beginning teachers are likely to leave the profession after only one year on the job (Fletcher, Chang, & Kong, 2008; Ingersoll & Smith, 2004).

There have been many times throughout the years when teacher shortages have plagued public schools. Traditionally, a somewhat cynical solution to this reality was simply to wait for downturns in the economy so that more individuals would turn to teaching as a safe source of income. Since the dawn of the 21st century, economic problems in the United States, Canada, and many other nations around the world have led to higher unemployment rates, so one might assume that school districts would be able to report an increase in applicants for teaching positions, particularly since many states offer alternative routes to teacher certification that might improve the number of potential teachers. This pattern might remain true were it not for the fact that conditions of a slow economy have led to reductions in tax revenues that result in having less money available to hire more teachers in many school systems. This, in turn, leads to increasing demands on current teachers to accept larger class sizes and other measures to reduce operating costs in public schools. Old assumptions that there will always be a need for teachers are no longer valid in many cases; there is simply not enough financial support for some school districts to find replacements for each teacher who walks away from the classroom. School districts will, of course, continue to need to replace teachers, but it may be that large numbers of departing educators will result in a smaller number of teachers recruited to take their places. Retaining teachers is an important component in preventing the continuation of such a cycle, especially considering the effect it can have on the quality of education students in these classrooms receive.

Above any other reasons for providing assistance to new teachers is the fact that there is a clear link between the success of teachers in the classroom and student learning. Researchers have noted how the revolving door for new teachers has many negative effects on the quality of education in individual schools (Barnes, Crowe, & Schaeffer, 2007). Money spent on seeking new teachers each year might be better used to improve classes or supplement limited funds for instructional materials; the kind of massive turnover among school teachers has a negative impact on students. The cost associated with the annual search for new teachers to replace what has become the yearly exodus of newly hired teachers is enormous. A 2007 study by researchers from the NCTAF reviewed the typical costs to local school districts in different areas of the country and determined that the range of expense associated with replacing teachers ranged from $4,366 for the recruitment and selection of a new teacher in a small rural district in New Mexico to $17,872 per teacher in the Chicago Public Schools (Barnes et al., 2007). That equaled an overall expense of approximately $86 million in the United States' third largest school district in 2006–07. In all school districts, there will be vacancies in the teaching ranks every year, but with a predictable dropout rate of around 30–50 percent among newly hired teachers each year in many school systems, a huge amount of money is being diverted from classroom expenses just to find and hire teachers who may or may not stay more than five years. As a principal of a school that is strapped, consider what might be possible if your school district could save and return to each school even half of the money now spent in hiring new teachers each year.

Success for students is not limited solely to their ability to perform well on standardized tests. Their learning can also be judged in terms of how they mature and grow as human beings. Often that process is guided by teachers who care and are available for several years after students leave their classrooms. In today's climate where teachers disappear rather quickly, it is likely that the kind of collegial dialogue that should occur to benefit students as they proceed through future grade levels will disappear. It is easy to understand how many students who thought they had found heroes and friends can become easily disillusioned when they feel that their heroes have abandoned them. Keeping stability in a faculty's composition is an important tool to guide learning in a school.

It is also important to note that while it has traditionally been assumed that the primary reasons for teachers leaving the profession have been low pay and poor working conditions (NEA, 2007), they are but a part of what influences newly hired teachers to leave the classroom. Other issues educators we've spoken with now identify as factors causing beginners to leave schools include lack of parental support and involvement, pressure due to emphasis on student performance on standardized testing, and provisions of the No Child Left Behind (NCLB) Act. Additionally, teachers and administrators have explained to us that feelings of professional isolation, and a lack of support from school districts in general and administrators in particular are among the strongest reasons behind people deciding to leave the field of professional education after only a few years. As a principal, you can do very little to increase salaries in your district for anyone, but fortunately, some strategies and programs have been developed to decrease the feelings of isolation and increase support available to new teachers.

Questions to Consider

- In your opinion, what are some of the reasons why beginning teachers seem to leave the profession during the first five years of service?
- What steps do you think can be taken to increase the retention rate of beginning teachers in your school district?
- What strategies might be used to increase teacher retention rates across the country?
- What might you, as a principal, do to increase the likelihood that beginning teachers will want to continue in the profession?

Organizational Efforts to Support New Teachers

The problem with retaining teachers has been recognized widely as a critical issue facing schools. Since the late 1980s, progress has been made to provide specialized support to beginning teachers to make this transition more successful. Many states and individual school districts now provide induction programs for new teachers. Mentoring is also part of the welcome package made available to incoming staff members so they can focus on getting off to a good start in the classroom without wondering about the nuances of local district policies and procedures that are familiar only to experienced colleagues.

In chapter 8 (page 65), we provide an in-depth look at how induction and mentoring programs can be very helpful to beginning teachers in a school. At this point, however, we simply note the presence of induction programs and mentoring as institutional responses to problems new teachers often face. Later in this book, we will discuss a few strategies that have been suggested as ways to help new teachers succeed in their roles, including district induction programs, formal mentoring arrangements, and other programs that may be available to beginners. In fact, we believe that supporting new teachers and assisting them so they stay are such important objectives that all forms of assistance are valuable. But we also believe that whatever strategies are used to assist rookies, the active involvement by the principal of a school with new teachers is the most powerful force in helping individuals successfully begin their professional careers. Principals have little to no control over such variables as the salaries of teachers or the physical environment that comprises the working conditions of the staff, but principals can certainly contribute greatly and directly to the quality of the experience that all teachers will have in the school. That experience will likely pay off for the individual teachers and students, the school, the profession, and also for the principal as an educator.

Conclusion

The accounts from Jane Crewe and other educators that we shared in this chapter illustrate the demands placed on principals to support new teachers, as well as new teachers' need for this support. While support programs may require commitments of time and money, the cost of doing nothing is far greater in terms of the compromise in education quality that results and the amount of time and resources that districts must devote to continued teacher recruitment when teachers do not have the support they need to be successful and remain in classrooms.

All of this points to the need for a personal commitment to the added responsibilities for principals who must now also find ways and time to work with beginning teachers. Personal commitment to a course of action requires that principals have values consistent with service as staff developers. All the suggestions in the world for techniques that may help principals in assisting new teachers will be simply words on paper unless campus administrators assume a direct role in working with rookies, which is linked to personal professional values, a topic considered in the next chapter.

How Your Values Define Your Task

In the first chapter, we noted how critical it will be to find, hire, and keep good teachers to ensure effective educational programs for all students. We also noted that the principal of each school will be a factor in the teacher recruitment and hiring process. The days of site-based management are here, and activities like selecting new teachers will increasingly be an action shifted from central offices to individual schools.

In this chapter, we consider an extremely important part of the teacher selection process that relates directly to principals. Simply put, the ways in which the right teachers can be found for an individual school will, in large measure, be determined by the values and beliefs of school leaders.

Site-Based Teacher Selection

Principals have always been expected to monitor their teaching staffs to determine as early as possible the likelihood of any turnover for the next school year. Keeping an eye (and ear) open to who may be retiring next year or which teachers may be looking for jobs in other districts or seeking transfers to other sites in the school system has always been an important part of the principal's job. The principal should be able to predict where new teachers might be needed; there is a need to maintain a constant eye on who might be back next year or who may be ready to leave.

Prior to the development of the trend to emphasize school- or site-based management of schools, the role of a school principal was defined largely as an intermediary between the district central administration and the teachers, students, and parents of an individual school. Such matters as budget management, curriculum, and personnel selection have traditionally been the responsibilities of the central office, while principals were responsible for the effective management of their individual schools and implementation of the central office decisions.

Since about 1990, it has been increasingly recognized that effectiveness of an individual school will most often be determined by actions of decision makers at the local level. After all, who can best determine what is most beneficial for a particular neighborhood, part of the city, or precinct than the people who interact with that community each day? Consequently, principals have had to face the reality of considerably more work coming to their in-baskets. While many are now involved at the local school level, the principal is responsible for leading the direction of the school.

The existence of site-based decision-making groups can have a significant effect on how teacher selection activities are conducted in a school, depending on a few basic realities. First, there may be either a statutory mandate or policy of a local school district concerning the need to involve site-based councils in the selection of teachers. Second, in some cases, site-based groups may be required to participate in personnel issues regardless of the preferences of the school principal, or even the preferences of group members. Third, simply involving parents and other site group members in the interviewing process for teacher candidates does not mean that input from such individuals will always have a direct effect on the principal's choices.

> ### Questions to Consider
>
> - As a principal, how do you assess the value of emphasizing decentralized management of schools in most districts across the United States?
>
> - According to your personal values and perspectives, what are the positive aspects of principals having the opportunity to work with site-based decision-making groups for their schools? What do you believe are some of the limitations to site-based decision-making groups?

Personal Vision and Personnel Issues

Values define actions, and actions are determined by values. These simple words describe a critical issue that will determine what the individual principal must keep in his or her mind when engaging in the work described here.

The personal values and beliefs of a school principal are likely to have a great impact on how she or he treats trends such as efforts to decentralize management in school districts. Quite obviously, when the topic of site-based decision-making councils and groups comes up among principals, some administrators are quite pleased to receive regular input into their decisions, and others are content to work with local councils but would not care if they disappeared, either. On the other hand, there are some principals who view site-based groups as unwanted mandates that are intrusive on the administrator's rights as the school leader. The issue here is not whether one of these perspectives is right or wrong. Rather, there are various outcomes depending on how the principal views the validity of ideas that arise through local community involvement. It is important that principals not merely "play at" broad-based involvement without taking the group's input into consideration. One consequence of doing so may be the eventual lack of confidence by group members in terms of engaging in the decision-making process. No one likes to waste time with ceremony not related to actual practice.

The values, beliefs, and perspectives held by a school principal have a great deal to do with how a school operates in ways well beyond periodic meetings of school-based decision-making bodies. As noted, values have a profound impact on the choices and actions of a school principal when the principal is faced with selecting teachers to work in her or his school. Since the principal is the formal leader of the school and is responsible for the articulation of the school's vision, his or her values and beliefs will have a role in the identification of a teacher who will help implement the school's vision. To put it quite simply, if a principal has an idea of what a school is to achieve, that principal has a responsibility to find people who will be able to ensure that the desired goal is attained. In a very important way, the values and beliefs of the principal serve the school by influencing the process of finding, recruiting, and selecting the right people for the job.

The link between vision and staff selection is extremely important to a school's ultimate success. Consider, for example, that a principal has articulated a vision in which a school would function as a community of learners and that collaborative working relationships would be evident throughout the school. All energy would be directed toward the needs of students, and learning would not be defined solely through the student scores on each year's statewide achievement exam. Instead, the school would be considered successful primarily through demonstration of students' abilities in areas such as critical thinking or by student engagement in a variety of projects requiring the development of collaborative problem-solving skills. If this is the principal's vision of the type of school desired, the selection of teachers must be based on finding people with the appropriate knowledge, skills, and above all, attitudes to enable them to join the direction the school is headed. One candidate might note how he or she has always believed in the importance of working as a part of a team, while another candidate with similar skills may express a reluctance to spend too much time talking to other teachers because it might take away from precious instructional time. The recruitment, interviewing, selection, and actual hiring of new teachers (whether they are rookies or veterans) must be guided by the school's vision. And the primary director of this vision is the principal.

Identifying and Articulating Beliefs and Values

One activity that has long been recommended to help school principals and other leaders more clearly articulate their fundamental views regarding the challenges of school leadership has been the development of an individual educational platform. Thomas Sergiovanni and Robert Starratt (2007), Bruce Barnett (1991), John Daresh (2007), and others have reported it as a helpful way for individuals to reflect on their core educational beliefs. The idea is a simple one, namely asking questions regarding what an individual educator sees as important, such as:

- What does a "good school" look like?

- What is the proof that a school is really good?

- Research shows that schools function as communities. How do we build a strong sense of community in our school?

- What will be the role of teachers in a school that functions as a community? What about administrators? Staff? Parents? And above all, what will be the role of students in a community?

- In a school community, what should be the interaction that takes place each day between teachers and administrators?

- What about interaction among teachers?

- What should the prevailing attitudes be about students in a good school that functions as a community?

- How should teachers in a school community look at relations with parents and other members of the local external community?

Two things should be noted about these questions. First, they should not necessarily be used in prospective teacher interviews. Rather, they are meant to stimulate the principal's thinking regarding his or her own values and the way those values can contribute to forming a vision for the school. That vision can then be shared with the site-based decision-making group and, eventually, the interviewee. For example, if the vision the principal shares with current teachers is that a "good school" would be one where the organizational climate is characterized by open communication and a sense of collegiality and shared leadership, he or she would likely have a fairly clear idea of what goes on in an ideal school.

Second, this list of questions is neither exhaustive nor complete. In the truest sense of creating an individualized professional platform, each principal needs to consider the issues that she or he would relate to personal philosophy and perspective.

> ## Questions to Consider
>
> - How would you personally respond to the questions listed in the previous section?
> - What additional questions would you ask of yourself in determining the qualities that you seek in a good school?

How Values and Beliefs Affect Teacher Recruitment and Selection

Now that a principal has taken the time to articulate personal responses to questions related to the implementation of a desired vision in a school, he or she is equipped to begin the process of searching for members of the teaching team who will help the school actually achieve the vision.

The greatest probability of a school achieving the principal's desired outcome is found when the principal is able to hire people who subscribe to the same views, beliefs, and values inherent in the school's vision. If a principal's goal is to have a great school, the fulfillment of that goal begins with putting together a team that at least has the great potential to work toward important goals. The days of simply looking for teachers who are appropriately certified or who have the desired experience to fit in a school faculty are waning. Principals need to put forth an attainable vision, and they must be very intentional in their selection of teachers. Once these initial objectives are achieved, the principal must put into effect a plan to ensure as much as possible that the new teachers will continue to thrive in the school. Without such support, they may take their skills to another team or even leave the game entirely.

A Word of Caution

The purpose of raising the issue of a principal's personal views or values as a legitimate and necessary step in selecting new teachers is meant to help decision makers reflect on the importance of locating not just highly qualified teachers but, more importantly, teachers who will fit in the culture of a particular school, at least from the perspective of the school leader. We are not attempting to condone the practice of the principal simply setting out to find teachers based solely on personal preferences or, at times, even personal prejudices. The key here is that there are likely to be many good teaching candidates available, particularly in a slow economy. But of these qualified applicants, some are likely to have more potential than others to increase the quality of educational practice and student learning in a particular school.

Conclusion

Once principals have assessed their educational values and vision for their schools, they can more effectively search for the right candidates to help fulfill that vision. But principals also need to be aware of the variety of avenues available to find the most promising talent. As technology and changing economies affect the teaching profession, so too do they influence the ways open positions are advertised and pursued. In the next chapter, we provide insight into these methods as well as practical tips to assist principals as they assume, to a greater degree, the role of personnel decision maker in their schools and for their schools.

How to Start the Search

There are several time-tested approaches used by school districts and individual school leaders when searching for new teachers. In this chapter, we note strategies that may be followed by the leader of a school as she or he moves forward with the increased responsibilities of engaging in personnel recruitment, and we suggest some of the right places to find the talent needed to make a good school even better. We will discuss the most frequent strategies, which involve relying on student teachers or substitute teachers with whom a principal might already be familiar, attending job fairs, contacting local colleges or universities for recommendations, advertising, and using technology.

Looking at Local Talent

When filling teacher openings, many principals make extensive use of candidates who already know about the school. Two traditional sources are student teachers who have recently worked in the school and regular substitute teachers. There is an assumption that someone who has already spent time in a particular building will be ready to step in as a regular member of the teaching staff. It would certainly simplify searching for new teachers if a principal could discover someone who already had some knowledge of local priorities, practices, and policies.

Student Teachers

While the assumption that a person already in the school could be the right choice makes sense, it can be unwarranted. For one thing, student teachers are working under the direction of cooperating teachers who generally give clear directions about expectations, curricular coverage, and many other factors associated with "real" teaching. Student teaching is a way for aspiring educators to learn to deliver information to classes, respond to student behavior through classroom management techniques, and gain many other skills needed to start a new career. They might also get insights into the stress and fatigue of the daily grind of teaching (Lieberman, 1988). But for the most part, the student teaching experience is brief—usually no more than fifteen or sixteen weeks in a school year. Student teachers' experience of school life might range from a half day to a full day, but after-school meetings and night duties such as parent-teacher conferences are rarely part of student teaching. In some instances, the student-teaching assignment is split between two or more schools.

A short-term school placement will likely enable an individual to see no more than the formal or public side of life in school—the way things are supposed to be. What is missing is the opportunity to learn about the underlying issues, concerns, and problems in a school. Student teachers are not around to hear the discussions related to the school's vision, for example. The result is that while a student teacher might know the layout of the school, rules, general characteristics of the student population served by a school, the neighborhood, and many other features, he or she is not aware of the culture or climate of the school. On the other hand, student teachers have gotten to know other teachers, routines, and some parents. They have seen the school, even if they have not been privy to some aspects of the school's culture. It is also important to remember that if a student teacher had a positive experience in the school or with her or his cooperating teacher, it is likely to be an easier task to convince an individual to work in the same school.

Substitute Teachers

Substitute teachers are likely to come with a variety of backgrounds, some of which may enable them to become strong candidates for teaching positions in a school. Of course, not all who serve as substitute teachers are qualified to serve as full-fledged teachers. Depending on local, state, or school district policies, it may be possible for an individual without any formal training in education to be qualified as a substitute teacher. In several cases across the United States, substitutes do not even need to have completed a university degree program. In addition, there are many people who serve as substitutes in local schools deliberately because they are not interested in pursuing full-time employment as regular teachers. There are also a fair number of people for whom substitute teaching is synonymous with highly paid babysitting.

There are definite limitations of looking to substitutes to take full-time jobs. There are also many individuals who are very interested in finding a regular teaching position, but for one reason or another, they cannot do so yet. In order to keep their feet in the door for the future, they now work as substitutes. Schools have been eager to employ such individuals on a regular basis and have gladly classified them as "permanent substitutes" who come to school each day to cover a class somewhere in the building. In addition, there are frequently situations in which substitute teachers are hired for a single day, but due to circumstances that were unpredictable (a serious long-term illness, sudden resignation, and so on), the single day becomes a much longer-term appointment.

In cases in which substitutes are waiting for full-time teaching positions to open, serving as regular fill-ins at one specific school or working long-term appointments, there may be opportunities for a principal to find someone able to step in as a regular teacher. Just as with student teachers, less frequent substitutes may be removed from inside aspects of how a school and its staff function, and they do not have a continuing stake in what is happening each day, but they do have some knowledge of a school. If substitutes have had a long-term appointment, however, they may have been involved with many activities all teachers normally participate in, including after-school staff meetings, department or grade-level meetings, and even parent-teacher conferences. Despite any limitations of substitutes, they may serve as potentially strong candidates for teaching positions.

Teacher Recruitment Fairs

One staple of the teacher search process has been the reliance on teacher recruiting fairs as sources of possible candidates for new teachers. Each year, hundreds of local teacher fairs are held across the United States and Canada. School districts from across a region are invited to spend part of a day in a central location and promote their school districts to teachers looking for jobs for the next school year. The tone of the fairs has changed. There used to be a sense that the school districts were actually competing for teachers in every grade level, every subject area, and from every corner of each region. There was a nationwide shortage of individuals interested in the teaching field. When people from personnel departments went to the fairs, they carried mental shopping lists that simply said *find lots of teacher candidates*. This perspective has changed drastically with the economic downturn. There are, of course, many school systems that need new teachers each year. But the shopping lists of recruiters have become more refined and limited to specific teaching fields. Math, science, and bilingual education teachers are still in great demand, regardless of the overall economic situation. School districts have been so keen to hire individuals in these areas that they continue in many cases to offer signing bonuses to individuals even as they walk through job fairs. There are often no interviews at the local school, and staff members from individual schools are not directly involved in the selection of these new colleagues in many cases. This approach to staffing is not viewed favorably by principals and teachers, but it is understandable that districts may wish to jump quickly at strong candidates with needed skills. Teaching candidates from high-need areas still go through interviews, but once they do so with administrators present at the job fairs, they are often offered teaching contracts on the spot, without the necessity of going through further review at individual school campuses. While this may violate the practice established for additional scrutiny at the site level, the need to get highly qualified teachers under contract sometimes leads to apparent contradictions in the hiring process. The need to comply with state standards sometimes supersedes local policy.

The recruiting fair is an effective way to give schools and districts some idea of what the prospects for hiring new faculty members may look like. But the limitations of this type of event do not allow a quick meeting to be a substitute for more intensive reviews of potential teachers in a school. Schools must recognize that they are now the buyers in a buyers' market. Even in high-need areas, there is not an absolute need to hire people without a complete view of the fit between a school and a new teacher.

Principals must find time to get to the job fairs in person, if possible. If a school needs new teachers, and if there is a sincere desire to fill openings not only with properly certified teachers but also with quality teachers who fit the needs of a good school, it is important for principals to see what candidates are available. When principals are able to spend time at the job fair recruiting booth, a few tips for making the most of one's time include:

- Think of the meeting with potential candidates as a sort of pre-interview during which you can get a sense of who might do well in your school.

- Go with a clear sense of what (or who) you really need to improve your school in the future. Bring a copy of your school's vision statement if you have one, and share that with passersby who stop at the table to hear about working in your school district.

- Bring photos of the school and the people who work and learn there.

- Invite a recently hired teacher to come along with you from your school. There is no better way to recruit new teachers than to bring along someone who can share personal experiences and enthusiasm for working in a particular school.

- Come with an attitude that suggests that you want everyone who stops at your table to have a favorable impression.

It may be much more convenient to turn over the task of attending job fairs to the human resources department of a school system, but principals and teachers can bring a lot of heart and sincere care for individual student needs to the table as well. Many potential applicants want to apply to school systems where there are more important things than the salaries, fringe benefits, and general working conditions.

Working With Local Colleges and Universities

One of the great hiring resources available to principals is local colleges and universities. The departments or schools of education with teacher preparation programs are likely to have numerous candidates who might fit the needs and vision of neighboring schools.

Building positive relationships with faculty of higher education institutions may lead to mutually beneficial interactions in a variety of ways. From the university perspective, building and maintaining strong bonds with schools in the community provide opportunities for recruiting students to attend its institutions. In addition, for departments and schools of education, connections with school districts lead to opportunities for placement of student teachers, counseling and administrative interns, and collaborative research and development action. Inviting local practitioners to serve as guest speakers and resource persons in undergraduate- and graduate-level classes is an effective instructional activity at the university. Furthermore, for professors of education, open doors to nearby schools often mean opportunities for personal and professional development by getting away from campus offices to get back inside schools and classrooms and talk with teachers and students.

When local school teachers and administrators visit colleges and universities, many important benefits are realized. It is a way for practitioners to stay in touch with research expertise so that they may improve student learning in schools. While professors are often too far removed from daily practice to have insights into solutions to everyday problems, the distance of the university campus often provides an environment for thinking beyond the next phone call or school crisis. Engagement with the rarified air of academe can be a refreshing moment for many busy practitioners.

Finally, and most relevant, going where most future trainers attend classes to become teachers is a very important strategy to help school principals in their hunt for new talent. Many principals who have relationships with colleges, such as serving on committees, teaching classes as adjuncts, appearing as guest speakers, or simply visiting friends on the faculty, have reported to us that they often get suggestions concerning strong teacher candidates going through the university training programs. In many cases, these leads concern teachers a year or two away from graduation, but waiting for outstanding talent may be worth it for a principal who knows in advance where openings may occur in a school staff.

As noted earlier, there are many reasons for schools and colleges or universities to develop strong collaborative relationships. But principals need to remember the old adage about one hand washing the other; both schools and universities receive benefits from collaboration.

Questions to Consider

- Do you currently have any contacts at local institutions of higher education with whom you chat about possible referrals of future teachers?

- Have you had any successes in developing relationships with universities or colleges in the ways described here?

- How can the recruitment of new teachers be made more effective in your school or district through the process of collaboration with teacher education programs at local colleges and universities?

Advertising

As more candidates for teaching positions become available and begin to engage in more proactive job-searching practices on their own, there may be less need for school districts to spend as much money to advertise teaching positions as they did in the past when there were more teacher positions open across the country than there were qualified teacher candidates. School districts had to invest a significant amount of money into paying for advertisements in local newspapers or even national outlets such as *Education Week* in an effort to find qualified candidates. Some larger cities bought ad time on local radio and television channels to advertise for teaching candidates. Alternative teacher certification programs, which provided streamlined preservice teacher training and certification to individuals with college degrees but no formal teacher training, appeared across the United States on university campuses, in state educational agencies, and even through for-profit organizations. Even with the resulting increase in terms of available candidates, school systems continued to scramble to find certified (if not always well-qualified) applicants for teaching jobs.

Technology

Technology has had significant influence in changing the way jobs are advertised. This has been an additional factor in why some modes of advertising discussed in the preceding section have become less popular. A large number of job seekers today learn of and apply for job openings through online job search engines (such as Monster, CareerBuilder, and Indeed as well as more specialized sites geared toward educators). *Education Week* now has a separate website dedicated to career development and job postings (www.topschooljobs.org). School or district websites are another popular and convenient place to list vacancies. Posting job openings online is also less expensive than some of the traditional methods mentioned previously. Additionally, word of mouth has long been a popular method for learning of job openings and is now even more pervasive with the advent of social and professional networking sites and online teacher communities, which connect more people and allow for convenient distribution of information.

Questions to Consider

- What amount of money is currently available in your district to advertise teacher job openings?
- Have you used or considered using low-cost or no-cost strategies involving the use of social networking (LinkedIn or Facebook, for example) as a way to communicate openings for teaching positions in your school?

Conclusion

The downturn in the national economy has had a marked impact on the stock of teachers looking for jobs, and because there are fewer tax dollars coming from traditional sources such as income and property tax, school systems are not able to recruit or hire as they did in the past. But certain instructional areas continue to have critical shortages that must be filled, and of course, despite the economy, teachers continue to retire, and children keep coming to school. In some areas of the country, there are still massive increases in the school-age population that require new buildings, new classrooms, and new teachers.

New teachers are needed, but it is certain that resources to find those teachers are now limited. Recruitment trips by human resources staff are largely a thing of the past, but other pathways to find good teachers noted earlier in this chapter (teacher job fairs, contacts with local teacher training institutions, and reviews of student teachers or substitutes) remain effective strategies. The days of print ads in *Education Week* may be on their way out, however. New ways of finding teaching talent, including online job search engines, websites, and social networking, deserve attention.

Once you have found a number of promising applicants, you will need to use effective interviewing techniques to increase the likelihood that those found will become not only promising new teachers, but teachers who promise to be strong additions to a school committed to serving the ever-changing needs of students. We describe these techniques in the next chapter.

4

How to Plan and Carry Out Interviews

Many principals have considerable skill and knowledge meant to improve the efficacy of teachers who, in turn, will work to increase learning in schools. They are excellent at providing strong instructional leadership, and many are very effective managers of their schools. However, there are also many principals—including strong instructional leaders and effective managers—who are not great interviewers of candidates for teaching jobs. That fact does not in itself make a principal an unsuccessful leader, but it may indirectly result in a school with fewer strong and competent teachers. To help avoid this outcome, we discuss processes for planning and conducting effective initial interviews in this chapter.

The Basics

Effective job interviewing involves much more than sitting in a comfortable chair with a notebook and pencil and chatting with a candidate for a job. It is more appropriate to think of it as an activity in which a carefully planned set of questions is asked of each finalist for a job. It is a way to go beyond all other devices used in gathering information about potential teachers in a school.

Application Materials

The traditional method of gaining information about job seekers includes reviews of application materials, including letters of interest and letters of reference. In addition, there may be an expectation that applicants send a résumé or curriculum vitae as well as proof of certification or licensure in the state in which the teacher will work, official transcripts from all universities attended, and in some cases, scores received as part of the licensing or certification in the state. Criminal background checks are often required. Some school districts request that applicants complete a personality survey online or in person at the district office of human resources or personnel. In many places, social network sites such as LinkedIn or Facebook are reviewed for information about applicants for a job. It is not unusual for teaching candidates to be excluded from a pool of finalists because of some indiscrete statements or photos appearing online.

Prior to scheduling interviews of any teaching candidates, principals must become familiar with the full range of materials that have been submitted to the human resources office. Inviting candidates in for an interview is costly in terms of finances but moreover in terms of time taken away from the principal and classroom teachers who are part of the selection process. It is much better to read material submitted earlier by a candidate than to discover a bad fit when a person is waxing eloquent about what he or she will do as a teacher in a school while sipping water or coffee in the principal's office. Yet the interview is a critical step in the selection process. Letters of application may be written by people other than the actual job applicants, references obviously come from trusted referees, personality tests are often criticized for any predictive value, and people are getting smarter about what they include in Facebook profiles. A face-to-face interview is still likely to be a most effective tool to use in selecting new colleagues.

Interview Protocol

The appropriate decision makers for the school system should determine the possible number of interviews to which applicants may be subjected. In many schools, the number of highly qualified (that is, properly certified) teachers who are applying for jobs may be such that interviews must be conducted first to screen out wholly unsuitable applicants while decisions are made about those who may be considered semifinalists for openings in a school. We suggest that, at minimum, two levels of interviews be carried out. The first would involve a committee comprised of different individuals such as teachers, staff, parents, and community members. See the section on interview committees on page 27 for more information about their composition and responsibilities. The second level of decision making might be the principal who must make the final decision about the best choice for the school. In some larger schools, additional interviews involving teachers from a certain grade level or subject department might also be a wise addition to the review process.

Overall Interview Practices

A job opening in a school—particularly a school that has a good reputation or is located in a desirable community—will likely draw applicants from a few different pools, including those who are about to take on their first full-time teaching jobs as well as those with prior teaching experience. Regardless of varying experience levels, the principal must ensure that the interview process is fair to all candidates. This is difficult at times when a strong candidate with several years of experience is compared with the potential shown by someone coming directly from a university preparation program, or someone with an alternative certification who has little experience as a teacher but who has many years of previous professional activity in some other field. However, there are both advantages and disadvantages to selecting a candidate from any of these pools.

While experienced teachers bring with them a set of learned skills and knowledge of procedures and practices, there are downsides to their selection, particularly if the principal is dedicated to change in a school. They might be limited in their thinking by the way things were done at their previous schools and may not be as open to changing their practice for the benefit of their new school's vision. Teachers' experience may also include the past acquisition of bad habits and questionable practices. Hiring a rookie will involve more oversight and care than hiring a person who has already had experience as a teacher, but a grass-green rookie teacher may walk into a job with a type of energy and insight that comes from fresh eyes looking at old problems without any preconceived notions of the best (or only) way to do things; new teachers are naïve at times, but that naïveté should be looked at as a positive feature. The same is true of those candidates who come with prior experience in the military or in private business. On the one hand, they provide insights that may not be found in teachers coming into a school directly from college. On the other hand, teachers with alternative backgrounds that are beginning their careers as teachers will need to learn more about the expectations of the new culture they are entering.

Fairness in the interview process is important because all candidates have a variety of strengths and weaknesses. Regardless of experience levels, each candidate selected for onsite interviews must be treated in the exact same way all other candidates are treated. This is essential information that the principal should make all those involved in interviewing a candidate aware of.

Questions to Consider

- To what extent do you or other principals in your district seek nontraditional information about applicants by reviewing social networking sources? What value has this review given to your selection process?

- If you had a choice, and all other characteristics of the best applicants were equal, would you prefer to hire beginners or teachers with years of experience? What do you see as advantages or disadvantages of either choice?

Interview Committees

The school community should consider who, besides the principal, should be invited to interview a candidate. Clearly, the principal will have the ultimate duty of recommending individuals for employment to the superintendent, who will in turn decide whether to recommend certain candidates to the district board of education, but it is essential that a variety of stakeholders have a chance to participate in the interview process if possible. As a result, other teachers need to interact with applicants. Parents also have an interest in seeing what teaching candidates might offer the school. Classified or noncertificated staff and, depending on age and maturity, students may be included as interviewers. Together, stakeholders from these groups can be assembled to create an interview committee.

The overall size of the committee need not be large. We are suggesting three or four teachers, two or three parents, a staff member, perhaps a student, and the principal and possibly an assistant principal. In order for the interview committee to be effective, before agreeing to serve the school in this capacity, committee members should be reminded of the importance of their task and adhere to certain expectations. If people want to be committee members and participate in the teacher selection process, they need to attend all required meetings and interview sessions and also follow established protocols. The number of expected meetings of an interview committee may depend on several factors, as logistics to bring together groups that include parents, teachers, and staff are often difficult to arrange. In general, however, the school district will identify the exact nature of the work of the committee.

Rules of Participation in Interviews

In addition to agreeing to interview teaching candidates, committee members (including the principal) must observe a number of rules in order to participate in this critical activity for ensuring effective schools. Some of these rules might be classified as effective or important practices, while others are related to laws regarding general hiring procedures. In many cases, the first meeting of an interview committee might be chaired by the principal who can provide an overview of such things as the timeline to be followed, the importance of complete participation, the avoidance of illegal questions, and so forth. While the principal might wish to serve as an *ex officio* committee member, he or she has the authority to provide definition to the task of the committee, and also parameters that need to be observed.

The committee needs to engage in some discussions with the principal prior to inviting any candidates to visit the school. During this time, it is essential that the principal lay out the ground rules for the actual interviews. Two very important sets of ground rules are critical. The first is based on the need to inform all committee members of the limitations to the types of questions they may ask. The second set of ground rules concerns the need for all committee members who will ask questions of candidates not to stray from the script of the questions that the committee will agree to use with each candidate. Failure to follow this expectation may result in charges of unequal treatment of candidates during interviews. All must understand that they, by law, may not question candidates about the following:

- Marital status

- Family issues (for example, if they have children)

- Sexual orientation

- Religion

- Physical condition

- Any other background information concerning matters totally unrelated to an applicant's ability to perform any or all duties related to the job

Failure to recognize these boundaries could result in rather harsh limitations on the process, fines, or other penalties that may be applied after a legal review of the hiring process. Courts may require hiring bodies to redo searches and screening activities if any violations of an applicant's individual rights or privacy are found.

Most individuals who have been involved in personnel practices are aware of questioning practices that are not permitted. Rarely does such a breach of professional practice occur in the selection of teachers, but when others who may be less familiar with these practices are involved in committees, this information needs to be made very clear. An even more critical issue to be considered when setting up interviews by a committee involves the actual questions to be asked concerning the candidate's ability to perform the tasks a job requires.

Questions to Consider

- What school district policies need to be followed as you plan for the interviews you will conduct?
- How will you address the demands of your local policy so that your search for new teachers can most benefit the fulfillment of the vision for your school?

Interview Objectives and Timing

A principal must determine ahead of time what he or she wants to know about an applicant coming in for an interview, while acknowledging that the time allocated for an interview may be no more than twenty to thirty minutes. This amount of time may be considerably less if a district policy (or traditional practice) requires all applicants who pass the paper screen at the district's human resources office (that is, they meet all minimum requirements for proper certification) to be sent to interview at all district schools with openings for teachers. Lining up appropriate questions to be used in a job interview should be guided by no less an important question than, Will this person contribute to the school we want?

Interviews must be sharpened to a point where candidates are asked the most critical questions. Traditional warm-up questions, such as *Why did you select teaching as a career choice?* might be interesting, but these may be irrelevant to the search for a new teacher. The issue must always be to determine if a person will fit in a school and if he or she is more or less likely to join the faculty in contributing to a school achieving its vision and mission.

A key point to remember when it comes time to begin the actual screening or selection process for new teachers is that there may be only a limited time to catch the right person to fill a position.

Interview Methods and Content

After working with teachers and others to create a clear vision for the school, after the teachers and staff have truly begun to buy into the school being crafted or refined through their efforts, and after the procedures and ground rules for interviewing candidates for teaching positions have been clarified, the next step is to ensure that the interview will be carried out in an effective manner. This consists largely of deciding the content of the interviews as well as the methods that will be used to keep the process of selection consistent with laws and school district policy. This should be a part of the work that goes on in the days before candidates are actually brought forward. As stated previously, interviewers must ensure that all candidates are treated fairly. That means everyone must be asked the same questions. Scripted interviews are a way to achieve this practice and help ensure fairness.

Scripted Interviews

Using a scripted interview is a way to ensure that the interviewing process is fair for all who are being interviewed. Determining who will ask questions is generally an informal process in which interviewers simply indicate which question they prefer to ask of each candidate. Scripted interviews are controlled so that the person asking the questions reads the same questions verbatim to each applicant, and the questions are always asked in the same order for each person. The only variation permitted to the script is when clarification is needed to help the interviewer understand a response. Some educators we spoke with complain that these types of interviews are boring and limiting to decision makers who often read the same questions in a manner suggesting that adherence to standardization is more important than listening to responses made by a candidate. We believe that such a criticism is better directed toward the attitude of those asking the questions. The people answering the questions are likely to be hearing and considering issues and concerns never encountered before. Interviewers should listen to applicants and give them their undivided attention.

It is important to remember that there are no absolutely correct answers to any question for any job interview. At times, there have been efforts to provide scoring rubrics to be followed in interviewing so that candidates can be evaluated numerically. The problem with such an approach may become even more apparent when we consider questions for use in the interviews, but for now, think about the issue of trying to quantify the "correctness" of an answer provided for the rather traditional beginning question: Why are you interested in working in this school? The possible responses to such an open question might range from "I went to school here as a student X years ago, and I loved this place and now want to return" to "This is but one of several schools to which I have applied, and I am quite honestly interviewing here because you invited me to. It's a good school, and I hope the fact that I need a job as a teacher can match the needs you have for a teacher." The first answer might be very pleasing, more so than the straightforward second response. But in truth, neither response is "correct." People need jobs, and sometimes there are special reasons why a particular job may be more appealing. We know of no research that has scored one of these examples higher than any other response. The "correct" answer must be the one that makes the most sense to the principal and others involved with the interview.

Behavior-Based Interviews

Behavior-based interviewing (BBI) is a good strategy for focusing the interviewing process on concrete teaching issues and avoiding any legal problems while concentrating on the essential requirements for the principal and the school to hire the most effective teachers possible. This strategy involves a technique that combines research-based knowledge of effective teaching practice with an effort to move those who are interviewed into a framework of responses based not on vague general principles but rather concrete past or future actions. Questions for prospective teachers at all grade levels and subject areas include those on the following fundamental educational topics:

- Curriculum

- Planning for instruction

- Instructional methods

- Classroom management

- Assessment and grading

- Meeting the needs of individual students

- Communication with parents and others

- Professionalism

- Technology in the classroom

- Supporting the school's vision

Not only are these areas based on essential issues facing all educators, but interviewers are able to gauge responses by job candidates as they relate to the mission and vision of the particular school they intend to serve.

Interview Questions

A basic rule to remember when preparing the actual interview questions is that anything can be asked as long as it has a direct bearing on whether an individual can handle the responsibilities and effectively perform the job. As noted previously, there can be no inquiry made of a person's religious beliefs, marital status, lifestyle preferences, and so forth. But interviewers have a responsibility to ask candidates about their professional and employment history, criminal background (if any), their preparation to become teachers, professional beliefs and values, perspectives regarding policies and procedures associated with the school in which they are to work, experiences directly related to the expectations for performance of the available job, and attitudes about major educational issues associated with a contracted work assignment. Thus, questions such as the following are permissible:

- At our school, we have adopted a mission that requires teachers and administrators to promote the belief that all children can learn, regardless of background. How do you think you will be able to demonstrate your adherence to that mission as a teacher here?

- We work as a team here. How will you demonstrate your commitment to that shared belief?

- As a teacher, how have you provided evidence in the past, or how do you plan to demonstrate in the future, that you will work with parents as partners in the educational process?

- What is your understanding of the type of effective instructional strategies that you might employ as a teacher in this school?

- What is your approach to classroom management and student discipline? Can you provide some specific examples of how you have exercised this approach in the past or how you plan to implement this approach in the future here?

Some examples of interview questions for a variety of different teacher candidates are provided as reproducibles at the end of this chapter, beginning on page 34. Visit **go.solution-tree.com /leadership** to download these pages. As you review all of these questions, note that we don't suggest that you use *all* of these questions, since doing so would certainly not conform to the time limitations of most interviews. Questions here are meant only as models of the kinds of questions that a principal and an interview team might include in sessions with teacher candidates. The only thing we reinforce here is that all teaching candidates must be asked the same questions by the same interviewer or committee member in all interviews.

Questions to Consider

- In what ways will you be able to involve stakeholders in your school that are not participants in the interview process but who have an interest in the new teacher who will be hired?

- What additional broad areas of teaching responsibilities (for example, curriculum, individual student needs, instructional methods, and so on) might be added to the areas included in these lists of potential questions?

- Are there questions related to specific responsibilities associated with a teacher's work in a school that might be included? For example, should questions also be directed toward work with specific student populations such as special needs, bilingual groups, homeless students, and so on?

Efforts to Substitute for Interviews

While we have emphasized throughout this book that the interview is a critical activity, there are some who find this to be an unimportant traditional practice. As we've stated, the terms of federal legislation guiding No Child Left Behind have been quite clear that the expectation is for school districts to hire only what the legislation defines as highly qualified teachers. This is a commendable goal, but not always an easy one to achieve. As a result, some school systems have begun to seek ways to satisfy federal demands by employing what some might call more foolproof or scientific ways to ensure the quality of their teaching staffs. Despite the value traditionally associated with the interview, some believe that interviews are simply prone to a great deal of subjective interpretation, and quality can be determined in different ways (Johnson, Berg, & Donaldson, 2005).

Online Questionnaires

One practice adopted and utilized in several school districts is the administration of a computer-based questionnaire designed to acquire valid and reliable indicators of teaching knowledge by applicants. In this case, multiple-choice questions are asked of job applicants concerning their approaches to typical challenges faced by classroom teachers. Responses are analyzed according to a standardized scoring template, which assures school districts that teachers are selected based on their ability to be high-quality candidates who are well-suited to serve as classroom teachers.

A popular method to provide "scientific" assessment of teacher capability has been the TeacherInsight™ instrument, developed and marketed by the Gallup Polling Service Corporation as a readily available online instrument to provide school districts with data concerning the probable success of teacher applicants (Gallup, 2004). Gallup invested a significant amount of resources to develop a valid and reliable process to identify the most "correct" actions that a highly qualified and effective teacher would take in certain situations in the real world. Perceptions of successful teachers, principals, central office administrators, parents, university scholars, students, and community members were used in creating the scoring norms for the instrument (Gallup, 2004) which could, in effect, provide a rather easily administered alternative to the costly (and often ineffective in terms of finding correct answers to questions of practice) employment interviews. And since the TeacherInsight instrument is administered through the Internet, a wider array of potentially strong teaching candidates could be reached for consideration to fill current openings. However, as we noted earlier, there are no perfect answers to open-ended questions used in employment interviews. To believe that there may be a "correct" versus "incorrect" response could in fact be an inhibitor to people who may offer perspectives that are outside the box but worth considering.

And despite its popularity, reviews of the value of the TeacherInsight survey as a technique to identify new teacher skills that increase student learning have not been conclusive. Only very minor (statistically insignificant) increases in student achievement seem to be related to the adoption of TeacherInsight as a feature of new teacher selection in many school districts (Wilson, 2008). This leaves strong doubt about the use of an online instrument replacing the more traditional teacher interview as the primary method for selecting new teachers.

Conclusion

The heart of the teacher selection process is the initial interview of large numbers of applicants, and the most critical issue to be addressed during the interview process is the extent to which an applicant for a teaching position will truly fit the needs of a school, district, and community. But it is important that interviewers are prepared to take on this responsibility, and that they have planned a process to ensure the interview goes smoothly and results in learning the desired information. The processes and sample questions provided in this chapter can be used as a guide to help interview committees achieve this goal. In the next chapter, we explore additional ways to identify the actual teachers selected for recommendation for teaching positions in a school.

Generic Interview Questions for All Teacher Applicants

Curriculum

✓ • What influence would Common Core *[instructional shifts]* or other standards have on the way you teach your subject(s)?

✓ • What are important curriculum topics *[major clusters / fluency]* for the grade and subject area that you would be teaching?

Planning for Instruction

• Your school is dedicated to integrating all learners into every class. As a result, your classes will have students representing many different ability groups. How would you plan to provide effective instruction for all students?

• Tell us about how you would prepare a lesson plan. How important is the preparation of weekly lesson plans for you?

• What are some of your favorite ways to begin and end a class?

✓ • Describe how you would teach a two-week unit in your class. *(assessment)*

Instructional Methods

• Describe how you would teach a lesson.

• How would you plan to integrate technology into your lessons?

Classroom Management

✓ • Describe a classroom that you have visited that exhibited what you believe to be effective student discipline, was well-managed and orderly, and was an inviting environment for learners. What were the key features of that classroom, and how would you create a similar setting in your class?

✓ • What kinds of rules, positive behaviors, and consequences for bad student decisions are appropriate for students at the age that you would be teaching here?

✓ • If you are selected as our new teacher, what do you anticipate as appropriate activities for you to use during the first week of the new school term?

Assessment and Grading

✓ • Describe a homework assignment that you would give to students in the class that you would teach here. What is the purpose of this assigned work?

✓ • There has always been a problem here with students who simply do not complete homework assignments. How would you change this in your class(es)?

• If you could design a grading system just for your class, what would it look like?

• As you are teaching a lesson, how can you tell if students are really getting it?

Meeting the Needs of Individual Students

✓ • Describe an approach that you would take in helping students with learning disabilities succeed.

✓ • What modifications would you make in your teaching so that lessons could be more easily learned by students with learning disabilities, or with other special populations such as students classified as English learners?

• You note that students in your class have divided themselves into small groups or cliques that do not seem to have anything to do with the other groups. This has led to a lot of mocking behavior, back stabbing, and situations where students make fun of others. What would you do to change this situation and promote tolerance and acceptance among your students?

• If one of your students complained that he or she was being bullied by another student in class, what steps would you take to address this issue?

Communicating With Parents and Others

• Describe what you would view as indicators of positive parent communications.

• How will you know if a contact with a parent has been successful in terms of changing a student's behavior or academic progress?

Professionalism

• How would you evaluate your own teaching?

✓ • How would you stay current with trends and issues in education and in your subject area?

—reword

Technology in the Classroom

✓ • Provide an example in which you have made use of technology in your classroom. *reword for blended learning*

• How would you make use of an interactive whiteboard in your classroom?

Supporting the School's Vision

✓ • Have you reviewed the vision statement for this school? What do you plan to do as a teacher that would advance this vision?

Sample Questions for Preschool Teacher Applicants

Curriculum

- What are the most significant curricular topics for a preschool student to master?

- What would you use from national and state standards to guide your teaching?

Planning for Instruction

- Describe a successful lesson.

- A child comes to you and expresses a concern that he or she ran out of time to complete an assigned task. How would you respond?

- What would you do to capture the attention of young children?

Classroom Organization and Management

- What special safety precautions must be considered when working with very young students (two to four years old)?

- You have a four-year-old student who is extremely bright but has persistent behavioral problems and frequently slaps and pushes other students. What approach would you take in disciplining this child so that he or she learns the consequences of bad behavior?

- A child consistently tests the limits you established at the beginning of the term for class behavior. What would you do, and what results would you expect?

Assessment and Individual Needs

- How do you intend to assess student progress?

- Based on your observations during the first six weeks of the school year, you are quite sure that a student who had never attended any type of school in the past shows many characteristics of autism. How would you approach this in a way that would be helpful to the student as well as his parents?

- Young children need a great deal of attention. How would you plan to create opportunities to individualize the attention that you provide to each of the children who will be in your room?

- What modifications in your teaching practice would you use to accommodate learning disabilities or language minority students in your room?

- Explain a task that might be developmentally inappropriate for a three-year-old, yet could be done easily by a kindergarten student.

Professionalism and Communication With Parents

- Describe what you expect to see in a successful parent conference.

- What new research or pedagogical methods have you encountered recently that will influence your teaching practices?

Sample Questions for Elementary Teacher Applicants (K–6)

Reading and Literacy

- Describe the way in which you plan to teach reading through the district's curriculum and incorporate your own ideas at this school.

- Describe your experiences in teaching phonics.

  — infon text vs. literary
  → Guided reading

- Describe your experiences teaching with a balanced literacy approach. How would you differentiate your teaching through an assessment of different levels of student comprehension?

- How would you use material found on websites and through other forms of technology to supplement your teaching of reading?

Instructional Methods

- Describe ways in which you would use successful techniques to help students learn and improve their writing skills.

- How can manipulatives be used to enhance instruction for elementary school–aged students?

  — social studies

- How would you integrate teaching reading into science instruction for children?

- How do you plan on using small-group work as a way to enhance learning in your classroom?

Assessment

- Without falling prey to the problem of strictly teaching to the tests, how would you plan to prepare students in your grade for the statewide standardized achievement tests each year?

- In your opinion, what other ways can be used to determine if students have achieved basic competency in curricular areas normally covered in standardized tests?

- What is your view of making use of portfolios to guide assessment of student progress?

- How can a teacher tell if students are actively engaged in learning without testing or assigning a grade to an activity?

Classroom Organization and Management

- How do you plan on making your classroom an inviting learning environment for students?

- How do you plan to transition students from one activity or subject area to the next successfully?

- What research or personal experience would you rely on to indicate the kinds of rewards and consequences that are particularly effective in working with students at the age group to which you will be assigned at this school?

Working With Peers

- What is your attitude about working in a school where you might be called on to engage in either team teaching or co-teaching? Under what circumstances would such practices be effective, in your opinion?

- How do you intend to plan with other teachers at your grade level?

— RTI — assessment

Communication With Parents

- Describe the techniques that you plan to use to keep parents involved with their children's education.

- What challenges do you anticipate in your efforts to communicate with parents? How would you deal with those challenges?

Sample Questions for Middle School Teacher Applicants

Working With Peers

- What would your thoughts be about an expectation that you work with other teachers on a teaching team?

- Have you had experience with team planning? If so, how do you think it worked to achieve important instructional goals?

- What are middle school subjects that you believe you are particularly well-suited to teach in a team arrangement?

Curriculum

- What does the phrase *writing across the curriculum* mean to you? How would you implement this concept in your class?

- Can mathematics be taught in other curricular areas? Provide an example.

- How would you challenge students to be more effective readers in all other areas of the curriculum?

Instructional Methods

- What techniques do you use to make learning something that can be fun for students?

- In addition to the traditional practice of posting student papers on a bulletin board, how can you highlight student work?

- In what ways can you help students get ready for high school?

- How will you go about preparing students to excel on standardized achievement tests?

Student Needs

- Early adolescents often demonstrate feelings of self-doubt and a lack of confidence. How can you help these children overcome these feelings so that they are more productive learners?

- What would you do if a student's problem were beyond your comfort level or expertise?

- How can you encourage middle school students to open up about issues that concern them?

School Climate

- What kinds of discipline issues do you believe you will face in a middle school, and how will you deal with them?

- How do you plan on making your students accept responsibility for their own behavior?

Communication and Professionalism

- Explain how you would work with a parent who heard a rumor that his daughter was being bullied or sexually harassed by some boys in your class.

- If you heard a rumor that your students were sexting, how would you address this problem? What if there were a suggestion that intimidation or bullying was going on among your students?

Sample Questions for High School Teacher Applicants

Working With Peers

- Two other recently hired teachers ask if you would be interested in working with them in developing two or three lessons that integrate your subject area with the work of these other teachers in their subject areas. How would you respond? What questions might you ask your colleagues?

- This school has a policy requiring that each teacher provide coverage for at least one extra-curricular or sporting event during each academic quarter of the school year. How do you react to that expectation for you as a teacher?

Instructional Methods

- You learn that there is an expectation for teachers to take students on at least two field trips in the community each year. Where would you plan to go with the students? Why did you select those places?

- How do you plan to integrate technology into your daily class activities?

Student Needs and Motivation

- As the school year approaches the winter break, spring break, or end of the year, you want to keep students engaged and motivated to continue learning. How would you do this?

- You have some very active and involved students from the school orchestra, athletic teams, and student government in your sixth-period class. You are receiving requests from different coaches, directors, and sponsors to allow at least one student each day to leave your class early to go to practice, go to a basketball game, play in a concert, or engage in some other school-sponsored activity. How would you gracefully end this practice without indicating displeasure with the actions of your colleagues?

Communication With Parents

- You note that parents who are in need of conferencing with you never show up at parent nights. What would you do to ensure that you get in touch with parents on a regular basis?

- You suspect that one of your students might be using some form of illegal substance at school. How would you approach parents about your concern regarding their son or daughter?

Classroom Management

- If you had a concern about gang behavior (signing, sending text messages about gang meetings after school, wearing colors, and so on) in your class or in places where you pass on occasion throughout the day, what would you do?

- Two students regularly fall asleep in your class. What do you do?

- A student begins to punctuate his response in class through the use of profanity. What do you do?

How to Interview, Hire, & Retain High-Quality New Teachers © 2013 Solution Tree Press • solution-tree.com
Visit **go.solution-tree.com/leadership** to download this page.

Professionalism

- Despite all the time that you spend on your job each week, you know that you must also keep up with your learning in your chosen instructional field. How do you plan to balance your personal needs, professional responsibilities, and professional development?

- You hear from some of your students that one of your teaching colleagues is sexually involved with a student in your class. Without making any unwarranted accusations, how would you find out if this were true, and if so, what would you do about it?

5

How to Draw Additional Questions From State and National Standards

Numerous lists of effective teacher characteristics have been adopted as standards to guide certification and licensure. These standards represent sets of performance expectations by teachers. As such, they would hardly be appropriate for direct use in the interviewing process. However, they may serve as the basis for areas of potential development for those who work in classrooms. In many cases, they have been used as the basis for evaluating performance of teachers in their jobs, and in some cases, standards have also been used as guides for teacher professional development activity. They may also be used as a way to determine the potential skills and abilities desired in job seekers. In this case, they can serve as frameworks to be used by administrators or others who need to gauge potential performance through the questioning process suggested in the preceding chapter.

InTASC Standards

The Interstate Teacher Assessment and Support Consortium (InTASC) standards were developed by the Council of Chief State School Officers (CCSSO) primarily to guide the development of future teachers. There are ten standards ranging from knowledge of subject matter to classroom management to the development of partnerships with colleagues, parents, and the community. Following are the standards as described by the CCSSO (2011), accompanied by examples of interview questions based on the standards.

1. **Learner development:** "The teacher understands how learners grow and develop, recognizing that patterns of learning and development vary individually within and across the cognitive, linguistic, social, emotional, and physical areas, and designs and implements developmentally appropriate and challenging learning experiences" (p. 8). Examples of a few prompts that might be derived from this standard are—

> Select a topic that you might address early in the school year. Explain how teaching this topic would be different for students at the age that you teach, as contrasted with older or younger students.

✓ > Describe how you might integrate a social skill into an academic lesson.

2. **Learning differences:** "The teacher uses understanding of individual differences and diverse cultures and communities to ensure inclusive learning environments that enable each learner to meet high standards" (p. 8). Possible interview questions include—

> How would you present a lesson that would combine auditory, visual, or kinesthetic teaching strategies?

> What might be some modifications that you could make to an assignment or test so that a student could master material successfully despite having an exceptionality?

3. **Learning environments:** "The teacher works with others to create environments that support individual and collaborative learning, and that encourage positive social interaction, active engagement in learning, and self motivation" (p . 8). Possible interview questions include—

> How would you set up your classroom to facilitate time on task?   *—Station rotations*

> How would you set up a classroom management plan to improve the behaviors of individual students?

4. **Content knowledge:** "The teacher understands the central concepts, tools of inquiry, and structures of the discipline(s) he or she teaches and creates learning experiences that make the discipline accessible and meaningful for learners to assure mastery of the content" (p. 8). Some interview questions that might be based on this standard are—

Pick a power standard → fluency standard

> Can you describe an activity or project that students might do to reflect their understanding of subject matter being taught? How would you assess the success of their efforts?

> Describe a topic that is traditionally hard to teach in your field, and describe a lesson or strategy that you might employ that would enable students to understand this topic.

5. **Application of content:** "The teacher understands how to connect concepts and use differing perspectives to engage learners in critical thinking, creativity, and collaborative problem solving related to authentic local and global issues" (p. 8). Possible interview questions include—

> Describe a lesson you might develop that illustrates for students how the content is significant to life outside the classroom.

How have you expanded your understanding of blending learning & tech integration? How can students benefit from an increased use of online tech?

> How might you integrate a variety of forms of media to supplement a lesson and encourage students to work together to find creative solutions?

6. **Assessment:** "The teacher understands and uses multiple methods of assessment to engage learners in their own growth, to monitor learner progress, and to guide the teacher's and learner's decision making" (p. 9). Possible interview questions include—

    > What variety of assessments might you use to gauge and further students' learning?

    > How will you use assessments to encourage students to take an active part in their own learning?

7. **Planning for instruction:** "The teacher plans instruction that supports every student in meeting rigorous learning goals by drawing upon knowledge of content areas, curriculum, cross-disciplinary skills, and pedagogy, as well as knowledge of learners and the community context" (p. 9). Possible interview questions include—

    > What practices might you implement to ensure that students stay on track toward achieving their learning goals?

    > How would you plan an instructional unit to address specific state or national standards?

8. **Instructional strategies:** "The teacher understands and uses a variety of instructional strategies to encourage learners to develop deep understanding of content areas and their connections, and to build skills to apply knowledge in meaningful ways" (p. 9). Possible interview questions include—

    > How might you use higher-order questions to challenge students?

    > Can you describe an activity that would enable you to ask students to do something with material from a text other than merely answering simple questions?

9. **Professional learning and ethical practice:** "The teacher engages in ongoing professional learning and uses evidence to continually evaluate his/her practice, particularly the effects of his/her choices and actions on others (learners, families, other professionals, and the community), and adapts practice to meet the needs of each learner" (p. 9). Possible interview questions include—

    > What professional development opportunities have been most beneficial to you?

    > In what organizations do you have membership, and what materials do you read or review to stay current in your career as a teacher?

10. **Leadership and collaboration:** "The teacher seeks appropriate leadership roles and opportunities to take responsibility for student learning, to collaborate with learners,

families, colleagues, other school professionals, and community members to ensure learner growth, and to advance the profession" (p. 9). Possible interview questions include—

> › How would you ensure positive parent or community involvement?

> › How do you anticipate being able to communicate effectively with your colleagues?

Questions to Consider

- What are some additional questions that might be asked of job applicants in terms of these InTASC standards?

- Of the standards noted here, how would you assess the overall skills of all teachers currently working in your school? Are there some areas that are particularly strong so that newcomers will have models?

Research on Teacher Behavior

Another potentially valuable resource to guide the development of interview questions comes from Daniel Heller's research related to the characteristics of effective teachers, derived from numerous studies of teachers. Following are features of the best teachers, as noted by Heller (2004), accompanied by possible interview questions related to those qualities.

- Effective teachers exhibit positive, flexible, and supportive attitudes that enable them to work effectively with parents.

  Sample question: A parent comes to you and confides that, as a single parent, she feels inadequate with her ability to handle many of the problems her son seems to be having in terms of academic and social issues in the school. How might you comfort her and turn her concerns into a positive and proactive strategy to help her child?

- The effective teacher relies on pedagogical practice that is student-centered, uses multiple techniques, matches techniques to student needs, and relies on valid knowledge from the field.

  Sample question: You learn during the first week of school that each of your classes at this middle school includes students with a variety of backgrounds and needs. For example, your first-period class has gifted and talented students, two students who are autistic, one child with a severe auditory disability, and at least three children who are classified as homeless. How will you prepare for this class?

- The effective teacher is a continuing learner who engages in reflective thinking, is comfortable with risks, tries again when he or she fails, accepts criticism, and demonstrates a desire to learn and improve.

  Sample question: You are assigned a class that includes many students of varying ability. As a result, you try several strategies to enable you to reach out to students with many different individual needs. Unfortunately, by the end of the first semester, you realize that many of your efforts to address diverse learning needs and abilities are not working. What do you do in the second term?

- Effective teachers treat all students with respect, keep students engaged, put students at the center, handle difficult students with understanding and compassion, and continue to handle their own personal problems.

  Sample question: Students at this school come from many different socioeconomic groups, different religions, a variety of racial and ethnic groups, and family backgrounds that range from ideal to situations that make their daily lives a challenge because of poverty, lack of parental care or presence, and many other conditions that would challenge any teacher. How would you address this diversity?

- Effective teachers can work with others, flow with challenging situations, are willing to share, and demonstrate respect to others.

  Sample question: You are new to this school and are asked to serve in a team of teachers where there is clearly a degree of animosity present in terms of personal interactions at meetings. How would you be able to cope with this situation, and how might you engage in actions that improve the organizational climate of your team?

Questions to Consider

- What are some additional questions that might be asked as a way to determine how an applicant for a teaching position can function as an effective teacher in terms of the skills identified by Daniel Heller?
- What additional skills for effective teachers might you add to this list?

State Teacher Standards

Individual state standards are a third potential source of questions that may be used in interviewing applicants for teaching positions. The California Standards for the Teaching Profession are one example. These standards identify characteristics that at least one state has determined should be found in all teachers, whether they are veterans or new to the profession. It should also be noted that there are significant overlaps between the California vision and the InTASC standards as well as the features of effective teachers identified through the research of Heller. We do not advocate using every item in these three sources, but rather, those who are involved in the teacher applicant interviews might wish to pick and choose which appear to be the most appropriate items for the identification and selection of teachers who will fit the desired vision of an individual school.

The following teacher professional standards and accompanying questions were first articulated by the California Commission on Teacher Credentialing and the California Department of Education in 1997 to provide guidance and direction to both the initial preparation of future teachers, and also the ongoing professional development of classroom teachers in the state.

- **Engaging and supporting all students in learning:** Key elements include—

  › Connecting students' prior knowledge, life experience, and interests with learning goals

  › Using a variety of instructional strategies and resources to respond to students' diverse needs

  › Facilitating learning experiences that promote autonomy, interaction, and choice

  › Engaging students in problem solving, critical thinking, and other activities that make subject matter meaningful

  › Promoting self-directed, reflective learning for all students

Some potential interview questions related to this standard include—

  › How will you help students to see connections between what they already know and the new material?

  › How will you use a variety of strategies to introduce, explain, and restate subject matter concepts and processes so that all students understand?

  › How will you use the classroom environment to provide opportunities for independent and collaborative learning?

  › How will you help students to learn, practice, internalize, and apply subject-specific learning strategies and procedures?

  › Give an example of how you would explain clear learning goals for all students for each activity or lesson?

- **Creating and maintaining effective environments for students:** Key elements include—

  › Creating a physical environment that engages all students

  › Establishing a climate that promotes fairness and respect

  › Promoting social development and group responsibility

  › Establishing and maintaining standards for student behavior

  › Planning and implementing classrooms and procedures that support student learning

  › Using instructional time effectively

Some potential interview questions related to this standard include—

  › How can a teacher arrange a room to facilitate positive classroom interaction?

> Describe how you intend to encourage students to take risks and be creative.

> How can a teacher help all students accept and respect different experiences, ideas, backgrounds, feelings, and points of view?

> How will you intervene when student behavior does not meet agreed-upon classroom standards?

> How do you plan to develop classroom procedures and routines that promote and maintain a climate of fairness and respect?

> How will you structure time to support student learning?

- **Understanding and organizing subject matter for student learning:** Key elements include—

  > Demonstrating knowledge of subject matter and student development

  > Organizing curriculum to support student understanding of subject matter

  > Interrelating ideas and information within and across subject matter areas

  > Developing student understanding through instructional strategies that are appropriate to the subject matter

  > Using materials, resources, and technologies to make subject matter accessible to students

  Some potential interview questions related to this standard include—

  > How do you ensure that your knowledge of subject matter will incorporate different perspectives?

  > How will you use your knowledge of development to organize and sequence the curriculum to increase student understanding?

  > How will you help students to apply learning from different curricular areas to solve problems?

  > How will you use your knowledge of subject matter to help students construct their own knowledge?

  > How will you use technology to convey key concepts in the subject matter?

- **Planning instruction for designing learning experiences for all students:** Key elements include—

  > Drawing on and valuing students' backgrounds, interests, and developmental learning needs

> Establishing and articulating goals for student learning

> Developing and sequencing instructional activities and materials for student learning

> Designing short-term and long-term plans to foster student learning

> Modifying instructional plans to adjust for student needs

Some potential interview questions related to this standard include—

> How will you incorporate students' knowledge and experience in your curriculum and instructional planning?

✓ > How do you establish short-term and long-term goals for student learning?

> How will you choose and adapt instructional materials to make subject matter relevant to students' experiences and interests?

> How will you incorporate diverse subject matter perspectives in your planning?

- **Assessing student learning:** Key elements include—

> Establishing and communicating learning goals for all students

> Collecting and using multiple sources of information to assess student learning

> Involving and guiding all students in assessing their own learning

> Using the results of assessments to guide instruction

> Communicating with students, families, and other audiences about student progress

Some potential interview questions related to this standard include—

✓ > How do you plan to use subject matter standards from state, district, and other sources to guide how you establish learning goals for each student?

> How will you use a variety of assessments to determine what students know and are able to do?

✓ > How will you help all students build their self-reflection skills?

> How can you use assessment data to meet students' individual needs?

> Explain some of the ways you might involve parents as active partners in the assessment process.

- **Developing as a professional educator:** Key elements include—

> Reflecting on teaching practice and planning professional development

> Establishing professional goals and pursuing opportunities to grow professionally

> Working with communities to improve professional practice

> Working with families to improve professional practice

> Working with colleagues to improve professional practice

> Balancing professional responsibilities and maintaining motivation

Some potential interview questions related to this standard include—

> What are some ways that you might be able to collaborate with your colleagues?

> What will you do to find a balance between your needs and professional responsibilities?

> What will you do to increase your understanding of the cultures and dynamics of your students' communities?

Source: California Commission on Teacher Credentialing and California Department of Education, 1997.

There are many sources available to guide the preparation of an interview protocol. As we will discuss in the next chapter, remember that, while interview questions and answers are a good tool to use in selecting teachers for a school, there are many other factors to take away from face-to-face encounters with job candidates that may also be important determinants of probable success in working in a particular school. As is so often the case, there is no perfect way to find the perfect teacher.

Conclusion

Standards that reflect values and views of ideal teaching behaviors, skills, and attitudes are helpful sources that may be used as the basis for questions in interviews of teacher candidates. Understanding the key characteristics, derived from research, of effective teachers can also assist interviewers in developing productive questions. Asking questions based on these formal frameworks is important because, in addition to finding a good fit between a teacher applicant and what you need in your school (as described in chapter 4), it is also important to find faculty who meet the standards of wider audiences. In short, you need not only a good teacher in general, but a good teacher for *your* school. Although examples of questions reflecting important ideas from various standards are provided here, it is important that the questions used to guide the interviewing process always reflect and include attention to the vision of education that is important to your individual school.

6

What Comes After the Interview

Once an interview process is complete, committees face the task of determining which candidates they want to continue pursuing. It is important that groups are able to reach consensus on the status of candidates. In order to do so, there are a number of processes to complete and topics to consider. Here, we describe these and provide helpful questions to guide you through this decision-making process.

Remember that the process of finding good teachers to add to your school (or at least replace departing staff members) is not simply finding someone to take a job. If a school is truly committed to providing excellent educational opportunities for children, teacher selection can be a powerful tool to ensure that what takes place in the classroom leads to learning. Simply finding people who meet the minimal standards associated with a particular opening is only a start to improving the school in its effort to address the learning needs of students. In this chapter, we suggest some actions that might ensure that the interviewing process leads to hiring and keeping high-quality teachers.

What to Consider

As we explained in chapter 4, applicants are asked to submit a great deal of paper to a school district when they apply initially. But in the long run, this material provides only flat data such as name, contact information, eligibility, attestations from friendly sources, and years of prior professional experience. In many cases, information is limited because the applicant is coming directly from a university and past experience consists almost exclusively of student teaching. The employing district may require a criminal background check to ensure the applicant does not have a police record. One additional item included in the application process typically asks applicants to pledge that all information provided is truthful.

The application form (the first document provided by an applicant) yields very little solid information to guide the selection process. Of course, if there is any doubt about an applicant's honesty, the screening process will reveal this and the automatic termination of an application will likely result.

In addition to the actual application form, the candidate must also submit official transcripts from colleges or universities attended, verification of appropriate state certification (including scores showing successful completion of the certification or licensing examination required in the state), and two or three names of references or letters of recommendation commenting on the applicant's actual or potential success as a classroom teacher. Applicants for all teaching jobs are now required to submit a statement authorizing the employing district to carry out a criminal background check through the FBI to determine that there is no previous record of any criminal behavior. Normally, the district will not initiate this review until an applicant has already completed the interview(s) and is either the chosen candidate or finalist. In some cases, school districts also require finger printing of all faculty as a condition of the receipt of a contract. Obviously, the fingerprinting process must not lead to any record of criminal activity. Each of these items is meant to serve a specific purpose in the completion of an application for a teaching position.

Official university transcripts are important in a number of ways. First, they will be an indication that the applicant has, in fact, completed an academic degree program at an approved college or university. Beyond that, principals and others who review applicants may review transcripts even more carefully to determine, for example, grades that potential teachers received in subject areas that they would teach. And some administrators look at transcripts to determine what overall grade point averages might reflect. For example, a 3.0 (B) average may be achieved by a graduate having straight As in general, required courses, but no grades higher than a C in advanced classes for future teachers. The reverse may also be true. It may also be noteworthy to see how long it took the applicant to complete a degree program.

Letters of reference (or completed reference checklist forms) are a virtual universal requirement for applicants for teaching positions. This has remained true for many years, even though researchers have long recognized that references are generally the least valid predictors of probable future success in jobs (Peterson, 2002a). The fact is, no one is likely to invite someone to write a letter of support unless there is a high degree of certainty that a referee will provide a glowing recommendation.

Questions to Consider

- What application materials does your district require from teacher candidates? Which are most helpful for decision makers? Are there other materials that the district should also consider requiring that would improve the process?

- How are application materials reviewed and verified for accuracy in your district? Is there anything about these procedures that can be changed to better identify the right candidates?

Rating the Interviewees

Ultimately, there is a time when those who conducted the interview have to decide what to do with what they have heard and seen. In general terms, we recommend that the interview committee consider the following steps during the process of collectively rating the interviewees' performances. Discussions of these steps should ideally take place soon after all interviews have been completed so that committee members' memories are fresh:

1. Review broad issues concerning the interviews—

    › To the knowledge of interviewers, were answers provided by interviewees truthful?

    › Was information provided in the answers accurate?

    › Did applicants answer questions that were asked, or did they appear to evade questions?

    › In questions about classroom management and discipline, were the descriptions provided by applicants consistent with the practices and philosophy related to behavior at the school?

    › Did answers by applicants match the vision adopted by the school?

    › Does it seem that the applicants will be able to work effectively with other teachers, staff, students, parents, and community members?

    › Were any answers provided by applicants contrary to established school philosophy, policy, or practice?

2. In a similar fashion, review nonverbal behavior of interviewees in terms of demonstrated consistency with the needs of a specific school—

    › Did the nonverbal actions of applicants signal a sense of openness and warmth to members of the interview committee?

    › Did applicants show any disrespectful or unfriendly behavior to members of the committee?

    › Did applicants indicate a willingness to listen actively during the interviews?

    › Did applicants engage in eye contact with those who were asking the questions?

    › Were any behaviors or actions of applicants indicative of negative attitudes (for example, smirking, glancing around the room, doodling on a piece of paper, and so on) they may have?

    › Did the applicants exhibit any behaviors that might detract from their ability to provide effective classroom management and student discipline?

    › Can candidates serve as effective contributors to school effectiveness and work effectively as colleagues to assist other teachers' efforts to support student learning?

3. Work toward building a consensus recommendation regarding interviewees. The committee will not be making the final decision regarding the applicants, but an important last

step in the delivery of a recommendation to the principal regarding the most appropriate choice for a teaching position must involve the process of developing some level of consensus regarding the interviewees. In most cases, committees will be asked to provide a list of three or four finalists to those charged with making the final decisions. Typically, the list is not to be provided in any order, but rather, in some fashion that highlights the committee's views concerning positives and negatives regarding each of the recommended candidates. In this final step of the committee's review process, the following actions and pieces of information may help in moving toward consensus—

> › The person chairing the committee might request that the members begin by identifying the worst possible candidates first. This may be a unanimous listing, or one so full of agreement that the list of finalists is narrowed rather quickly.

> › Of the candidates still remaining for consideration, the committee may first be invited to indicate if they believe that there are any candidates who immediately stand out as the strongest candidates. Often, this is an easy way to thin the list down to a few manageable names.

> › If the first two steps here make it clear that only a small number of finalists (three to five individuals) remains, the list may be reduced further after the committee begins to identify specific strengths and limitations for each person.

> › In most cases, the above actions result in limited lists, and potential selected candidates will emerge to enable the committee to complete its charge.

> › A situation may arise in which one specific interviewee does such a good job that there may be a temptation to provide the name of only one finalist to the principal as the person who must be selected for a job. This outcome should be avoided. Committee members must be aware that a candidate recognized as the only choice in one school might also be recognized as a strong candidate at one or several other schools where they may have also interviewed. The principal needs some choices to pursue if the first choice is not available.

Developing absolute consensus is a commendable goal for any committee. But remember that the decision need not be unanimous. On occasion, there may be one or two members of a committee who dissent from the majority recommendation. Time for selecting the best teachers is limited, and we strongly recommend that the committee might best serve the needs of a school by not devoting too much time to working toward absolute consensus. Submit minority observations without prejudicial commentary (for example, "Despite the protests of only one or two committee members . . .") to whomever must make the final decision regarding the selection for a teaching position. The fact is, the principal's final decision—after looking at two or three excellent choices—will always be a tough duty. If this is the case, though, it is also likely that good teachers will be found and, ultimately, this carefully conducted process will result in good things happening for students.

Quantitative Scoring Processes

Creating a quantitative scoring process to rate answers provided during interviews is a strategy used to remove highly subjective interpretation by individuals who will be making local decisions concerning the employment of candidates. While this is often viewed as a much more precise and objective approach to selecting teachers, it—like the online questionnaires discussed in chapter 4—implies that answers can be scored in a way that will yield numerically acceptable outcomes. Simply stated, in theory, the higher the scores acquired by the ranking of responses means that better applicants will be chosen for teaching positions. A person who gets 98 points out of a possible 100 is identified as a better choice than a person who gets only 96 points.

Approaches to developing numerical scoring processes to evaluate teacher employment interviews have been proposed by James Stronge (2002) as a way to enable people to compare and contrast the strengths and limitations of multiple job applicants in a fair and subjective fashion. This perspective certainly has some merit, but the same outcome of ensuring fairness can be attained through avenues other than the adoption of numerical scoring. For example, the use of multiple interviews involving multiple interviewers with a variety of perspectives can be most effective in ensuring that objective reviews of applicants can take place (Peterson, 2002a).

The advantages of not relying on numerical rating schemes to identify the best applicants for teaching jobs are twofold. First, not falling back on simply tabulating points awarded to various applicants could lead to a process of open discussions among committee members who might need to communicate with each other about a matter of mutual concern. Such an activity is often absent from many schools. Second, having the staff members on the committee talk through the selection process means that whoever is invited to be a teacher in a school was deliberately chosen by the faculty. As the new teacher comes on board, he or she is likely to recognize that their offer of employment was an intentional action by colleagues, not an accidental event.

Conclusion

The theme of this chapter was perhaps the most critical of all concerns associated with the selection of new teachers for a school: how will those involved with the interviewing process make use of all their hard work to select the perfect teacher? The ultimate answer to that question is, of course, the perfect teacher may not always be found, and the selection process will not ever be absolutely ideal. But if those making important decisions consistently direct their attention toward finding people who will have powerful and significant effects on student learning, the opportunity to find the right match will be more easily achieved. Your work isn't finished once you've found that match, however. It's important for principals to provide newly hired teachers with guidance and support to ensure that those teachers reach their full potential and have successful experiences that motivate them to remain in their positions. The next chapter provides strategies for how you can achieve this.

How to Guide New Teachers After They Sign on the Dotted Line

Each year, principals have an opportunity to add some new blood to their schools, but they also face a challenge with the arrival of rookies. The question is, How do you take the enthusiasm and awe often exhibited by new teachers and help them translate their energy into creative and productive work in classrooms? Another reality facing most new staff members and their principals is that new teachers are not only entering a new job, but a new profession. Teaching is a very important and satisfying world, but also a tiring and frustrating occupation in many ways, and new teachers need to be supported so they can cope with these challenges.

There are many effective recruiting and hiring practices to ensure that schools will be able to enjoy the benefits of excellent teachers. But the job of selecting new staff is not the end of the road. The first days on a job are, in fact, the beginning of a long journey for new teachers. Even in cases where teachers new to a school have had prior experience as teachers in other schools, or experiences in other life endeavors, being new can be a real and daunting challenge. Experienced teachers have at least been treated to the ups and downs of a school year. Newly minted members of the teaching profession are not familiar with the rhythm of a school year, and they are often unaware of the subtle nature of interpersonal relationships that are likely to occur in their first full-time job as a teacher.

This chapter considers the kinds of issues that may frustrate new teachers, whether experienced in other settings or fresh out of a preservice teacher training program. Our observations will not in themselves solve all of the orientation woes of new teachers, but we offer a few ideas that might be of value to principals helping newcomers adjust to their new work environments and become the most effective teachers they can be.

Predicting Trends and Disruptions

When people ask teachers why they have gone into their profession, they often hear stories about how others used to tell them that they should teach or how they were inspired by a teacher who once touched their lives in some significant way. They also volunteer that they continue to enjoy life as a teacher because teaching is a job during which one cannot get bored. Every day is completely different because students behave differently every day, year, and over an entire career. All of this is based on the fact that teachers do not teach math, or fourth grade, or any subject or grade level. They teach students, and students are people, and no two people are alike. Each of the roughly 180 days in a school year is unique and represents dozens or even hundreds of new challenges. But in total, the 180 days follow a more or less predictable pattern or rhythm that is generally similar to the school years of the past and is likely to be similar in school years of the future.

For example, certain aspects of the beginning of a new school year are very predictable. Experienced primary grade teachers enter each school year knowing that overly protective parents are quite likely to stay within arm's length of their children by sitting in the backs of classrooms, sitting out in the hallway near classrooms well after the sounding of the first bell, and making many other similar efforts to hold on too long. New teachers can easily believe that they are creating bonds with parents and other family members by allowing parents easy access to their children at the beginning of the school year, only to discover that parents are still sitting in the back of the classroom in May. Similar examples can be found at all grade levels.

In high schools, teachers must realize the potential disruptions that occur as adolescents get ready for football games and homecoming dances, for example. One novice teacher we spoke with taught a late afternoon class in a high school in which respect for academic traditions was high, but football was almost a religion. In the fall of his first year on the job, he noted that at least half of his junior and senior students simply did not show up for sixth period American history class. No excuse requests appeared the following Monday. The explanation, quite simply, was that it was game day, and all band members, cheerleaders and, of course, football players and managers were *always* excused. The new teacher quickly scheduled meetings with coaches, cheerleader moderators, and the band director to find a way in which American history class was not taking a back seat to Friday night football.

Other times during the school year are also predictable and recognized by veteran teachers (for example, the holiday stretch from Halloween to Thanksgiving to Christmas and Hanukkah and Kwanzaa). Whether it is the arrival of trick or treat night, or turkey dinners and the Macy's parade followed by Santa Claus, young children (and older students as well) become increasingly distracted during this time of year. Academic focus is on midyear testing in secondary schools, but students' concentration on this work sometimes takes a back seat to social activities. For new teachers, it is a time to recognize that lessons must be filled with serious content but also some more entertaining ways of keeping distracted students engaged in schoolwork. Discipline must also be maintained by teachers even if cries of "Scrooge!" might fill the air at times.

After the holidays are concluded comes the longest and arguably the most focused time in all grade levels and schools. From January until spring break (usually the middle to the end of March), there is typically only one holiday, Martin Luther King Jr. Day, and that is only about a week or two after the students return from the winter break. Most school districts do not observe any official holidays until March. Valentine's Day comes during this time of the year, and while it is certainly a day that often brings about a lot of distractions in a school, it is not a day off for students. Also add statewide testing to this long stretch of uninterrupted school days. This period is filled with long hours, anxiety, and tension for teachers, principals, and above all, students. Smiles suddenly begin to disappear as testing dates approach. Teachers work extra hours tutoring students and providing extra instruction in Saturday school programs. They generally realize that more is at stake than students simply getting high average scores. In terms of state and national education accountability expectations, jobs are at stake and so may be salary increases. Terminations of staff may result if scores are not high enough. New teachers, of course, know that high-stakes tests are important, but they may not fully comprehend the impact that testing time has on the climate and even emotional status of a school.

As the school year begins to wind down, getting students excited about learning is often a significant challenge between the first part of April and the end of May. After all, the standardized tests are over, and many in the school—teachers as well as students—show signs of burnout after the intensity of pretest preparation. New teachers, of course, do not generally succumb to the temptation of turning things off a month or more before the school year ends. But they are easily drawn into the culture of a school where senior, veteran teachers begin using more DVDs, small-group discussions, and other activities that allow students more freedom than earlier in the year. It is truly unfortunate, but the high-stakes testing phenomenon has had the unanticipated result of signaling to students and teachers that the goal of a school year is to test student achievement to ensure the attainment of minimum standards for accountability purposes. New learning simply ends in many schools.

There are, of course, some differences in schools. For example, some schools we have observed have been able to create a culture and collective attitude that is more relaxed about testing time. By contrast, we've seen some other schools begin the school year in a sort of high-alert status that creates even more tension—usually because the test scores from the previous school year were too low. Now there is a need to get the school year off to a good start by focusing on test performance improvement from the first day that teachers and students report for the new school year.

The important thing for new teachers and their principals to remember is that school years have predictable life cycles. Principals who have a few years of experience in a particular school have the ability to reduce the frustrations of newcomers with a rather simple technique: talk with the new staff and provide frequent warnings and alerts about what situations they will likely encounter during each six- to nine-week period of a school year. The idea is not to list every possible example of what might happen at different points of a school year but rather to make new teachers aware of certain predictable behaviors. Principals with long histories working in the same schools with many of the same teachers can often forget that not everyone is aware of the way things get just before the holidays or how tense it is just before testing begins in March. While there is no easy solution to offer new teachers for how to approach these challenges, acknowledging them in the form of a pep talk, debriefing session, email, phone call, or note is usually welcome and can go a long way in reassuring and encouraging new teachers. Such communication can create a kind of road map showing what to expect next, and it will be an appreciated form of support for recently hired people.

Questions to Consider

- What are some predictable patterns occurring at your school throughout the year that are important to make sure new teachers are aware of?

- How can you incorporate time into your schedule to regularly touch base with new teachers?

Understanding Local Culture and Informal Organizational Structures

Helping new arrivals learn who is who and the informal aspects of operations within a building is also important. Knowing who does what in the environment of a school is simple to describe on paper. The formal, official organizational chart will show the board of education at the top, followed by the superintendent, then central office administrators, and so on. Unfortunately for someone new to the system and to the job, the formal organization often does little to answer questions or solve real problems, especially if the problems need to be addressed immediately. Often, responsibilities and activities of people in the titled jobs change, and informal arrangements between staff members are not reflected in the official map. This requires a bit of ongoing advisement by people who have worked in a school or district for a number of years, which can be provided informally or through an internal newsletter.

In the next chapter, we talk about the importance of mentoring and coaching for new teachers, and we point out that a significant way to help new staff is by providing experienced people to identify the ways in which daily tasks are accomplished in a school, as compared with the way things are supposed to function according to school or district policy. For example, veterans often inform new teachers that, in many cases, contact with the principal is best orchestrated through a key secretary rather than by trying to have direct contact. Experienced teachers and administrators can also be important resources in terms of providing subtle, unofficial descriptions of the traditions or cultural idiosyncrasies in a particular school. An example of this, provided by a new teacher, was the fact that one table in the teachers' lounge was traditionally the unofficial territory of coaches at lunch time. For years this group used lunch time as a way to review last Friday's football game, plan for the next basketball game, or simply discuss the local baseball team. No signs were posted indicating the table was for coaches only. Instead, there was an unspoken expectation that one table out of seven or eight was reserved each day. Simply having a veteran teacher point out the table where the coaches always eat lunch might have been a helpful bit of news for a newcomer.

Another example we heard was about the head custodian at a high school. He was a very popular figure who not only took care of the building but also served as an active contributor to the formation of an exceptionally talented staff dedicated to the learning needs of more than two thousand students. He was truly an individual who went beyond the minimum requirements of his job description by doing many small things to help teachers and administrators, from staying late into the night (without overtime pay) to fix burners in the chemistry lab, to changing tires for teachers who didn't know how to use a jack, to counseling troubled students who were unable to connect with teachers or counselors. All of these contributions were done without hesitation or financial compensation, provided one thing: a simple expectation that staff who saw him around the building each day would greet him by name and bid him a good morning or good afternoon. Although this may sound like a trivial matter, he was proud of his work, and there was no doubt about his dedication to the school, students, and staff. He wanted to be recognized by name and a simple greeting. A new teacher who might need some special favor in the future would be well-advised of this expectation by a person who could do much to ensure a more pleasant and effective start to a new career. Many new teachers at this high school were shocked when they initially seemed to be ignored by a custodian described frequently by veteran teachers as one of the most important educators they had. But when the experienced staff members had the chance to counsel their new colleagues about this expectation, it became a regular practice that benefitted the newcomers.

Understanding the culture of a school also involves appreciating a lot of small items if a person wants to fit in. Is the principal addressed as Janet, or is she always Mrs. Craig? What are the personalities of the people who work in the school's main office? Are they businesslike, or do they joke around with teachers or administrators? Do certain teachers appear to always park in the same spots? Do teachers talk openly about their families? Is the talk over lunch exclusively non-work-related? Are there informal get-togethers at local watering holes every Friday? These issues may seem trivial, but if they are not addressed, big problems can result for new teachers.

Quite simply, if a principal wants to ensure that all the time and effort invested in finding and hiring good new teachers has been worth it, she or he should be prepared to provide support to new members of a school's teaching team. Part of the support provided to each newly hired teacher can best be delivered at the individual school, and specifically by the principal and teacher leaders. Principals can help beginning teachers feel more directly involved in the school community through open discussions and information concerning the kinds of events, emotions, issues, and problems that traditionally appear each year in every school. Principals and staff can do this quite simply by clearly identifying important deadlines and dates to be remembered and met by every teacher in the school. It is critical that this information be provided via email or other concrete (not simply verbal) means. If the first parent night will be held on Thursday, September 22, that fact and the expectation for all teachers to participate should not be left solely to a statement on the school's calendar that might have been distributed at the beginning of August. Instead, reminders must come out in a timely fashion as important dates approach. Remember, rookies often feel overwhelmed with their new duties and responsibilities. If the principal wants them there to meet parents in two weeks, it is certainly worth a brief email.

New teachers quickly realize that there is much more to being a successful educator than simply teaching students. All schools are complex organizations that are held to very clear expectations from the district and the public, but they also have many expectations that are not always well publicized. Newcomers need to know, for example, if no one on the faculty ever misses the first home football game of the season. If they do not adhere to subtle expectations and traditions, they may feel quite apart from colleagues rather quickly, just as they would if they missed some mandated training program for all new teachers. A new person in any organization has a lot to learn. The principal must recognize this and do what can be done to make all new teachers feel welcome and aware of the culture of a school.

Conclusion

There are many unspoken and undocumented intricacies regarding the culture and inner workings of a school, and these are different for each school. Alerting new teachers to these informal details from the beginning, rather than merely letting them discover them through trial and error, will increase the confidence of new teachers to become an active part of the school team. Furthermore, principals who take the time to provide simple reminders and prepare new teachers for the predictable trends that occur in a school throughout the year can help them stay ahead of the game and increase their chances for success. But these methods alone are not always sufficient in terms of support for beginners. In the next chapter, we take a look at some additional efforts to provide support for new teachers through the resources of the school district.

How the Central Office Supports New Teachers

The previous chapter included ways in which rookie teachers can receive support at the individual school level. This chapter considers two ways in which support for beginning teachers (as well as veteran teachers) may be provided by school districts. One is through structured mentoring programs, and the second is through comprehensive and focused professional development throughout the first few years for new teachers. As we have noted repeatedly in this book, teachers make a difference for students. If you find caring, dedicated, and talented classroom teachers, you are not simply filling a job; you are adding to the quality of learning. And while some leave the teaching profession because they feel mistreated, others give up life in the classroom because teaching is increasingly very demanding, hard work. While we note the absence of magical ways to keep teachers, we also recommend that school districts keep trying to assist newcomers in the hope that such effort will keep a high percentage of teachers who are hired each year.

Mentoring for Beginning Teachers

It is increasingly more evident that beginning teachers are becoming frustrated during their first few years in the classroom (Brown, 2003). Newly hired teachers are often discouraged because they are expected to perform their teaching duties with the same skill and confidence as experienced colleagues (Feinman-Nemser, 2003). Specialized support for beginners is needed.

Fortunately, many school districts and states have recognized the importance of support programs for novice teachers. Induction programs have been developed as a way to assist those who are entering classrooms for the first time. A central ingredient in these programs for beginning teachers has generally involved the adoption of some form of mentoring involving experienced teachers serving as one-on-one consultants to assist new teachers in beginning their careers. Throughout the 1980s, 1990s, and now in the beginning years of the 21st century, arranging mentoring support for new teachers has become a fairly standard practice in a vast number of school systems across the United States (Daresh, 2003).

Mentor Training

Contrary to the former practice of a newly hired faculty member developing an informal relationship with an experienced colleague to learn about school life, teacher mentoring programs today are highly structured in most cases, and mentors are typically not simply found but rather assigned to beginning teachers in a school district. Mentors are no longer teachers who simply volunteer to help newcomers. Now mentors are selected deliberately for special skills and are provided with training to assist them in their work.

We believe that a formal process of mentoring new teachers needs to be more substantive and frequent than simply brief encounters between veterans and novices. If a school district wants to provide a well-planned and consistent mentoring program, it must make training available to experienced teachers who provide valuable, regular assistance to new colleagues. Our view of mentoring includes activities in several domains (Daresh, 2003):

> **Domain 1—Orientation to mentoring.** Here the focus should be on developing a consensus as to what mentoring on a regular and formal basis would include, the potential benefits and limitations of mentoring, and, in general, how formal mentoring differs from simply serving as a periodic helping hand to new teachers.

> **Domain 2—Effective planning and managing of instruction.** Since the greatest impact that any teacher has in a school is the extent to which instruction is improved and learning by students is increased, training for mentors needs to be directed to that fact, and mentoring must always be directed toward that important goal—not simply making new teachers more comfortable in their new roles.

> **Domain 3—Human relations skills.** Training in this domain can identify some areas in which people may need some refinement. For example, even the best teachers who work well with students have some areas (such as providing feedback to adults in a nonthreatening fashion) where they might profit from some additional work.

> **Domain 4—Mentor process skills.** The skills mentors need to have to perform the job and create strong relationships are described. These are generally problem-solving, listening, and observation skills.

> **Domain 5—Local implementation skills.** How local issues may affect the way mentoring programs are approached should be taken into consideration.

The Broader Agenda of Mentoring

Mentoring can help the beginning teacher deal with challenges that are unique to that individual educator. The principal and veteran teachers have a major role to play in terms of assisting beginning teachers at individual schools with developing insights into how things operate at the school site level. As school districts take on the challenge of providing support for new teachers across the entire system, it is useful to think about a broader agenda to follow for all those who are starting their teaching careers in a district as well as experienced teachers who have just relocated to a new school system. Following are general suggestions for ideas to be considered throughout a school year. If possible, it is best for mentors and beginning teachers to review these issues as a team:

- **Developing a personal educational platform**—Earlier, we made the case for principals starting their recruitment and selection process for new teachers by pausing first to review their personal assumptions and beliefs regarding the vision for their school. This reflection is one that might drive the connections made between mentors and new teachers. What are some of the most important and central values of the new teacher? What are the non-negotiable values that the new teacher believes should not be violated by any demands of the new job?

- **Articulating a vision**—What does the teacher hope to accomplish during the first year on the job? Besides simply surviving, what are some indications that the newcomer might demonstrate as an affirmation of success during the first year?

- **Personal identity**—Since people who are new to professional roles often must make conscious decisions about how they present themselves in those roles, a reasonable question to ask might be, What will it feel like to have students, parents, other teachers, staff, and administrators look to the beginner as a professional educator and expert?

Essential Skill Areas for Mentoring

There are a variety of essential skill areas in which a mentor can help teachers when they assume a new role. Some of these include:

- **Framing issues**—For an individual who is taking on a new role, the job can be overwhelming, considering all of the issues that need to be addressed. The first thing that needs to be done when working with a new teacher is to frame the broad issues to consider. For example, novice teachers are often very concerned about classroom management and student discipline. Although it may be easy to broadly identify a general concern such as student discipline, it takes the intervention of a mentor or coach to help a new teacher pick apart the broad concern and begin to identify the specific issue that needs to be addressed. There are very broad concerns, such as teaching effectively, that may never be addressed if one does not know where to start.

- **Identifying goals**—Once a mentor has worked with a new teacher to identify broad issues that need to be addressed, the pair is better able to begin to set long-term as well as immediate personal and professional goals. While discussions of long-term goals are important fuel for new teacher and mentor dialogue, mentors often find that they also provide an important service for new teachers by keeping them on track toward immediate goals.

- **Promoting self-directed learning**—A big part of mentoring, particularly when working with new teachers, is to help novices grow into their new roles. The key to a successful mentorship is the extent to which a new teacher becomes comfortable with taking control of personal learning experiences. In a sense, good mentoring should eventually make reliance of a new teacher on the insights and wisdom of a mentor disappear.

- **Assisting and guiding the work of others**—The power of mentoring is most felt when beginning teachers decrease reliance on the knowledge of their mentors. This transition is achieved through the mentor's willingness to empower the teacher as an equal and a colleague.

- **Summarizing**—An effective mentor must, in discussions with the new teacher, summarize any agreements that are reached. This procedure produces a more complete understanding of what has been discussed and any plans that have been made. A major part of this closing agreement must include a mutual commitment to confidentiality as a foundation of any helping relationship such as mentoring or coaching. If a mentor and new teacher cannot converse without fear of disclosure of issues discussed, the trusting dimension of the supportive relationship will quickly erode.

Some additional responsibilities for mentors include helping teachers develop the following strengths:

- Feelings of personal and professional competence

- Self-confidence

- A greater sense of direction on the job

- Increased professionalism

Questions to Consider

- Have you ever participated in a program in which a person with experience and expertise in a field has served as your mentor? If so, do you believe any additional mentoring skills or responsibilities should be added to the previous list?

- What additional skills might be taught to those experienced practitioners who would like to serve as mentors to new teachers?

Topics for Discussion

During the first few weeks after the school year has begun, the following topics might deserve some conversation between mentors and beginning teachers:

- **Lesson development**—Modify the lesson plans in response to student needs and performance. Beginning teachers often have an idealized view of how to develop lessons each day. But what happens if the idealized vision is not consistent with the students actually sitting in a classroom?

- **Classroom management and school procedures**—Maintain class control without becoming a tyrant. What do you do if your discipline plan does not seem to be working with the students in your class?

- **District policies and school procedures**—Continue to enforce school and district policies in the classroom. Why have some of these policies been implemented in the first place?

- **Motivation**—Keep the interests, focus, and efforts of students alive as the school year begins. What are some strategies that veteran teachers have used to stimulate continuing interest?

- **Interpersonal relationships**—Maintain positive and productive working relationships with other teachers and staff members. What if you simply do not get along with a few of the other teachers?

- **Taking time for student needs**—Get to know students as people and provide honest and effective feedback. How can you create a climate in your classes that promotes this type of open communication with students?

- **Housekeeping details**—Remember not to miss important deadlines, maintain accurate records and dates, get students ready for statewide testing, and so forth. What are some very important dates and events that are soon approaching?

As the school year progresses, the following topics might also be considered as part of the ongoing dialogue between the new teacher and her or his mentor. Note that some of these are recurring topics, as they are ongoing issues that are necessary to revisit multiple times throughout the year:

- **Communication**—Maintain open communication with parents or other caregivers, both in terms of formal conferencing and through other approaches.

- **Classroom management**—This is an ongoing concern of beginning teachers and deserves ongoing attention in conversations between mentors and beginning teachers.

- **Focusing on learning and teaching**—As beginners become more comfortable with their surroundings, it is nonetheless critical that intensity and focus are maintained on instruction and student learning.

- **Housekeeping**—It is important to stay on top of all major deadlines and other housekeeping chores expected of teachers.

As the school year continues, it may also be helpful to mentors and new teachers to have conversations on topics related to development of the teacher as a professional, including the following:

- **Platforms**—Again, discussions of personal beliefs, educational platforms, and philosophies represent dialogue concerning fundamental values. These always deserve attention.

- **Adjustments**—This includes the ways in which students, teachers, and other staff seem to be adjusting to the new teacher, as well as ways in which the new teacher is adjusting to new people, duties, and places.

- **Personal issues**—How is the new teacher adjusting to the strains now placed on her or his personal life as a result of the new job and its time demands?

- **Self-evaluation**—How can you tell if the beginning teacher is actually doing a good job?

Finally, trained mentors can assist newly hired teachers in many other ways. Regardless of the competence and ability of people who were recently hired, it is not likely that they will possess all the knowledge, skills, and insights that have been acquired by teachers with several years of experience. As a result, discussions between new teachers and mentors might include the following:

- The prevailing technology expectations for all teachers and how to learn more if these skills are a problem

- The vision of effective teaching and learning and instruction that exists in the school district

- Expectations for teachers in terms of ensuring high passing rates on statewide standardized tests for students

Questions to Consider

- As you look at the suggested topics for discussions between mentors and new teachers throughout the school year, can you think of any additional topics that might be added to the lists provided here?

- During your first few days, weeks, or months as a teacher, how could a mentor have helped you, or how did a mentor help you?

Benefits of Mentoring

When a district chooses to initiate a mentoring program for new teachers, a strong commitment is needed to support this effort, whether it is directed to assist beginning teachers or for all teachers in a school system. Districts must recognize that it does no good to simply call some veteran teachers mentors and tell them to go help newcomers; years of service as a teacher does not equal automatic skill as a mentor. A degree of training is needed if experienced personnel are to provide effective support. While it may require a significant commitment, quality school systems provide mentoring programs because of many benefits for the whole district as well as new teachers and those who are chosen to serve as mentors. The following descriptions of these benefits are adapted from Daresh (2003).

Benefits to Mentors

Many people have been informally mentored in a variety of settings including school or work, or in sports, music, or other areas of interest. While these relationships are often developed with the objective of benefitting mentees, it is also possible that mentors benefit from these relationships. Though serving as a mentor is not typically a financially lucrative activity, a number of benefits to mentors of new teachers have been identified:

- After serving as mentors, people report overall greater satisfaction with their jobs as teachers.

- Mentors often get increased positive recognition from their peers.

- Mentoring gives people opportunities for personal career advancement.

- Mentors often gain a renewed enthusiasm for their profession.

In short, people who have served as mentors to teacher colleagues report that they have gained much in this type of relationship. Perhaps the best way to summarize this finding is to note that despite the amount of time involved in maintaining effective mentoring relationships, mentors express a desire to serve in this capacity again in the future.

Benefits to New Teachers

Individuals who have been mentored in more formal programs report the following benefits:

- New teachers feel more confident in their professional competence.

- New teachers find they can see how theory learned at the university translates into practice.

- Communication skills are enhanced.

- Mentoring is a way to learn the "tricks of the trade."

- Mentoring makes new teachers feel as if they belong.

In general, formal mentoring arrangements are powerful learning opportunities in which teachers can learn about their professional lives and gain more insights into their needs, personal visions, and values.

Benefits to Districts

School systems also gain from the implementation of mentoring programs for beginning classroom teachers in the following ways:

- Districts have more capable staffs.

- An attitude of lifelong learning is created among all teachers.

- More effective and enthusiastic professional performance results when teachers understand that the school system demonstrates employees are worthy of the resources spent in establishing and maintaining a mentoring program.

- Greater productivity results.

However, as states have mandated support for newly hired educators, there has been a distressing tendency in some cases to comply with the mandate in name only (Ingersoll & Kralik, 2004). For these benefits to become a reality, a mentoring program needs oversight and commitment by the school district to make assistance to newcomers a true priority and to act accordingly. In some cases, principals of schools with new, innovative teachers may need to speak out in support of districtwide induction programs in order to reap the benefits mentioned in the preceding lists.

Questions to Consider

- If you have ever participated as either a mentee or mentor in a support program for new teachers, what additional training might you suggest for those who would be involved with providing support in such a program?

- Do you know any additional benefits to the establishment of a mentoring program, beyond those listed here?

Induction Programs

There is nothing really novel about the creation of induction programs in organizations. In large corporations, there has long been recognition that new employees need some type of structured support to receive information regarding company benefits, expectations for performance, rules, regulations, and procedures of the new workplace. The purpose of such activity has typically been to provide newcomers with a clear understanding of what the company expects, and in turn, what employees can expect from their new employer. The most consistent goal of such programs is to develop a sense of predictability which in itself is a benefit to all employees who realize that, if they do their jobs as required, they will be rewarded in ways comparable to all employees—either as newcomers or veterans. In our view, these efforts are important, but not sufficient when talking about providing support for new teachers. Efforts in most companies tend to be more aptly defined as orientation programs. Participants are oriented to the company, and not the reverse. We believe that newly hired educators would profit not only from initial orientation but more importantly from a process of induction.

Induction Versus Orientation

The key distinction between orientation and induction is that orientation—based on required meetings to learn about traditional topics selected by the school district—is dictated and controlled by the interests and priorities of the school system, while induction is personalized for the specific needs of teachers. The required orientation sessions have been carefully selected and planned in accordance with district-defined priorities of such matters as discipline, parent and community contact, and above all, contributions to the district in terms of student learning as demonstrated by test scores. Examples of the kinds of topics driving these frequent sessions might be:

- Establishing classroom management and discipline plans

- Working effectively with parents

- Addressing students with learning and physical disabilities

- Maintaining wellness and perspective as a new teacher

- Getting students ready for the annual state achievement tests

- End-of-the-year close-out procedures

Clearly, sessions focusing on these and many other similar topics are of great value to individuals stepping into the world of full-time teaching for the first time. Many topics are also appropriate for teachers with experience but in different school systems. As such, periodic information sessions focused on traditional local topics are valued by the majority of beginning teachers (Liu & Johnson, 2006). But they are simply not all that might constitute a comprehensive program for new teachers in the district, particularly if there is a desire to engage in induction.

Induction by its very nature requires much more of an individualized model of delivery, and does not consist of a preplanned schedule of topics for mandated meetings of all beginning teachers, as orientation does. But both forms of support are critical elements for new teachers. There are many items that are typically needed by all teachers. A classic example is effective classroom management and student discipline. The school district has not only a right but a responsibility to address the need for teachers—old and new—to be able to create safe and secure learning environments for the students in their care. And the district has sufficient experience to know that beginning teachers often have difficulty establishing an orderly environment in their classrooms. At the same time, a vast majority of newly hired teachers will openly admit to the fact that they enter schools with anxiety associated with maintaining discipline in a fair and consistent fashion, not as a punishment of students but as a needed aspect of development and personal learning. In this matter, it is perfectly reasonable to note the clear overlap between the institutional needs of the school system in alignment with the concerns of virtually all beginning teachers. The same is true with many other topics provided by the district throughout the school year.

Beginners need to learn more than the information designed primarily to address basic survival skills, however. Each teacher joining a school comes with unique talents, skills, and experiences. New teachers also have very diverse personalities. Some walk into the classroom for the first time with considerable confidence in their ability to do the job. Others are not as sure of their ability. For some, there has been no break in their schooling from elementary schools to high schools, then college and finally into their classrooms as teachers. Other teachers have spent years in noneducational roles and have entered teaching later in life. The list of possible different backgrounds and personalities among new teachers is almost endless.

Diverse support is needed to assist a diverse teaching staff. There must be more ways for newcomers to connect with their first jobs than just through the large group sessions required by many school districts. Induction programs are an important resource to be employed if there is a serious district commitment to beginning teacher success.

Components of Induction Programs

Induction is described as an approach to teacher professional development that is driven not by organizational priorities, but rather by the needs, concerns, and interests of individual teachers (Dilworth & Imig, 1995). Barbara Brock and Marilyn Grady (2007) explain that the "development [of individual teachers is] viewed as the shared responsibility of the school community, [and it] occurs within a collegial context" (p. 65). These induction programs are designed to supplement preservice preparation programs for future teachers by providing structured learning experiences throughout the beginning years of a new teacher's career.

Our view is quite simply that the more forms of support that a rookie can receive during the first two or three years on the job, the better. In terms of a comprehensive program, we think that most of the activities in a model for an ideal induction program suggested by Brock and Grady (2007) are worth considering by a school system committed to supporting new teachers. The following induction program components seem to be most valuable:

- **Needs assessment**—If the ideal induction program will be devoted to serving the developmental needs of each new teacher, the logical starting point must be a needs assessment to determine the specific needs of each of them, as well as the shared concerns of each incoming group of rookies each year. Not only is the content of the learning activities important to determine at this point, so is the preferred delivery strategy (Gordon, 1991). The most appropriate way to identify the different needs of all incoming teachers is through the completion of surveys (Ondak, 1996). For example, one simple survey question might be, What aspects of your job as a teacher would call for more professional development? How may that development be provided?

- **Commitment to ongoing assistance**—It is a simple task to offer information and assistance to teachers at the beginning of a school year, but a strong induction program must help teachers throughout the first and perhaps second and even third years of a new teacher's career. The challenges facing new teachers do not end in the first three months, let alone the first or even second years of their work (Perrachione, Rosser, & Petersen, 2008).

- **Periodic meetings with the principal of the new teachers' schools**—The most powerful force in the development and support for new teachers is the person who hired them, sees them most every day, and will evaluate them at the end of each school year. This, of course, is the principal. The principal also tends to have the clearest understanding of the values, goals, mission, and statement of the school in which the new teachers work (Sergiovanni, 2006; Wiebke & Bardin, 2009).

- **Informational meetings**—In addition to the continuing orientation sessions that might be provided for new teachers by the district, there may be many additional learning experiences for rookies. In states requiring the completion of continuing education experiences each year for teachers to renew their certification, it may also be helpful to participate in additional in-service each year.

- **Support seminars conducted by and for new teachers**—While veteran teachers, experienced principals, and experts from the central office may generally be a good source of information for new teachers during the year, it is also important to provide the opportunity for new teachers to take responsibility for periodic meetings or support seminars during which the new teachers are able to talk openly with peers about issues arising during the year. So often, beginners encounter challenges that they believe are unique to them. Having the opportunity to talk with others in the same boat can go a long way toward helping new teachers lose their sense of isolation (Perrachione et al., 2008).

- **Peer observation**—Periodically giving new teachers the opportunity to watch veterans at work in their classrooms is an excellent activity. Unfortunately, teachers—both novice and veteran—rarely get to observe the work of their peers.

- **Coaching and mentoring**—As we noted earlier in this chapter, there is little more powerful than the interaction between a new teacher and a trained mentor or coach throughout the school year.

- **Co-teaching lessons**—New teachers can learn a great deal by working alongside experienced colleagues. This is not necessarily an activity that should take place frequently, but it is worth doing once a month or once each grading period (six or nine weeks). It is not an evaluation process; many veteran teachers enjoy this activity since they often learn a great deal from ideas that come from new teachers.

- **Social functions**—Sometimes the best place for learning about schools is at gatherings far from school. Making certain that new teachers from around the district are present at the dinner, breakfast, picnic, or other events adds to the opportunities for learning.

- **Professional reading**—Many principals have a regular practice of creating book-of-the-month clubs or reading circles for teachers to consider new practices, research on learning, motivation, change, and other issues facing educators. It may be even more powerful to have a special interest group of readings directed to new teachers as a focus group.

Few, if any, school districts might attempt all of the activities listed here. At the same time, however, school systems need to direct resources, time, and attention toward finding ways to help support the most recently hired teachers as they transition into the classroom. The critical thing to remember is that a true induction program must begin with a sincere commitment in the district to support newcomers. It is far more than simply offering special meetings once in a while for the new folks. And it is much more challenging than what is traditionally done for new teachers, reflected here in the words of one veteran teacher we heard from: "Let them be. They can stumble around and make mistakes just like I did. They'll learn." That experienced educator just does not appreciate the realities faced by today's new teachers.

Questions to Consider

- Does the school district in which you now work offer a specialized induction program for all newly hired teachers? (Does "newly hired" refer only to first-year teachers, or may others also participate in the program?)

- Of the ten activities for a comprehensive induction program described on pages 74—75, how many of these items are part of the professional development of newly hired teachers in your district?

- What additional activities might you add to the list presented here?

Successful Induction Programs

Formal induction programs are found in school districts in virtually every state. In fifteen states, these programs are mandated by state law and policy (American Association of State Colleges and Universities, 2006). All induction programs have stated goals of assisting new teachers as they adjust to their new professional roles, but the fact is, the limited resources available to school districts have made it increasingly difficult for many programs to achieve their intended potential. In a few cases, induction programs have continued as they were first intended, namely as programs that give all newly hired teachers a good start to their professional roles. Examples of these successful efforts include the California Mentor Teacher Project (Brown & Wambach, 1987), the Montana Beginning Teacher Support Program (Spuhler & Zetler, 1995), and the Texas Beginning Educator Support System (Fuller, 2003). In each of the California, Montana, and Texas projects, evaluation studies showed that second-year retention rates were higher for those beginning teachers who participated in the statewide programs.

Ineffective Induction Programs

While the notion of structured induction is simple enough, there have been limitations on the effectiveness of these efforts. Some of the induction programs schools have in place are, unfortunately, simply window dressings to make applicants believe that if they sign a contract to teach in a particular school system, resources will be provided to enable beginners to succeed. Telling teacher candidates that "if you come to our school, you will be provided with resources that will enable you to succeed" is often little more than a recruiting device. In a comprehensive review of experiences by new teachers in several school districts in the United States, Edward Liu and Susan Moore Johnson (2006) note that words of support are easily heard, but follow-through with focused and planned induction efforts is sorely lacking. Once these individuals sign on the dotted line, they quickly learn that *induction* means requiring all new teachers to attend a day of orientation to the policies, procedures, and benefits associated with working in a school district and, perhaps, the identification of experienced teachers who may be available to mentor newcomers if questions arise from time to time. Furthermore, Richard Ingersoll and Jeffrey Kralik (2004) note,

> Like the induction processes common to other occupations, there are a number of different, and sometimes conflicting, purposes behind teacher induction programs. Among them are support, socialization, adjustment, development and assessment. Moreover, teacher induction can refer to a variety of different types of activities—classes, workshops, orientations, seminars, and especially, mentoring. (p. 1)

It is important that schools and principals are on the same page about the objectives of their induction programs and that they carefully structure these programs to best achieve those objectives.

Conclusion

Implementation of mentoring and induction programs is important if districts want to protect the investments they have made in the selection of new teachers. These programs may be helpful in changing the minds of some young or beginning teachers who are often discouraged by the real world of current education (Guarino, Santibanez, Daley, & Brewer, 2004; Mancheno-Smoak, Enders, Polak, & Athanasaw, 2009). Protecting and supporting new teachers is also important if districts want to improve over time. Since teachers are the most significant factors in improving student learning, when new people take on teaching roles, they must be guarded in a way that ensures that the district's future efforts will truly be stronger than they were in the past.

The "danger" in starting a support program and mentoring for new teachers is that it may have the unanticipated effect of developing a hunger by veteran teachers to continue to learn and discover more effective ways of teaching. Such a result will likely mean the investment of resources by a district to support all teachers. While costly, this may be yet another positive benefit of a mentoring program.

Final Reflections From New Teachers

The basic argument of this book is that the selection of new teachers is both a responsibility and an opportunity for a principal to move his or her school to excellence. Other members of the school community are also important partners in the selection of teachers who are likely to add to the quality of a school and help pursue its goals and objectives.

But the one voice not reported until now comes from the "customers" of the searching, interviewing, hiring, and supporting actions noted throughout the book. This last chapter offers comments often made by people who have gone through the selection process from the other side of the interview. Teachers who have recently gone through the frequently frustrating process of finding and getting a good job are full of stories about their experiences. The items listed here came straight from responses to the question, If you could advise the people who hired you in terms of what were (or what should have been) questions and issues to ensure that the best applicants for teaching jobs would be hired, what things would you suggest to improve the process?

What Teachers Want to Know

Some of the teachers we talked with noted that these were issues they were either very glad to have pursued when the interviewers asked if they had any questions, or they wish they had inquired of these things:

- **Do teachers in this school work together, plan cooperatively, provide cover for each other when needed, and basically serve as a team?** In short, teachers seeking jobs in schools want to know what type of climate they will encounter when they walk into a school for the first time. Do most teachers in the school see each other as colleagues or simply people with whom they will have to work each day? And how does the school ensure that teachers are able to engage in team planning during the school day?

- **Does the district provide teachers with a clear statement of expectations for curriculum (scope and sequence) coverage by each teacher?** Candidates searching for teaching jobs know that there will be pressure for each teacher to cover all facets of the district curriculum. To what extent is there an expectation that all teachers of the same grade levels or subject area remain synchronized with other teachers each day across the school system? What might be the consequences to a teacher who is not able to cover all elements of the formal district curriculum? Are there any sanctions imposed on teachers who choose to follow a different sequence than the one identified in district (or state) guidelines for the curriculum in each subject area at each grade level?

- **As part of this interview, is it possible for me to see and spend a bit of time learning about the students with whom I would be working here? Can I observe some typical students in a regular working environment?** Test scores, enrollment figures, and graphs showing the diversity of a school paint a rather limited view of what a new teacher is likely to encounter in his or her classes each day. Is it a friendly school, or are there tough students who do not seem to want to learn? How can a prospective teacher see and begin to get a feel for the kinds of students with whom he or she will be expected to work?

- **What about parents here? What level of involvement can I expect as a teacher in this school? How would you describe the majority of teacher-parent interactions that occur here?** Teachers—whether new or experienced—know that parent involvement is an extremely important part of developing positive learning experiences for students. Do parents actually respond to teachers who wish to provide more effective instruction and learning experiences for their children? Is there true support for the school by parents? Are they likely to take time to provide support for their children as learners? Do parents come to meetings with teachers as a way to guide their children and form partnerships with the staff of the school? Answers to these questions can provide incoming teachers with food for thought about how one can form productive relationships with parents to assist students in learning.

- **Can I show you that I can teach?** Many new teachers noted feelings like the following: "The school knows that I am certified and licensed and I meet all the prerequisites for being a teacher. But you want a teacher, and I know I can teach well. Can I demonstrate my talent?" In many school districts, those who are considered finalists for teaching positions are expected to prepare and teach a class (or a brief lesson) with students from the grade level in which the applicant will teach if hired. Surely adding this activity to the teacher selection will increase the time required to hire a teacher. However, if good teachers make good schools, principals should consider whether a few extra hours in hiring teachers might be a wise addition.

- **Are there any political issues that I need to know about if I come here?** People deserve full disclosure of important factors in place that may be foreseen as likely to have an effect on them. Unfortunately, this is not always practiced. For example, consider a teacher who decides to take a job teaching sixth grade, believing that sixth graders would be included in the organization of the local middle school. Soon after the teacher decides to take the job, however, it becomes apparent that there has long been a plan to move sixth grade to the elementary school. An organizational plan has been under review for the district, and had applicants been aware of the probable changes that were on the horizon, they may very well have decided not to even apply for certain positions. No lies were told, but all relevant information was not shared. This is a type of political reality that needs to be disclosed. The same might be true if the principal who has hired new teachers is later discovered to be relocated to a new campus soon after all the hiring for next year has taken place. This may or may not have had an effect on decisions made by job seekers. But if there is to be an openness created in schools, that candor needs to be present in all actions of the school system.

- **What type of support will I receive as a new teacher if I decide to take a job here?** Those who are applying for teaching positions clearly have a personal agenda. They want to have a job next year, and because of that, they may be so intent on getting a paycheck that they will ignore or forget momentarily that the job they are seeking can be very difficult. Schools and districts looking for talented new teachers may also forget that they need to ensure that the talented individuals they are now seeking will need to be provided with support to do these difficult jobs. They cannot be told, "You are important to us, but you will need to sink or swim on your own."

Is there a mentoring program already established in your district for new teachers? What kinds of continuing professional development opportunities exist for newly hired teachers? What has been the track record of the principal in this school regarding support for new teachers? What about the attitudes of current veterans regarding assistance for less experienced colleagues?

- **There is a lot of talk about how important it is for teachers to be paid based on performance. What is this school district's plan to address this issue in terms of teacher salaries?** Performance-based pay for teachers and school administrators is indeed a hot topic. Inexperienced teachers may be concerned about the way teacher performance will be judged. What are the indicators that a child has learned during the course of a school year? To date, the answer to this question in the minds of many is performance on mandated achievement testing required at different grade levels. According to this practice, students learn and teachers deserve financial recognition only if their students score at high levels on annual standardized tests. But if scores fall from past years, or lag behind other schools in a district, region, or across the state, the teacher is at fault.

For a new teacher in a district that has established a policy of performance-based salary increases, and where performance is defined in terms of increased student scores on standardized achievement tests, how can pay be increased if the teacher is a kindergarten, first-, or second-grade teacher? And what about a high school teacher whose assignments are with seniors only—those who long ago completed their last state tests? Normally, those who are seeking jobs are advised not to discuss salary or fringe benefits when they are being interviewed for a teaching job, but in a situation where there is an attempt to apply performance-based criteria for all financial rewards, it would be understandable for applicants to raise questions such as those listed here.

- **What can you tell me about the amount of technology and support I would receive if I were to come to this district as a teacher?** Today's teachers have come to the profession as products of the age of high-tech innovation. They text, tweet, and use Facebook as forms of everyday communication. They use iPads, iPhones, and numerous other types of new innovative hardware each day. In short, teachers coming to work in schools are comfortable with and attuned to a world of technology that most other teachers are less familiar with. Along with the gadgets they bring to school, they also bring different ways of thinking than that of many veterans. For many new teachers, devising instructional materials such as video presentations is a second-nature activity. This is a world of high-tech whiteboards, not blackboards and chalk.

  The natural question that will become increasingly a part of the expectations for teachers will be, What is the status of technology hardware and software in this school system? Even more critical may be the accompanying concern, Does this district have personnel who are trained and knowledgeable enough to help me fix tech problems or come up with new uses of equipment available in terms of technology?

  Having people who are aware of and skilled in the use of technology was not an issue when the majority of classroom teachers across the United States were hired in the 1970s or 1980s. But the innovations in material and more imaginative uses of technology have become something that will increasingly be second nature to new teachers of the future.

- **How much out-of-pocket expense will I need to assume as a teacher here?** It will certainly not be a major surprise for new teachers that they may end up paying for some instructional materials out of their own pockets, but how much funding for these materials is likely available in the district? For young teachers who may still be facing the challenges of paying off student loans and other debts from their university days—while in some cases also setting up a new apartment, taking care of car repairs, and addressing many other financial issues—it may be too much to expect incoming teachers to also pay for crayons for young children who come from impoverished homes, snacks in primary grades classrooms, videos to use in social studies classes, or the many other costs incurred from frequent trips to the local teacher store. While the principal is likely unable to estimate a figure, it may be helpful for him or her to describe the ways in which limited resources for teachers are provided. Is it a decision guided by some kind of proposal process, or is money for additional resources simply allocated in equal amounts to each teacher, regardless of planned activities?

Questions to Consider

- In some cases, principals seek input concerning questions that should be asked during teacher selection interviews from first- and second-year teachers. What kinds of questions do you think a good candidate might ask about working in your school?

- What additional questions do you think should be anticipated by interviewers talking with job applicants?

A Few Concluding Thoughts

To return to a thought we expressed at the outset of writing this book, finding, interviewing, hiring, and supporting new teachers is a critical responsibility for principals and their staffs. The reason? Good teachers make good schools. Whatever schools can do to ensure that they are staffed with good, enthusiastic, knowledgeable, and caring professionals is a task whose importance cannot be overemphasized.

We conclude this work by sharing a concern we heard from virtually every beginning teacher with whom we spoke. When asked what they wanted most from the people who are trying hard to convince them to come to a school, the issue of respect surfaced again and again. We often heard statements along the lines of "When I come to a school (for the interview or when I first start at the beginning of the next term), I hope that I will be treated as a true professional by the people with whom I will work."

Of course, the demonstration of this type of respect can be something easily promised during the hiring process, but there are times when the best intentions disappear as soon as the school year starts. New teachers are frequently treated as if they have been around as long as all the other teachers, and their colleagues assume that they know as much about daily life in a classroom as a teacher with ten or more years of experience. "They should know better" is an attitude frequently adopted around the rookies. But the rookies often know quite a bit more than some of their senior coworkers, as newly appointed teachers are most typically coming directly from university programs where they have learned a great deal about the latest developments in research on teaching, curriculum, and more aspects of their professional work. Above all, it should be recognized that the new people are professional educators who are trying to do the best possible job for their students. No school works effectively without all members working together as a team.

How can an employing school show that the new teacher will be a valued colleague? Maybe the best way to answer this question is by providing an example of how a school staff signals disrespect to a possible new teacher. One person with whom we talked pointed out that she decided not to accept one position offered for what might appear a small reason. When she was invited to take a teaching job, the offer was made over the phone by a secretary in the principal's office. Her question was simply, If I am to be an important part of this school's team, am I not worth a quick call from the principal? In other cases, we have also seen members of interviewing panels doodling on notepads during an interview session, or passing notes to other interview team members, or never making use of active listening skills when applicants are telling their stories. No doubt, some applicants are not terribly exciting during their interviews. But then again, they are worth everyone's attention when interviews are underway.

New teachers we spoke with frequently expressed their desire for others to demonstrate respect by listening to and considering their ideas. People interviewing for a first job do not necessarily have much experience, but they may have insights that do not necessarily require years of teaching in classrooms. Beginning with first impressions made during the interview, a type of mutual respect between new and veteran teachers can begin to be created if interviewers truly focus on the responses they receive from a potential colleague.

During a principal's career, he or she will be faced with the challenge of finding new teachers many times. This is a long and difficult task, as we have noted throughout this book. But it is certainly one that merits the greatest insights, skills, and commitment to ensure that the best people are being brought forward to make a difference for schools, and more importantly, for students.

REFERENCES AND RESOURCES

American Association of State Colleges and Universities. (2006). Teacher induction programs: Trends and opportunities. *Policy Matters, 3*(10), 1–4.

Barnes, G., Crowe, E., & Schaeffer, B. (2007). *The cost of teacher turnover in five districts: A pilot study.* Washington, DC: National Commission on Teaching and America's Future.

Barnett, B. (1991, April). *The educational platform: A developmental activity for preparing moral school leaders.* Paper presented at the Annual Meeting of the American Educational Research Association, Chicago, IL.

Behrstock, E., & Coggshall, J. G. (2009). *Key issue: Teacher hiring, placement, and assignment practices.* Washington, DC: National Comprehensive Center for Teacher Quality.

Brock, B. L., & Grady, M. L. (2007). *From first-year to first-rate: Principals guiding beginning teachers* (3rd ed.). Thousand Oaks, CA: Corwin Press.

Brown, J. G., & Wambach, C. (1987, February). *Using mentors to increase new teacher retention: The mentor induction project.* Paper presented at the Annual Meeting of the American Association of Colleges for Teacher Education, Arlington, VA.

Brown, S. (2003). Working models: Why mentoring programs may be the key to teacher retention. *Techniques, 78*(5), 18–21.

California Commission on Teacher Credentialing, & California Department of Education. (1997). *California standards for the teaching profession.* Accessed at www.ctc.ca.gov/educator-prep /standards/CSTP-prior.pdf on August 20, 2012.

Casey, C. E., & Childs, R. A. (2007). Teacher education program admission criteria and what beginning teachers need to know to be successful. *Canadian Journal of Educational Administration and Policy, 1*(67), 1–24.

Council of Chief State School Officers. (2011). *Interstate Teacher Assessment and Support Consortium (InTASC) model core teaching standards: A resource for state dialogue.* Washington, DC: Author.

Daresh, J. C. (2003). *Teachers mentoring teachers: A practical approach to helping new and experienced staff.* Thousand Oaks, CA: Corwin Press.

Daresh, J. C. (2007). *Supervision as proactive leadership* (4th ed.). Long Grove, IL: Waveland Press.

Darling-Hammond, L. (2000). Teacher quality and student achievement: A review of state policy evidence. *Education Policy Analysis Archives, 8*(1).

Dilworth, M. E., & Imig, D. G. (1995). Professional teacher development. *ERIC Review, 3*(3), 511.

Feinman-Nemser, S. (2003). What new teachers need to learn. *Educational Leadership, 60*(8), 25–29.

Feinman-Nemser, S., Schwille, S., Carver, P., & Yusko, M. (1999). *A conceptual review of literature on new teacher induction.* Washington, DC: National Partnership for Excellence and Accountability in Teaching.

Fletcher, E., Chang, J., & Kong, Y. (2008, October). *Teacher preparation, teacher induction, and teacher retention: An emerging conceptual framework of teacher development.* Paper presented at the Annual Meeting of the Mid-Western Educational Research Association, Columbus, OH.

Fuller, E. (2003). *Beginning teacher retention rates for TxBESS and non-TxBESS teachers* (Unpublished manuscript, State Board for Educator Certification, Austin, Texas).

Gallup. (2004). *TeacherInsight interview: Predictive validity study, 2003–04 school year.* Princeton, NJ: Author.

Gallup. (2007). *TeacherInsight frequently asked questions.* Princeton, NJ: Author.

Gordon, S. (1991). *How to help beginning teachers succeed.* Alexandria, VA: Association for Supervision and Curriculum Development.

Guarino, C., Santibanez, L., Daley, G., & Brewer, D. (2004). *A review of the literature on teacher recruitment and selection* (Technical Report). Santa Monica, CA: RAND.

Heller, D. A. (2004). *Teachers wanted: Attracting and retaining good teachers.* Alexandria, VA: Association for Supervision and Curriculum Development.

Ingersoll, R., & Kralik, J. (2004). *The impact of mentoring on teacher retention: What the research says* (Document No. 5036). Denver, CO: Education Commission of the States.

Ingersoll, R. M., & Smith, T. M. (2004). The wrong solution to the teacher shortage. *Educational Leadership, 60*(8), 30–33.

Johnson, S. M., Berg, J. H., & Donaldson, M. L. (2005). *Who stays in teaching and why? A review of literature on teacher retention.* Cambridge, MA: Project on the Next Generation of Teachers, Harvard Graduate School of Education.

Lieberman, A. (Ed.). (1988). *Building a professional culture in schools.* New York: Teachers College Press.

Liu, E., & Johnson, S. M. (2006). New teachers' experiences of hiring: Late, rushed, and information-poor. *Educational Administration Quarterly, 42*(3), 324–360.

Lortie, D. C. (1975). *Schoolteacher: A sociological study.* Chicago: University of Chicago Press.

Mancheno-Smoak, L., Enders, G., Polak, R., & Athanasaw, Y. (2009). The individual cultural values and job satisfaction of the transformational leader. *Organizational Development Journal, 27*(3), 9–14.

National Commission on Teaching and America's Future. (2003). *No dream denied: A pledge to America's children*. Washington, DC: Author.

National Education Association. (2007). *Teacher shortages and retention report*. Washington, DC: Author.

Ondak, R. (1996, August). *College based induction and mentoring programs and teacher attitude toward teaching*. Paper presented at the Annual Meeting of the National Council of Professors of Educational Administration, Corpus Christi, TX.

Perrachione, B. A., Rosser, V. J., & Petersen, G. J. (2008). Why do they stay? Elementary teachers' perceptions of job satisfaction and retention. *Professional Educator, 32*(2), 14–19.

Peterson, K. D. (2002a). *An ASCD study guide for effective teacher hiring: A guide to getting the best*. Alexandria, VA: Association for Supervision and Curriculum Development.

Peterson, K. D. (2002b). *Effective teacher hiring: A guide to getting the best*. Alexandria, VA: Association for Supervision and Curriculum Development.

Sergiovanni, T. J. (2006). *The principalship: A reflective practice perspective* (5th ed.). Needham Heights, MA: Allyn & Bacon.

Sergiovanni, T. J., & Starratt, R. J. (2007). *Supervision: Human perspective* (7th ed.). New York: McGraw-Hill.

Spuhler, L., & Zetler, A. (1995). *Montana Beginning Teacher Support Program: Final report*. Helena: Montana State Board of Education.

Stronge, J. H. (2002). *Qualities of effective teachers*. Alexandria, VA: Association for Supervision and Curriculum Development.

Ulrich, D., & Smallwood, N. (2007). *Leadership brand: Developing customer-focused leaders to drive performance and build lasting value*. Boston: Harvard Business School Press.

Wiebke, K., & Bardin, J. (2009). New teacher support: A comprehensive induction program can increase teacher retention and improve performance. *Journal of Staff Development, 30*(1), 34–38.

Wilson, S. (2008). *TeacherInsight: Preliminary findings*. Greeley: University of Northern Colorado, College of Education.

INDEX

Effective Program Evaluation, 2nd Edition
Mardale Dunsworth and Dawn Billings

Educators and administrators are increasingly coming to realize the importance of making decisions based on reliable, accurate data. This short guide provides a clear and easily implemented blueprint for evaluating academic programs, practices, or strategies using a simple framework.

BKF461

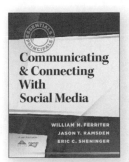

Communicating & Connecting With Social Media
William M. Ferriter, Jason T. Ramsden, and Eric C. Sheninger

In this short text, the authors examine how enterprising schools are using social media tools to provide customized professional development for teachers and to transform communication practices with staff, students, parents, and other stakeholders.

BKF474

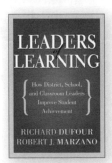

Leaders of Learning
Richard DuFour and Robert J. Marzano

Together, the authors focus on district leadership, principal leadership, and team leadership and address how individual teachers can be most effective in leading students—by learning with colleagues how to implement the most promising pedagogy in their classrooms.

BKF455

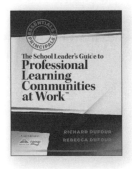

The School Leader's Guide to Professional Learning Communities at Work™
Richard DuFour and Rebecca DuFour

Are you a K–8 principal looking to implement the PLC at Work™ process? Explore the components needed to lay the foundation, including how to develop a structure that supports collaborative teams, how to focus on effective monitoring strategies, and more.

BKF489

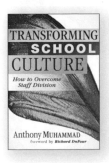

Transforming School Culture
Anthony Muhammad
Foreword by Richard DuFour

Busy administrators will appreciate this quick read packed with immediate, accessible strategies. This book provides the framework for understanding dynamic relationships within a school culture and ensuring a positive environment that supports the changes necessary to improve learning for all students.

BKF281

Solution Tree | Press

a division of
Solution Tree

Visit solution-tree.com or call 800.733.6786 to order.

Solution Tree

Solution Tree's mission is to advance the work of our authors. By working with the best researchers and educators worldwide, we strive to be the premier provider of innovative publishing, in-demand events, and inspired professional development designed to transform education to ensure that all students learn.

The mission of the National Association of Elementary School Principals is to lead in the advocacy and support for elementary and middle level principals and other education leaders in their commitment for all children.